CONTENTS

THE SHIFTING QUALITY

A CHOICE OF WEAPONS

A WORLD OF MADE

CONTENTS

STUDENT GUIDE

INTRODUCTION

In Your Own Words is a collection of stories, poems, plays, and articles presented in five units, each of which explores a different theme. In the first unit, you will be invited to "Imagine Them in the Past" through literature that reflects on the societies and individuals of times past. "The Deed Took Place" focusses on crime, criminals, and mysterious events, and challenges you to unravel puzzles. The selections in "A Shifting Quality" examine the human capacity for change and growth. In "A Choice of Weapons" the selections offer insights into conflict in a variety of situations. The final unit, "A World of Made," confronts the issues of technological development and calls for reflection on the consequences of human investment in science. Some of the selections may offer explanations for the issues that puzzle you, while others may stimulate new ideas and provoke new questions. It is through this process of inquiry and reflection that we all come to understand our world.

 In Your Own Words offers you many opportunities to speak and to write. The activities that follow each prose and dramatic selection in the book will help you to focus your discussion and writing in three directions. First, in the About the Lines section, you will be asked to consider the actual details of the piece of writing. Then you will share your views on what lies hidden Between the Lines. Finally, you will move Beyond the Lines to explore similar or related situations from a wide range of viewpoints. When you are working with the poetry in the book, you will be Looking In at the poet's message and Looking Out to discover other connections. Sometimes you may choose to do several of the activities, and at other times you may concentrate on only a few, depending on the objectives you and your teachers have.

 Talking and writing are ways of communicating with other people to share information, ideas, and opinions. However, an equally important function of talking and writing is the straightening out of your growing understanding of new concepts. As you gather ideas or information, recall experiences, or talk with other people, you will formulate your own viewpoints. You will shape your thoughts and their expression through this process of "roaming" around in your head and through conversing with others. After your initial attempts at expressing your thoughts, you will want to reshape and refine them, working toward a polished version of your oral presentation or your written piece.

Re-examining your written work with other people can help you to judge whether you have reached your audience and achieved your purpose. It is a good idea to work with partners, sharing perceptions and helping one another with observations and suggestions. In this way, you and your partners can act as editors and proofreaders for one another. When you help your partners in the reshaping of their expression you will consider its purpose as well as the audience for whom it is intended, and make recommendations accordingly. Then, your partners can think about your advice and make the changes that seem appropriate to them. To assist in this process of interaction, the Student Guide on pages 339-357 gives some ideas for re-seeing your work.

It has been said that language is the exposed edge of thinking. As you talk and write about what you have read and its impact on you, you will uncover what you have understood. You will also form links with other people's ways of seeing things. Reading, talking, listening, and writing are means to learning. *In Your Own Words* invites you to read, talk, listen and write, and revise and rewrite, "with a little help from your friends."

JOAN GREEN and IAN MILLS

1

IMAGINE THEM

Thy shores are empires, changed in all save thee —
Assyria, Greece, Rome, Carthage, what are they?
Thy waters washed them power while they were free,
And many a tyrant since: their shores obey
The stranger, slave or savage; their decay
Has dried up realms to deserts: — not so thou,
Unchangeable save to thy wild waves' play —
Time writes no wrinkle on thine azure brow —
Such as creation's dawn beheld, thou rollest now.

"Ocean"
(From Childe Harold's Pilgrimage)
George Gordon, Lord Byron

OZYMANDIAS

Percy Bysshe Shelley

I met a traveller from an antique land,
Who said — "Two vast and trunkless legs of stone
Stand in the desert . . . Near them, on the sand,
Half sunk a shattered visage lies, whose frown,
And wrinkled lip, and sneer of cold command,
Tell that its sculptor well those passions read
Which yet survive, stamped on these lifeless things,
The hand that mocked them, and the heart that fed;
And on the pedestal, these words appear:
My name is Ozymandias, King of Kings,
Look on my Works, ye Mighty, and despair!
Nothing beside remains. Round the decay
Of that colossal Wreck, boundless and bare
The lone and level sands stretch far away."

ON THE VANITY OF EARTHLY GREATNESS

Arthur Guiterman

The tusks that clashed in mighty brawls
Of mastodons, are billiard balls.

The sword of Charlemagne the Just
Is ferric oxide, known as rust.

The grizzly bear whose potent hug
Was feared by all, is now a rug.

Great Caesar's dead and on the shelf,
And I don't feel so well myself!

LOOKING IN

1 "Ozymandias" and "On the Vanity of Earthly Greatness" are ironic poems in that they show that human desires and the realities of history are very different. Develop this thought in a brief paragraph and compare your analysis with your partners'. Together, produce a polished paragraph.

2 List the words in the two poems that convey a sense of frailty in the face of time. Compare your list with your partners' and discuss the poets' choice of words.

3 In a small group discussion, compare and contrast the way the two poets have handled a similar theme.

4 In the voice of the sculptor, express your opinion of Ozymandias to a friend. You may present your ideas in a short letter or orally.

5 Present a polished reading of either "Ozymandias" or "On the Vanity of Earthly Greatness" to a small group. Justify your interpretation and then invite the comments of your audience.

LOOKING OUT

1 Invent a slogan or a jingle that would effectively convey the central ideas of these two poems.

2 Write a story for children in which an arrogant character learns the lesson of humility.

3 Make up a collage or a mobile that reflects the triumph of time.

4 Write a poem or a short story in which you refer to the vain ambitions of a character from the past who interests you, such as Napoleon, Genghis Khan, or Cleopatra.

5 Imagine that you are a traveller who has just returned from a journey to a distant land. Tape your reminiscences of the journey. Choose an incident that particularly pleases you and share it with a partner who has also gone on an imaginary journey. Travel brochures, guide books, travel sections of newspapers, and television travelogues will be helpful.

GAWAIN AND THE LADY RAGNELL

An English Tale

RETOLD BY ETHEL JOHNSTON PHELPS

A tale of love and magic in King Arthur's court

Long ago, in the days of King Arthur, the finest knight in all Britain was the king's nephew Gawain. He was, by reputation, the bravest in battle, the wisest, the most courteous, the most compassionate, and the most loyal to his king.

One day in late summer, Gawain was with Arthur and the knights of the court at Carlisle in the north. The King returned from the day's hunting looking so pale and shaken that Gawain followed him at once to his chamber.

"What has happened, my lord?" asked Gawain with concern.

Arthur sat down heavily. "I had a very strange encounter in Inglewood forest . . . I hardly know what to make of it." And he related to Gawain what had occurred.

"Today I hunted a great white stag," said Arthur. "The stag at last escaped me and I was alone, some distance from my men. Suddenly a tall, powerful man appeared before me with sword upraised."

"And you were unarmed!"

"Yes. I had only my bow and a dagger in my belt. He threatened to kill me," Arthur went on. "And he swung his sword as though he meant to cut me down on the spot! Then he laughed horribly and said he would give me one chance to save my life."

"Who was this man?" cried Gawain. "Why should he want to kill you?"

"He said his name was Sir Gromer, and he sought revenge for the loss of his northern lands."

"A chieftain from the north!" exclaimed Gawain. "But what is this one chance he spoke of?"

"I gave him my word I would meet him one year from today, unarmed, at the same spot, with the answer to a question!" said Arthur.

Gawain started to laugh, but stopped at once when he saw Arthur's face. "A question! Is it a riddle? And one year to find the answer? That should not be hard!"

"If I can bring him the true answer to the question, 'What is it that women most desire, above all else?' my life will be spared." Arthur scowled. "He is sure I will fail. It must be a foolish riddle that no one can answer."

"My lord, we have one year to search the kingdom for answers," said

7

Gawain confidently. "I will help you. Surely one of the answers will be the right one."

"No doubt you are right — someone will know the answer." Arthur looked more cheerful. "The man is mad, but a chieftain will keep his word."

For the next twelve months, Arthur and Gawain asked the question from one corner of the kingdom to the other. Then at last the appointed day drew near. Although they had many answers, Arthur was worried.

"With so many answers to choose from, how do we know which is the right one?" he asked in despair. "Not one of them has the ring of truth."

A few days before he was to meet Sir Gromer, Arthur rode out alone through the golden gorse and purple heather. The track led upward toward a grove of great oaks. Arthur, deep in thought, did not look up until he reached the edge of the oak wood. When he raised his head, he pulled up suddenly in astonishment.

Before him was a grotesque woman. She was almost as wide as she was high, her skin was mottled green, and spikes of weedlike hair covered her head. Her face seemed more animal than human.

The woman's eyes met Arthur's fearlessly. "You are Arthur the king," she said in a harsh, croaking voice. "In two days time you must meet Sir Gromer with the answer to a question."

Arthur turned cold with fear. He stammered, "Yes . . . yes . . . that is true. Who are you? How did you know of this?"

"I am the lady Ragnell. Sir Gromer is my stepbrother. You haven't found the true answer, have you?"

"I have many answers," Arthur replied curtly. "I do not see how my business concerns you." He gathered up the reins, eager to be gone.

"You do not have the right answer." Her certainty filled him with a sense of doom. The harsh voice went on. "But I know the answer to Sir Gromer's question."

Arthur turned back in hope and disbelief. "You do? Tell me the true answer to his question, and I will give you a large bag of gold."

"I have no use for gold," she said coldly.

"Nonsense, my good woman. With gold you can buy anything you want!" He hesitated a moment, for the huge, grotesque face with the cool, steady eyes unnerved him. He went on hurriedly, "What is it you want? Jewelry? Land? Whatever you want I will pay you — that is, if you truly have the right answer."

"I know the answer. I promise you that!" She paused. "What I demand in return is that the knight Gawain become my husband."

There was a moment of shocked silence. Then Arthur cried, "Impossible! You ask the impossible, woman!"

She shrugged and turned to leave.

"Wait, wait a moment!" Rage and panic overwhelmed him, but he tried to speak reasonably.

"I offer you gold, land, jewels. I cannot give you my nephew. He is his own man. He is not mine to give!"

"I did not ask you to *give* me the knight Gawain," she rebuked him. "If Gawain himself agrees to marry me, I will give you the answer. Those are my terms."

9

"Impossible!" he sputtered. "I could not bring him such a proposal."

"If you should change your mind, I will be here tomorrow," said she, and disappeared into the oak woods.

Shaken from the weird encounter, Arthur rode homeward at a slow pace.

"Save my own life at Gawain's expense? Never!" he thought. "Loathsome woman! I could not even speak of it to Gawain."

But the afternoon air was soft and sweet with birdsong, and the fateful meeting with Sir Gromer weighed on him heavily. He was torn by the terrible choice facing him.

Gawain rode out from the castle to meet the king. Seeing Arthur's pale, strained face, he exclaimed, "My lord! Are you ill? What has happened?"

"Nothing . . . nothing at all." But he could not keep silent long. "The colossal impudence of the woman! A monster, that's what she is! That creature, daring to give me terms!"

"Calm yourself, uncle," Gawain said patiently. "What woman? Terms for what?"

Arthur sighed. "She knows the answer to the question. I didn't intend to tell you."

"Why not? Surely that's good news! What is the answer?"

"She will not tell me until her terms are met," said the king heavily. "But I assure you, I refuse to consider her proposal!"

Gawain smiled. "You talk in riddles yourself, uncle. Who is this woman who claims to know the answer? What is her proposal?"

Seeing Gawain's smiling, expectant face, Arthur at first could not speak. Then, with his eyes averted, the king told Gawain the whole story, leaving out no detail.

"The lady Ragnell is Sir Gromer's stepsister? Yes, I think she would know the right answer," Gawain said thoughtfully. "How fortunate that I will be able to save your life!"

"No! I will not let you sacrifice yourself!" Arthur cried.

"It is my choice and my decision," Gawain answered. "I will return with you tomorrow and agree to the marriage — on condition that the answer she supplies is the right one to save your life."

Early the following day, Gawain rode out with Arthur. But not even meeting the loathsome lady face to face could shake his resolve. Her proposal was accepted.

Gawain bowed courteously. "If on the morrow your answer saves the king's life, we will be wed."

On the fateful morning, Gawain watched the king stow a parchment in his saddlebag. "I'll try all these answers first," said Arthur.

They rode together for the first part of the journey. Then Arthur, unarmed as agreed, rode on alone to Inglewood to meet Sir Gromer.

The tall, powerful chieftain was waiting, his broadsword glinting in the sun.

Arthur read off one answer, then another, and another. Sir Gromer shook his head in satisfaction.

"No, you have not the right answer!" he said raising his sword high. "You've failed, and now —"

"Wait!" Arthur cried. "I have one more answer. What a woman desires above all else is the power of sovereignty — the right to exercise her own will."

With a loud oath the man dropped his sword. "You did not find that answer by yourself!" he shouted. "My cursed stepsister, Ragnell, gave it to you. Bold, interfering hussy! I'll run her through with my sword . . . I'll lop off her head . . ." Turning, he plunged into the forest, a string of horrible curses echoing behind him.

Arthur rode back to where Gawain waited with the monstrous Ragnell. They returned to the castle in silence. Only the grotesque Lady Ragnell seemed in good spirits.

The news spread quickly throughout the castle. Gawain, the finest knight in the land, was to marry this monstrous creature! Some tittered and laughed at the spectacle; others said the lady Ragnell must possess very great lands and estates; but mostly there was stunned silence.

Arthur took his nephew aside nervously. "Must you go through with it at once? A postponement perhaps?"

Gawain looked at him steadily. "I gave my promise, my lord. The lady Ragnell's answer saved your life. Would you have me —"

"Your loyalty makes me ashamed! Of course you cannot break your word." And Arthur turned away.

The marriage took place in the abbey. Afterward, with Gawain and the lady Ragnell sitting at the high dais table beside the king and queen, the strange wedding feast began.

"She takes the space of two women on the chair," muttered the knight Gareth. "Poor Gawain!"

"I would not marry such a creature for all the land in Christendom!" answered his companion.

An uneasy silence settled on the hall. Only the monstrous Lady Ragnell displayed good spirits and good appetite. Throughout the long day and evening, Gawain remained pleasant and courteous. In no way did his manner toward his strange bride show other than kind attention.

The wedding feast drew to a close. Gawain and his bride were conducted to their chamber and were at last alone.

The lady Ragnell gazed at her husband thoughtfully.

"You have kept your promise well and faithfully," she observed.

Gawain inclined his head. "I could not do less, my lady."

"You've shown neither revulsion nor pity," she said. After a pause she went on, "Come now, we are wedded! I am waiting to be kissed."

Gawain went to her at once and kissed her. When he stepped back, there stood before him a slender young woman with gray eyes and a serene, smiling face.

His scalp tingled in shock. "What manner of sorcery is this?" he cried hoarsely.

"Do you prefer me in this form?" she smiled and turned slowly in a full circle.

But Gawain backed away warily. "I . . . yes . . . of course . . . but . . . I don't understand . . ." For this sudden evidence of sorcery, with its unknown powers, made him confused and uneasy.

"My stepbrother, Sir Gromer, had always hated me," said the lady Ragnell. "Unfortunately, through his mother, he has a knowledge of sorcery, and so he changed me into a monstrous creature. He said I must live in that shape until I could persuade the greatest knight in Britain to willingly choose me for his bride. He said it would be an impossible condition to meet!"

"Why did he hate you so cruelly?"

Her lips curled in amusement. "He thought me bold and unwomanly because I defied him. I refused his commands both for my property and my person."

Gawain said with admiration, "You won the 'impossible' condition he set, and now his evil spell is broken!"

"Only in part." Her clear gray eyes held his. "You have a choice, my dear Gawain, which way I will be. Would you have me in this, my own shape, at night and my former ugly shape by day? Or would you have me grotesque at night in our chamber, and my own shape in the castle by day? Think carefully before you choose."

Gawain was silent only a moment. He knelt before her and touched her hand.

"It is a choice I cannot make, my dear Ragnell. It concerns you. Whatever you choose to be — fair by day or fair by night — I will willingly abide by it."

Ragnell released a long, deep breath. The radiance in her face overwhelmed him.

"You have answered well, dearest Gawain, for your answer has broken Gromer's evil spell completely. The last condition he set has been met! For he said that if, after marriage to the greatest knight in Britain, my husband freely gave me the power of choice, the power to exercise my own free will, the wicked enchantment would be broken forever."

Thus, in wonder and in joy, began the marriage of Gawain and the lady Ragnell.

ABOUT THE LINES

1 Summarize the story of "Gawain and the Lady Ragnell" in three or four paragraphs. Ask your partner to check your summary. Delete every eighth word from your summary; you have now made a cloze exercise. Give your cloze exercise to another class member and ask him or her to complete it. Discuss the student's choice of words.

2 Working in a group, make a cartoon strip of the story of "Gawain and the Lady Ragnell." Provide captions for each illustration.

3 The lady Ragnell experiences a metamorphosis (undergoes a change in form) in this story. In one or two sentences, describe her as she appears at each stage.

BETWEEN THE LINES

1 "Gawain and the Lady Ragnell" mixes fantasy — the magical elements of the story — with an aspect of reality — the human emotions of the characters involved. Write a personal statement expressing your opinion of the effect of this mixture of the real and the unreal. Compare your statement with your partners' and see if you reacted in the same way.

2 Working with a partner, script and then dramatize the conversation between two of King Arthur's knights following the marriage reception of Gawain and the lady Ragnell.

3 Imagine that you are the lady Ragnell and write a letter to your stepbrother, Sir Gromer, after Gawain has broken the spell.

BEYOND THE LINES

1 Read some of the stories of King Arthur and the Knights of the Round Table. Pick your favourite story and either retell it in your own words as a written short story, or practise retelling it and then present it to a small group.

2 Script and dramatize the tale of Gawain and the lady Ragnell. Present your dramatization to a group of younger students.

3 In a group of four, debate the following resolution:
Appearance should be a minor consideration in the choice of friends or partners.

OF MURRAY **Anonymous**

Ye Highlands and ye Lawlands,
   O where have you been?
They have slain the Earl of Murray,
   And they laid him on the green.

"Now wae be to thee, Huntly,[1]
   And wherefore did you sae?
I bade you bring him wi' you,
   But forbade you him to slay."

He was a braw gallant,
   And he rid[2] at the ring;
And the bonny Earl of Murray,
   O he might have been a king.

He was a braw gallant,
   And he played at the ba';
   And the bonny Earl of Murray
   Was the flower amang them a'.
He was a braw gallant,
   And he played at the glove;[3]
And the bonny Earl of Murray,
   O he was the queen's love.

O lang will his lady
   Look o'er the Castle Down,
Ere she see the Earl of Murray
   Come sounding[4] through the town.

---

[1] Huntly, who killed Murray in 1592, had been ordered by King James VI of Scotland, the speaker of this stanza, to arrest the Earl.

[2] Rode. "The ring" was a hanging that mounted knights tried to catch on their spears.

[3] Either the goal in the race, or else a lady's favour.

[4] Blowing horns.

LOOKING IN

1 In point form, note the events of this ballad in chronological order. Adding in such details as you think should be included, present the incident either as:
a. a short story; or
b. a newspaper report.

2 Working in a group, prepare an oral reading of this ballad for presentation to the class. You might consider a choral reading (see p.350). Tape your version; listen to the tape and make any necessary improvements before presenting it.

3 Look up the definition of "ballad" in the glossary (see p. 349). List the features of this poem that classify it as a ballad.

LOOKING OUT

1 Choose a recent event from a newspaper, a news magazine, or from personal experience, and retell it in the form of a traditional ballad, such as "The Bonny Earl of Murray." Share your ballad with a group.

2 Select a story, poem, movie, song, or play that deals with a historical event. Make notes on the incident as it is presented in the chosen work, and then research the actual event in history books. In point form, note the similarities and the differences between the fictional version and the historical record. Write a paragraph comparing and contrasting the two renditions.

THE WEDDING GIFT

Thomas Raddall

Nova Scotia, in 1794. Winter. Snow on the ground. Two feet of it in the woods, less by the shore, except in drifts against Port Marriott's barns and fences; but enough to set sleigh bells ringing through the town, enough to require a multitude of paths and burrows from doors to streets, to carpet the wharves and the decks of the shipping, and to trim the ships' yards with tippets of ermine. Enough to require fires roaring in the town's chimneys, and blue wood smoke hanging low over the roof tops in the still December air. Enough to squeal under foot in the trodden places and to muffle the step everywhere else. Enough for the hunters, whose snowshoes now could overtake the floundering moose and caribou. Even enough for the always-complaining loggers, whose ox sleds now could haul their cut from every part of the woods. But not enough, not nearly enough snow for Miss Kezia Barnes, who was going to Bristol Creek to marry Mr. Hathaway.

Kezia did not want to marry Mr. Hathaway. Indeed she had told Mr. and Mrs. Barclay in a tearful voice that she didn't want to marry anybody. But Mr. Barclay had taken snuff and said "Ha! Humph!" in the severe tone he used when he was displeased; and Mrs. Barclay had sniffed and said it was a very good match for her, and revolved the cold blue eyes in her fat moon face, and said Kezia must not be a little fool.

There were two ways of going to Bristol Creek. One was by sea, in one of the fishing sloops. But the preacher objected to that. He was a pallid young man lately sent out from England by Lady Huntingdon's Connexion, and seasick five weeks on the way. He held Mr. Barclay in some awe, for Mr. Barclay had the best pew in the meetinghouse and was the chief pillar of godliness in Port Marriott. But young Mr. Mears was firm on this point. He would go by road, he said, or not at all. Mr. Barclay had retorted "Ha! Humph!" The road was twenty miles of horse path through the woods, now deep in snow. Also the path began at Harper's Farm on the far side of the harbour, and Harper had but one horse.

"I shall walk," declared the preacher calmly, "and the young woman can ride."

Kezia had prayed for snow, storms of snow, to bury the trail and keep anyone from crossing the cape to Bristol Creek. But now they were setting out from Harper's Farm, with Harper's big brown horse, and all Kezia's prayers had gone for naught. Like any anxious lover, busy Mr. Hathaway had sent Black Sam overland on foot to find out what delayed his wedding, and now Sam's day-old tracks marked for Kezia the road to marriage.

She was a meek little thing, as became an orphan brought up as house-help in the Barclay home; but now she looked at the preacher and saw how young and helpless he looked so far from his native Yorkshire, and how ill-clad for this bitter trans-Atlantic weather, and she spoke up.

"You'd better take my shawl, sir. I don't need it. I've got Miss Julia's old riding cloak. And we'll go ride-and-tie."

"Ride and what?" murmured Mr. Mears.

"I'll ride a mile or so, then I'll get down and tie the horse to a tree and walk on. When you come up to the horse, you mount and ride a mile or so, passing me on the way, and you tie him and walk on. Like that. Ride-and-tie, ride-and-tie. The horse gets a rest between."

Young Mr. Mears nodded and took the proffered shawl absently. It was a black thing that matched his sober broadcloth coat and smallclothes, his black woollen stockings and his round black hat. At Mr. Barclay's suggestion he had borrowed a pair of moose-hide moccasins for the journey. As he walked a prayer-book in his coat-skirts bumped the back of his legs.

At the top of the ridge above Harper's pasture, where the narrow path led

Two innocents, a snowstorm, and perhaps an answer to the prayers of both

off through gloomy hemlock woods, Kezia paused for a last look back across the harbour. In the morning sunlight the white roofs of the little lonely town resembled a tidal wave flung up by the sea and frozen as it broke against the dark pine forest to the west. Kezia sighed, and young Mr. Mears was surprised to see tears in her eyes.

She rode off ahead. The saddle was a man's, of course, awkward to ride modestly, woman-fashion. As soon as she was out of the preacher's sight she rucked her skirts and slid a leg over to the other stirrup. That was better. There was a pleasant sensation of freedom about it, too. For a moment she forgot that she was going to Bristol Creek, in finery second-hand from the Barclay girls, in a new linen shift and drawers that she had sewn herself in the light of the kitchen candles, in white cotton stockings and a bonnet and shoes from Mr. Barclay's store, to marry Mr. Hathaway.

The Barclays had done well for her from the time when, a skinny weeping creature of fourteen, she was taken into the Barclay household and, as Mrs. Barclay so often said, "treated more like one of my own than a bond-girl from the poorhouse." She had first choice of the clothing cast off by Miss Julia and Miss Clara. She was permitted to sit in the same room, and learn what she could, when the schoolmaster came to give private lessons to the Barclay girls. She waited on table, of course, and helped in the kitchen, and made beds, and dusted and scrubbed. But then she had been taught to spin and to sew and to knit. And she was permitted, indeed encouraged, to sit with the Barclays in the meetinghouse, at the convenient end of the pew, where she could worship the Barclays' God and assist with the Barclay wraps at the beginning and end of the service. And now, to complete her rewards, she had been granted the hand of a rejected Barclay suitor.

Mr. Hathaway was Barclay's agent at Bristol Creek, where he sold rum and gunpowder and corn meal and such things to the fishermen and hunters, and bought split cod — fresh, pickled or dry — and ran a small sawmill, and cut and shipped firewood by schooner to Port Marriott, and managed a farm, all for a salary of fifty pounds, Halifax currency, per year. Hathaway was a most capable fellow, Mr. Barclay often acknowledged. But when after fifteen capable years he came seeking a wife, and cast a sheep's eye first at Miss Julia, and then at Miss Clara, Mrs. Barclay observed with a sniff that Hathaway was looking a bit high.

So he was. The older daughter of Port Marriott's most prosperous merchant was even then receiving polite attentions from Mr. Gamage, the new collector of customs, and a connection of the Halifax Gamages, as Mrs. Barclay was fond of pointing out. And Miss Clara was going to Halifax in the spring to learn the gentle art of playing the pianoforte, and incidentally to display her charms to the naval and military young gentlemen who thronged the Halifax drawingrooms. The dear girls laughed behind their hands whenever long solemn Mr. Hathaway came to town aboard one of the Barclay vessels and called at the big house under the elms. Mrs. Barclay bridled at Hathaway's presumption, but shrewd Mr. Barclay narrowed his little black eyes and took snuff and said "Ha! Humph!"

It was plain to Mr. Barclay that an emergency had arisen. Hathaway was a good man — in his place; and Hathaway must be kept content there, to go on making profit for Mr. Barclay at a cost of only £50 a year. 'Twas a pity Hathaway couldn't satisfy himself with one of the fishermen's girls at the Creek, but there 'twas. If Hathaway had set his mind on a town miss, then a town miss he must have; but she must be the right kind, the sort who would content herself and Hathaway at Bristol Creek and not go nagging the man to remove and try his capabilities elsewhere. At once Mr. Barclay thought of Kezia — dear little Kezzie. A colourless little creature but quiet and well-mannered and pious, and only twenty-two.

Mr. Hathaway was nearly forty and far from handsome, and he had a rather cold, seeking way about him — useful in business of course — that rubbed women the wrong way. Privately Mr. Barclay thought Hathaway lucky to get Kezia. But it was a nice match for the girl, better than anything she could have expected. He impressed that upon her and introduced the suitor from Bristol

Creek. Mr. Hathaway spent two or three evenings courting Kezia in the kitchen — Kezia in a quite good gown of Miss Clara's, gazing out at the November moon on the snow, murmuring now and again in the tones of someone in a rather dismal trance, while the kitchen help listened behind one door and the Barclay girls giggled behind another.

The decision, reached mainly by the Barclays, was that Mr. Hathaway should come to Port Marriott aboard the packet schooner on December twenty-third, to be married in the Barclay parlour and then take his bride home for Christmas. But an unforeseen circumstance had changed all this. The circumstance was a ship, "from Mogador in Barbary" as Mr. Barclay wrote afterwards in the salvage claim, driven off her course by gales and wrecked at the very entrance to Bristol Creek. She was a valuable wreck, laden with such queer things as goatskins in pickle, almonds, wormseed, pomegranate skins and gum arabic, and capable Mr. Hathaway had lost no time in salvage for the benefit of his employer.

As a result he could not come to Port Marriott for a wedding or anything else. A storm might blow up at any time and demolish this fat prize. He dispatched a note by Black Sam, urging Mr. Barclay to send Kezia and the preacher by return. It was not the orthodox note of an impatient sweetheart, but it said that he had moved into his new house by the Creek and found it "extream empty lacking a woman," and it suggested delicately that while his days were full, the nights were dull.

Kezia was no judge of distance. She rode for what she considered a reasonable time and then slid off and tied the brown horse to a maple tree beside the path. She had brought a couple of lamp wicks to tie about her shoes, to keep them from coming off in the snow, and she set out afoot in the big splayed tracks of Black Sam. The soft snow came almost to her knees in places and she lifted her skirts high. The path was no wider than the span of a man's arms, cut out with axes years before. She stumbled over a concealed stump from time to time, and the huckleberry bushes dragged at her cloak, but the effort warmed her. It had been cold, sitting on the horse with the wind blowing up her legs.

After a time the preacher overtook her, riding awkwardly and holding the reins in a nervous grip. The stirrups were too short for his long black-stockinged legs. He called out cheerfully as he passed, "Are you all right, Miss?" She nodded, standing aside with her back to a tree. When he disappeared ahead, with a last flutter of black shawl tassels in the wind, she picked up her skirts and went on. The path climbed and dropped monotonously over a succession of wooded ridges. Here and there in a hollow she heard water running, and the creak of frosty poles underfoot, and knew she was crossing a small stream, and once the trail ran across a wide swamp on half-rotten corduroy, wind-swept and bare of snow.

She found the horse tethered clumsily not far ahead, and the tracks of the preacher going on. She had to lead the horse to a stump so she could mount, and when she passed Mr. Mears again she called out, "Please, sir, next time leave the horse by a stump or a rock so I can get on." In his quaint old-country accent he murmured, "I'm very sorry," and gazed down at the snow. She forgot she was riding astride until she had passed him, and then she flushed, and gave the indignant horse a cut of the switch. Next time she remembered and swung her right leg back where it should be, and tucked the skirts modestly about her ankles; but young Mr. Mears looked down at the snow anyway, and after that she did not trouble to shift when she overtook him.

The ridges became steeper, and the streams roared under the ice and snow in the swales. They emerged upon the high tableland between Port Marriott and Bristol Creek, a gusty wilderness of young hardwood scrub struggling up amongst the gray snags of an old forest fire, and now that they were out of the gloomy softwoods they could see a stretch of sky. It was blue-grey and forbidding, and the wind whistling up from the invisible sea felt raw on the cheek. At their next meeting Kezia said, "It's going to snow."

She had no knowledge of the trail but she guessed that they were not much more than half way across the cape. On this high barren the track was no longer straight and clear, it meandered amongst the meagre hardwood clumps where the path-makers had not bothered to cut, and only Black Sam's footprints really marked it for her unaccustomed eyes. The preacher nodded vaguely at her remark. The woods, like everything else about his chosen mission field, were new and very interesting, and he could not understand the alarm in her voice. He looked confidently at Black Sam's tracks.

Kezia tied the horse farther on and began her spell of walking. Her shoes were solid things, the kind of shoes Mr. Barclay invoiced as "a Common Strong sort, for women, Five Shillings"; but the snow worked into them and melted and saturated the leather. Her feet were numb every time she slid down from the horse and it took several minutes of stumbling through the snow to bring back an aching warmth. Beneath her arm she clutched the small bundle which contained all she had in the world — two flannel nightgowns, a shift of linen, three pairs of stout wool stockings — and of course Mr. Barclay's wedding gift for Mr. Hathaway.

Now as she plunged along she felt the first sting of snow on her face and, looking up, saw the stuff borne on the wind in small hard pellets that fell amongst the bare hardwoods and set up a whisper everywhere. When Mr. Mears rode up to her the snow was thick in their faces, like flung salt.

"It's a nor-easter!" she cried up to him. She knew the meaning of snow from the sea. She had been born in a fishing village down the coast.

"Yes," mumbled the preacher, and drew a fold of the shawl about his face. He disappeared. She struggled on, gasping, and after what seemed a tremendous journey came upon him standing alone and bewildered, looking off somewhere to the right.

"The horse!" he shouted. "I got off him, and before I could fasten the reins some snow fell off a branch — startled him, you know — and he ran off, over that way." He gestured with a mittened hand. "I must fetch him back," he added confusedly.

"No!" Kezia cried. "Don't you try. You'd only get lost. So would I. Oh, dear! This is awful. We'll have to go on, the best we can."

He was doubtful. The horse tracks looked very plain. But Kezia was looking at Black Sam's tracks, and tugging his arm. He gave in, and they struggled along for half an hour or so. Then the last trace of the old footprints vanished.

"What shall we do now?" the preacher asked, astonished.

"I don't know," whispered Kezia, and leaned against a dead pine stub in an attitude of weariness and indifference that dismayed him.

"We must keep moving, my dear, mustn't we? I mean, we can't stay here."

"Can't stay here," she echoed.

"Down there — a hollow, I think. I see some hemlock trees, or are they pines? — I'm never quite sure. Shelter, anyway."

"Shelter," muttered Kezia.

He took her by the hand and like a pair of lost children they dragged their steps into the deep snow of the hollow. The trees were tall spruces, a thick bunch in a ravine, where they had escaped the old fire. A stream thundered amongst them somewhere. There was no wind in this place, only the fine snow whirling thickly down between the trees like a sediment from the storm overhead.

"Look!" cried Mr. Mears. A hut loomed out of the whiteness before them, a small structure of moss-chinked logs with a roof of poles and birch-bark. It had an abandoned look. Long streamers of moss hung out between the logs. On the roof shreds of birch-bark wavered gently in the drifting snow. The door stood half open and a thin drift of snow lay along the split-pole floor. Instinctively Kezia went to the stone hearth. There were old ashes sodden with rain down the chimney and now frozen to a cake.

"Have you got flint and steel?" she asked. She saw in his eyes something dazed and forlorn. He shook his head, and she was filled with a sudden anger, not so much at him as at Mr. Barclay and that — that Hathaway, and all the rest of menkind. They ruled the world and made such a sorry mess of it. In a small fury she began to rummage about the hut.

There was a crude bed of poles and brushwood by the fireplace — brushwood so old that only a few brown needles clung to the twigs. A rough bench whittled from a pine log, with round birch sticks for legs. A broken earthenware pot in a corner. In another some ash-wood frames such as trappers used for stretching skins. Nothing else. The single window was covered with a stretched moose-bladder, cracked and dry-rotten, but it still let in some daylight while keeping out the snow.

She scooped up the snow from the floor with her mittened hands, throwing it outside, and closed the door carefully, dropping the bar into place, as if she could shut out and bar the cold in such a fashion. The air inside was frigid. Their breath hung visible in the dim light from the window. Young Mr. Mears dropped on his wet knees and began to pray in a loud voice. His face was pinched with cold and his teeth rattled as he prayed. He was a pitiable object.

"Prayers won't keep you warm," said Kezia crossly.

He looked up, amazed at the change in her. She had seemed such a meek little thing. Kezia was surprised at herself, and surprisingly she went on, "You'd far better take off those wet moccasins and stockings and shake the snow out of your clothes." She set the example, vigorously shaking out her skirts and Miss Julia's cloak, and she turned her small back on him and took off her own shoes and stockings, and pulled on dry stockings from her bundle. She threw him a pair.

"Put those on."

"I'm afraid they wouldn't go on."

She tossed him one of her flannel nightgowns. "Then take off your stockings and wrap your feet and legs in that."

He obeyed, in an embarrassed silence. She rolled her eyes upward, for his modesty's sake, and saw a bundle on one of the low rafters — the late owner's bedding, stowed away from mice. She stood on the bench and pulled down three bearskins, marred with bullet holes. A rank and musty smell arose in the cold. She considered the find gravely.

"You take them," Mr. Mears said gallantly. "I shall be quite all right."

"You'll be dead by morning, and so shall I," she answered vigorously, "if you don't do what I say. We've got to roll up in these."

"Together?" he cried in horror.

"Of course! To keep each other warm. It's the only way."

She spread the skins on the floor, hair uppermost, one overlapping another, and dragged the flustered young man down beside her, clutching him in her arms, and rolled with him, over, and over again, so that they became a single shapeless heap in the corner farthest from the draft between door and chimney.

"Put your arms around me," commanded the new Kezia, and he obeyed.

"Now," she said, "you can pray. God helps those that help themselves."

He prayed aloud for a long time, and privately called upon heaven to witness the purity of his thoughts in this strange and shocking situation. He said "Amen" at last; and "Amen," echoed Kezia, piously.

They lay silent a long time, breathing on each other's necks and hearing their own hearts — poor Mr. Mears' fluttering in an agitated way, Kezia's as steady as a clock. A delicious warmth crept over them. They relaxed in each other's arms. Outside, the storm hissed in the spruce tops and set up an occasional cold moan in the cracked clay chimney. The down-swirling snow brushed softly against the bladder pane.

"I'm warm now," murmured Kezia. "Are you?"

"Yes. How long must we stay here like this?"

"Till the storm's over, of course. Tomorrow, probably. Nor'easters usually blow themselves out in a day and a night, 'specially when they come up sharp, like this one. Are you hungry?"

"No."

"Abigail — that's the black cook at Barclay's — gave me bread and cheese in a handkerchief. I've got it in my bundle. Mr. Barclay thought we ought to reach Bristol Creek by supper time, but Nabby said I must have a bite to eat on the road. She's a good kind thing, old Nabby. Sure you're not hungry?"

"Quite. I feel somewhat fatigued but not hungry."

"Then we'll eat the bread and cheese for breakfast. Have you got a watch?"

"No, I'm sorry. They cost such a lot of money. In Lady Huntingdon's Connexion we —"

"Oh well, it doesn't matter. It must be about four o'clock — the light's getting dim. Of course, the dark comes very quick in a snowstorm."

"Dark," echoed young Mr. Mears drowsily. Kezia's hair, washed last night for the wedding journey, smelled pleasant so close to his face. It reminded him of something. He went to sleep dreaming of his mother, with his face snug in the curve of Kezia's neck and shoulder, and smiling, and muttering words that Kezia could not catch. After a time she kissed his cheek. It seemed a very natural thing to do.

Soon she was dozing herself, and dreaming, too; but her dreams were full of forbidding faces — Mr. Barclay's, Mrs. Barclay's, Mr. Hathaway's; especially Mr. Hathaway's. Out of a confused darkness Mr. Hathaway's hard acquisitive gaze searched her shrinking flesh like a cold wind. Then she was shuddering by the kitchen fire at Barclay's, accepting Mr. Hathaway's courtship and wishing she was dead. In the midst of that sickening wooing she wakened sharply.

It was quite dark in the hut. Mr. Mears was breathing quietly against her throat. But there was a sound of heavy steps outside, muffled in the snow and somehow felt rather than heard. She shook the young man and he wakened with a start, clutching her convulsively.

"Sh-h-h!" she warned. "Something's moving outside." She felt him stiffen.

"Bears?" he whispered.

Silly! thought Kezia. People from the old country could think of nothing but bears in the woods. Besides, bears holed up in winter. A caribou, perhaps. More likely a moose. Caribou moved inland before this, to the wide mossy bogs up the river, away from the coastal storms. Again the sound.

"There!" hissed the preacher. Their hearts beat rapidly together.

"The door — you fastened it, didn't you?"

"Yes," she said. Suddenly she knew.

"Unroll, quick!" she cried . . . "No, not this way — your way."

They unrolled, ludicrously, and the girl scrambled up and ran across the floor in her stockinged feet, and fumbled with the rotten door-bar. Mr. Mears attempted to follow but he tripped over the nightgown still wound about his feet, and fell with a crash. He was up again in a moment, catching up the clumsy wooden bench for a weapon, his bare feet slapping on the icy floor. He tried to shoulder her aside, crying "Stand back! Leave it to me!" and waving the bench uncertainly in the darkness.

She laughed excitedly. "Silly!" she said. "It's the horse." She flung the door open. In the queer ghostly murk of a night filled with snow they beheld a large dark shape. The shape whinnied softly and thrust a long face into the doorway. Mr. Mears dropped the bench, astonished.

"He got over his fright and followed us here somehow," Kezia said, and laughed again. She put her arms about the snowy head and laid her face against it.

"Good horse! Oh, good, good horse!"

"What are you going to do?" the preacher murmured over her shoulder. After the warmth of their nest in the furs they were shivering in this icy atmosphere.

"Bring him in, of course. We can't leave him out in the storm." She caught the bridle and urged the horse inside with expert clucking sounds. The animal hesitated, but fear of the storm and a desire for shelter and company decided him. In he came, tramping ponderously on the split-pole floor. The preacher closed and barred the door.

"And now?" he asked.

"Back to the furs. Quick! It's awful cold."

Rolled in the furs once more, their arms went about each other instinctively, and the young man's face found the comfortable nook against Kezia's soft throat. But sleep was difficult after that. The horse whinnied gently from time to time, and stamped about the floor. The decayed poles crackled dangerously under his hoofs whenever he moved, and Kezia trembled, thinking he might break through and frighten himself, and flounder about till he tumbled the crazy hut about their heads. She called out to him "Steady boy! Steady!"

It was a long night. The pole floor made its irregularities felt through the thickness of fur; and because there seemed nowhere to put their arms but about each other the flesh became cramped, and spread its protest along the bones. They were stiff and sore when the first light of morning stained the window. They unrolled and stood up thankfully, and tramped up and down the floor, threshing their arms in an effort to fight off the gripping cold. Kezia undid her bundle in a corner and brought forth Nabby's bread and cheese, and they ate it sitting together on the edge of the brushwood bed with the skins about their shoulders. Outside the snow had ceased.

"We must set off at once," the preacher said. "Mr. Hathaway will be anxious."

Kezia was silent. She did not move, and he looked at her curiously. She appeared very fresh, considering the hardships of the previous day and the night. He passed a hand over his cheeks and thought how unclean he must appear in her eyes, with this stubble on his pale face.

"Mr. Hathaway —" he began again.

"I'm not going to Mr. Hathaway," Kezia said quietly.

"But — the wedding!"

There'll be no wedding. I don't want to marry Mr. Hathaway. 'Twas Mr. Hathaway's idea, and Mr. and Mrs. Barclay's. They wanted me to marry him."

"What will the Barclays say, my dear?"

She shrugged. "I've been their bond-girl ever since I was fourteen, but I'm not a slave like poor black Nabby, to be handed over, body and soul, whenever it suits."

"Your soul belongs to God," said Mr. Mears devoutly.

"And my body belongs to me."

He was a little shocked at this outspokenness but he said gently, "Of course. To give oneself in marriage without true affection would be an offence in the sight of heaven. But what will Mr. Hathaway say?"

"Well, to begin with, he'll ask where I spent the night, and I'll have to tell the truth. I'll have to say I bundled with you in a hut in the woods."

"Bundled?"

"A custom the people brought with them from Connecticut when they came to settle in Nova Scotia. Poor folk still do it. Sweethearts, I mean. It saves fire and candles when you're courting on a winter evening. It's harmless — they keep their clothes on, you see, like you and me — but Mr. Barclay and the other Methody people are terrible set against it. Mr. Barclay got old Mr. Mings — he's the Methody preacher that died last year — to make a sermon against it. Mr. Mings said bundling was an invention of the devil."

"Then if you go back to Mr. Barclay —"

"He'll ask me the same question and I'll have to give him the same answer. I couldn't tell a lie, could I?" She turned a pair of round blue eyes and met his embarrassed gaze.

"No! No, you mustn't lie. Whatever shall we do?" he murmured in a dazed voice. Again she was silent, looking modestly down her small nose.

"It's so very strange," he floundered. "This country — there are so many things I don't know, so many things to learn. You — I — we shall have to tell the truth, of course. Doubtless I can find a place in the Lord's service somewhere else, but what about you, poor girl?"

"I heard say the people at Scrod Harbour want a preacher."

"But — the tale would follow me, wouldn't it, my dear? This — er — bundling with a young woman?"

" 'Twouldn't matter if the young woman was your wife."

"Eh?" His mouth fell open. He was like an astonished child, for all his preacher's clothes and the new beard on his jaws.

"I'm a good girl," Kezia said, inspecting her foot. "I can read and write, and know all the tunes in the psalter. And — and you need someone to look after you."

He considered the truth of that. Then he murmured uncertainly, "We'd be very poor, my dear. The Connexion gives some support, but of course —"

"I've always been poor," Kezia said. She sat very still but her cold fingers writhed in her lap.

He did something then that made her want to cry. He took hold of her hands and bowed his head and kissed them.

"It's strange — I don't even know your name, my dear."

"It's Kezia — Kezia Barnes."

He said quietly, "You're a brave girl, Kezia Barnes, and I shall try to be a good husband to you. Shall we go?"

"Hadn't you better kiss me, first?" Kezia said faintly.

He put his lips awkwardly to hers; and then, as if the taste of her clean mouth itself provided strength and purpose, he kissed her again, and firmly. She threw her arms about his neck.

"Oh, Mr. Mears!"

How little he knew about everything! He hadn't even known enough to wear two or three pairs of stockings inside those roomy moccasins, nor to carry a pair of dry ones. Yesterday's wet stockings were lying like sticks on the frosty floor. She showed him how to knead the hard-frozen moccasins into softness, and while he worked at the stiff leather she tore up one of her wedding bed-shirts and wound the flannel strips about his legs and feet. It looked very queer when she had finished, and they both laughed.

They were chilled to the bone when they set off, Kezia on the horse and the preacher walking ahead, holding the reins. When they regained the slope where they had lost the path, Kezia said, "The sun rises somewhere between east and southeast, this time of year. Keep it on your left shoulder for a while. That will take us back towards Port Marriott."

When they came to the green timber she told him to shift the sun to his left eye.

"Have you changed your mind?" he asked cheerfully. The exercise had warmed him.

"No, but the sun moves across the sky."

"Ah! What a wise little head it is!"

They came over a ridge of mixed hemlock and hardwood and looked upon a long swale full of bare hackmatacks.

"Look!" the girl cried. The white slot of the axe path showed clearly in the trees at the foot of the swale, and again where it entered the dark mass of the pines beyond.

"Praise the Lord!" said Mr. Mears.

When at last they stood in the trail, Kezia slid down from the horse.

"No!" Mr. Mears protested.

"Ride-and-tie," she said firmly. "That's the way we came, and that's the way we'll go. Besides, I want to get warm."

He climbed up clumsily and smiled down at her.

"What shall we do when we get to Port Marriott, my dear?"

"Get the New Light preacher to marry us, and catch the packet for Scrod Harbour."

He nodded and gave a pull at his broad hat brim. She thought of everything. A splendid helpmeet for the world's wilderness. He saw it all very humbly now as a dispensation of Providence.

Kezia watched him out of sight. Then, swiftly, she undid her bundle and took out the thing that had lain there (and on her conscience) through the night — the tinderbox — Mr. Barclay's wedding gift to Mr. Hathaway. She flung it into the woods and walked on, skirts lifted, in the track of the horse, humming a psalm tune to the silent trees and the snow.

ABOUT THE LINES

1 Draw a map of the journey taken by Kezia Barnes and Mr. Mears, and label the important places. In a legend underneath the map, indicate in point form the events that occur at each place.

2 Imagine that you are Kezia Barnes and explain in a short letter to a friend the steps you took to become Mr. Mears' wife.

3 Working with your partners, make a glossary of the words used in this story that have either gone out of everyday use or have changed in meaning since the time period in which "The Wedding Gift" is set. For each word, give the old meaning and the present-day meaning, if there is one. Compare your list with those of other groups, and together produce a combined glossary.

4 List the incidents that indicate that Mr. Mears is a naive newcomer to Canada.

BETWEEN THE LINES

1 In one paragraph describe the relationship between Kezia Barnes and the Barclay family. This opening sentence may help you to get started:
Although the Barclays treated Kezia well, it was quite obvious that she was not one of the family.

2 Speaking as Kezia Barnes, explain to your partners why the tinderbox lay on your conscience throughout that memorable night.

3 Imagine that you are Mr. Mears and confide in your journal why you see your upcoming marriage to Kezia Barnes as a "dispensation of Providence" (a great blessing).

or

Imagine that you are Kezia Barnes and confide in your journal your gratitude for the sudden snowstorm.

4 While the story is rather amusing and also has a happy ending, the writer gives several hints that life in Nova Scotia in 1794 was not equally enjoyable for all people. With your partners, identify the negative features of life at the time and together produce a paragraph on the topic of "The Good Old Days?"

5 Discuss with your partners how the first paragraph of the story prepares the reader for what is to come and how the last paragraph effectively concludes the story. Present your findings to another group, compare their conclusions with yours, and together produce a combined set of notes.

6 Look up the definition of "irony" in the glossary (see p. 352). Make sure that you understand the term. With your partners, find at least four places in this story where the author uses an ironic tone, and for each, explain in a sentence or two how the irony adds to the reader's enjoyment of the story.

BEYOND THE LINES

1 Working in a group of four, present to the class a debate on the following resolution:
Men are dreamers who would be helpless without the practicality of women.

2 Imagine that you are the casting director for a movie version of "The Wedding Gift." Choose a well-known actor or actress to play each character and justify each of your choices with a brief note. Compare your choices with your partners'.

3 Produce a copy of the *Scrod Harbour Times* of 1819, in which the community celebrates the twenty-fifth anniversary of the arrival of Reverend Mears and his wife. You should include: some of the events of the years the couple spent in the town, other local news, editorials, and perhaps classified advertisements. Note that a newspaper reflects the community in which it is published.

4 Script and then dramatize a conversation between any of the following people on the subject of Kezia's disappearance:
Mr. and Mrs. Barclay;
Mr. Hathaway and Mr. Barclay;
Miss Julia and Miss Clara.

THE OLD DEMON
Pearl S. Buck

An old woman and an "old devil of a river"

Old Mrs. Wang knew of course that there was a war. Everybody had known for a long time that there was war going on and that Japanese were killing Chinese. But still it was not real and no more than hearsay since none of the Wangs had been killed. The village of Three Mile Wangs on the flat banks of the Yellow River, which was old Mrs. Wang's clan village, had never even seen a Japanese. This was how they came to be talking about Japanese at all.

It was evening and early summer, and after her supper Mrs. Wang had climbed the dike steps, as she did every day, to see how high the river had risen. She was much more afraid of the river than of the Japanese. She knew what the river would do. And one by one the villagers had followed her up the dike, and now they stood staring down at the malicious yellow water, curling along like a lot of snakes, and biting at the high dike banks.

"I never saw it as high as this so early," Mrs. Wang said. She sat down on a bamboo stool that her grandson, Little Pig, had brought for her, and spat into the water.

"It's worse than the Japanese, this old devil of a river," Little Pig said recklessly.

"Fool!" Mrs. Wang said quickly. "The river god will hear you. Talk about something else."

So they had gone on talking about the Japanese. . . . How, for instance, asked Wang, the baker, who was old Mrs. Wang's nephew twice removed, would they know the Japanese when they saw them?

Mrs. Wang at this point said positively, "You'll know them. I once saw a foreigner. He was taller than the eaves of my house and he had mud-coloured

31

hair and eyes the colour of a fish's eyes. Anyone who does not look like us — that is a Japanese."

Everybody listened to her since she was the oldest woman in the village and whatever she said settled something.

Then Little Pig spoke up in his disconcerting way. "You can't see them, Grandmother. They hide up in the sky in airplanes."

Mrs. Wang did not answer immediately. Once she would have said positively, "I shall not believe in an airplane until I see it." But so many things had been true which she had not believed — the Empress, for instance, whom she had not believed dead, was dead. The republic, again, she had not believed in because she did not know what it was. She still did not know, but they had said for a long time there had been one. So now she merely stared quietly about the dike where they all sat around her. It was very pleasant and cool, and she felt nothing mattered if the river did not rise to flood.

"I don't believe in the Japanese," she said flatly.

They laughed at her a little, but no one spoke. Someone lit her pipe — it was Little Pig's wife, who was her favourite, and she smoked it.

"Sing, Little Pig!" someone called.

So Little Pig began to sing an old song in a high quavering voice, and old Mrs. Wang listened and forgot the Japanese. The evening was beautiful, the sky so clear and still that the willows overhanging the dike were reflected even in the muddy water. Everything was at peace. The thirty-odd houses which made up the village straggled along beneath them. Nothing could break this peace. After all, the Japanese were only human beings.

"I doubt those airplanes," she said mildly to Little Pig when he stopped singing.

But without answering her, he went on to another song.

Year in and year out she had spent the summer evenings like this on the dike. The first time she was seventeen and a bride, and her husband had shouted to her to come out of the house and up the dike, and she had come, blushing and twisting her hands together, to hide among the women while the men roared at her and made jokes about her. All the same, they had liked her. "A pretty piece of meat in your bowl," they had said to her husband. "Feet a trifle big," he had answered deprecatingly. But she could see he was pleased, and so gradually her shyness went away.

He, poor man, had been drowned in a flood when he was still young. And it had taken her years to get him prayed out of Buddhist purgatory. Finally she had grown tired of it, what with the child and the land all on her back, and so when the priest said coaxingly, "Another ten pieces of silver and he'll be out entirely," she asked, "What's he got in there yet?"

"Only his right hand," the priest said, encouraging her.

Well, then, her patience broke. Ten dollars! It would feed them for the winter. Besides, she had had to hire labour for her share of repairing the dike, too, so there would be no more floods.

"If it's only one hand, he can pull himself out," she said firmly.

She often wondered if he had, poor silly fellow. As like as not, she had often thought gloomily in the night, he was still lying there, waiting for her to do something about it. That was the sort of man he was. Well, someday, perhaps, when Little Pig's wife had had the first baby safely and she had a little extra, she might go back to finish him out of purgatory. There was no real hurry, though. . . .

"Grandmother, you must go in," Little Pig's wife's soft voice said. "There is a mist rising from the river now that the sun is gone."

"Yes, I suppose I must," old Mrs. Wang agreed. She gazed at the river a moment. That river — it was full of good and evil together. It would water the fields when it was curbed and checked, but then if an inch were allowed in, it crashed through like a roaring dragon. That was how her husband had been swept away — careless, he was, about his bit of the dike. He was always going to mend it, always going to pile more earth on top of it, and then in a night the river rose and broke through. He had run out of the house, and she had climbed on the roof with the child and had saved herself and it while he was drowned. Well, they had pushed the river back again behind its dikes, and it had stayed there this time. Every day she herself walked up and down the length of the dike for which the village was responsible and examined it. The men laughed and said, "If anything is wrong with the dikes, Granny will tell us."

It had never occurred to any of them to move the village away from the river. The Wangs had lived there for generations, and some had always escaped the floods and had fought the river more fiercely than ever afterward.

Little Pig suddenly stopped singing.

"The moon is coming up!" he cried. "That's not good. Airplanes come out on moonlight nights."

"Where do you learn all this about airplanes!" old Mrs. Wang exclaimed. "It is tiresome to me," she added, so severely that no one spoke. In this silence, leaning upon the arm of Little Pig's wife, she descended slowly the earthen steps which led down into the village, using her long pipe in the other hand as a walking stick. Behind her the villagers came down, one by one, to bed. No one moved before she did, but none stayed long after her. And in her own bed at last, behind the blue cotton mosquito curtains which Little Pig's wife fastened securely, she fell peacefully asleep. She had lain awake a little while thinking about the Japanese and wondering why they wanted to fight. Only very coarse persons wanted wars. In her mind, she saw large coarse persons. If they came one must wheedle them, she thought, invite them to drink tea, and explain to them, reasonably — only why should they come to a peaceful farming village . . . ?

So she was not in the least prepared for Little Pig's wife screaming at her that the Japanese had come. She sat up in bed muttering. "The tea bowls — the tea —"

"Grandmother, there's no time!" Little Pig's wife screamed. "They're here — they're here!"

"Where?" old Mrs. Wang cried, now awake.

"In the sky!" Little Pig's wife wailed.

They had all run out at that, into the clear early dawn, and gazed up. There, like wild geese flying in autumn, were great birdlike shapes.

"But what are they?" old Mrs. Wang cried.

And then, like a silver egg dropping, something drifted straight down and fell at the far end of the village in a field. A fountain of earth flew up, and they all ran to see it. There was a hole thirty feet across, as big as a pond. They were so astonished they could not speak, and then, before anyone could say anything, another and another egg began to fall and everybody was running, running. . . .

Everybody, that is, but Mrs. Wang. When Little Pig's wife seized her hand to drag her along, old Mrs. Wang pulled away and sat down against the bank of the dike.

"I can't run," she remarked. "I haven't run in seventy years, since before my feet were bound. You go on. Where's Little Pig?" She looked around. Little Pig was already gone. "Like his grandfather," she remarked, "always the first to run."

But Little Pig's wife would not leave her, not, that is, until old Mrs. Wang reminded her that it was her duty.

"If Little Pig is dead," she said, "then it is necessary that his son be born alive." And when the girl still hesitated, she struck at her gently with her pipe. "Go on — go on," she exclaimed.

So unwillingly, because now they could scarcely hear each other speak for the roar of the dipping planes, Little Pig's wife went on with the others.

By now, although only a few minutes had passed, the village was in ruins and the straw roofs and wooden beams were blazing. Everybody was gone. As they passed they had shrieked at old Mrs. Wang to come on, and she had called back pleasantly: "I'm coming — I'm coming!"

But she did not go. She sat quite alone watching now what was an extraordinary spectacle. For soon other planes came, from where she did not know, but they attacked the first ones. The sun came up over the fields of ripening wheat, and in the clear summery air the planes wheeled and darted and spat at each other. When this was over, she thought, she would go back into the village and see if anything was left. Here and there a wall stood, supporting a roof. She could not see her own house from here. But she was not unused to war. Once bandits had looted their village, and houses had been burned then, too. Well, now it had happened again. Burning houses one could see often, but not this darting silvery shining battle in the air. She understood none of it — not what those things were, nor how they stayed up in the sky. She simply sat, growing hungry, and watching.

"I'd like to see one close," she said aloud. And at that moment, as though in answer, one of them pointed suddenly downward, and, wheeling and twisting as though it were wounded, it fell head down in a field which Little Pig had plowed only yesterday for soybeans. And in an instant the sky was empty again and there was only this wounded thing on the ground and herself.

She hoisted herself carefully from the earth. At her age she need be afraid of nothing. She could, she decided, go and see what it was. So leaning on her bamboo pipe, she made her way slowly across the fields. Behind her in the sudden stillness two or three village dogs appeared and followed, creeping close to her in their terror. When they drew near to the fallen plane, they barked furiously. Then she hit them with her pipe.

34

"Be quiet," she scolded, "there's already been noise enough to split my ears!"
She tapped the airplane.

"Metal," she told the dogs. "Silver, doubtless," she added. Melted up, it would make them all rich.

She walked around it, examining it closely. What made it fly? It seemed dead. Nothing moved or made a sound within it. Then, coming to the side to which it tipped, she saw a young man in it, slumped into a heap in a little seat. The dogs growled, but she struck at them again and they fell back.

"Are you dead?" she inquired politely.

The young man moved a little at her voice, but did not speak. She drew nearer and peered into the hole in which he sat. His side was bleeding.

"Wounded!" she exclaimed. She took his wrist. It was warm, but inert, and when she let it go, it dropped against the side of the hole. She stared at him. He had black hair and a dark skin like a Chinese and still he did not look like a Chinese.

"He must be a Southerner," she thought. Well, the chief thing was, he was alive.

"You had better come out," she remarked. "I'll put some herb plaster on your side."

The young man muttered something dully.

"What did you say?" she asked. But he did not say it again.

"I am still quite strong," she decided after a moment. So she reached in and seized him about the waist and pulled him out slowly, panting a good deal. Fortunately he was rather a little fellow and very light. When she had him on the ground, he seemed to find his feet; and he stood shakily and clung to her, and she held him up.

"Now if you can walk to my house," she said, "I'll see if it is there."

Then he said something, quite clearly. She listened and could not understand a word of it. She pulled away from him and stared.

"What's that?" she asked.

He pointed at the dogs. They were standing growling, their ruffs up. Then he spoke again, and as he spoke he crumpled to the ground. The dogs fell on him, so that she had to beat them off with her hands.

"Get away!" she shouted. "Who told you to kill him?"

And then, when they had slunk back, she heaved him somehow onto her back; and, trembling, half carrying, half pulling him, she dragged him to the ruined village and laid him in the street while she went to find her house, taking the dogs with her.

Her house was quite gone. She found the place easily enough. This was where it should be, opposite the water gate into the dike. She had always watched that gate herself. Miraculously it was not injured now, nor was the dike broken. It would be easy enough to rebuild the house. Only, for the present, it was gone.

So she went back to the young man. He was lying as she had left him, propped against the dike, panting and very pale. He had opened his coat and he had a little bag from which he was taking out strips of cloth and a bottle of something. And again he spoke, and again she understood nothing. Then he made signs and she saw it was water he wanted, so she took up a broken pot from one of many blown about the street, and, going up the dike, she filled it with river water and brought it down again and washed his wound, and she tore off the strips he made from the rolls of bandaging. He knew how to put the cloth over the gaping wound and he made signs to her, and she followed these signs. All the time he was trying to tell her something, but she could understand nothing.

"You must be from the South, sir," she said. It was easy to see that he had education. He looked very clever. "I have heard your language is different from ours." She laughed a little to put him at his ease, but he only stared at her sombrely with dull eyes. So she said brightly, "Now if I could find something for us to eat, it would be nice."

He did not answer. Indeed he lay back, panting still more heavily, and stared into space as though she had not spoken.

"You would be better with food," she went on. "And so would I," she added. She was beginning to feel unbearably hungry.

It occurred to her that in Wang the baker's shop there might be some bread. Even if it were dusty with fallen mortar, it would still be bread. She would go and see. But before she went she moved the soldier a little so that he lay in the edge of shadow cast by a willow tree that grew in the bank of the dike. Then she went to the baker's shop. The dogs were gone.

The baker's shop was, like everything else, in ruins. No one was there. At first she saw nothing but the mass of crumpled earthen walls. But then she remembered that the oven was just inside the door, and the door frame still stood erect, supporting one end of the roof. She stood in this frame, and running her hand in underneath the fallen roof inside, she felt the wooden cover of the iron cauldron. Under this there might be steamed bread. She worked her arm delicately and carefully in. It took quite a long time, but, even so, clouds of lime and dust almost choked her. Nevertheless she was right. She squeezed her hand under the cover and felt the firm smooth skin of the big steamed bread rolls, and one by one she drew out four.

"It's hard to kill an old thing like me," she remarked cheerfully to no one, and she began to eat one of the rolls as she walked back. If she had a bit of garlic and a bowl of tea — but one couldn't have everything in these times.

It was at this moment that she heard voices. When she came in sight of the soldier, she saw surrounding him a crowd of other soldiers, who had apparently come from nowhere. They were staring down at the wounded soldier, whose eyes were now closed.

"Where did you get this Japanese, Old Mother?" they shouted at her.

"What Japanese?" she asked.

"This one!" they shouted.

"Is he a Japanese?" she cried in the greatest astonishment. "But he looks like us — his eyes are black, his skin —"

"Japanese!" one of them shouted at her.

"Well," she said quietly, "he dropped out of the sky."

"Give me that bread!" another shouted.

"Take it," she said, "all except this one for him."

"A Japanese monkey eat good bread?" the soldier shouted.

"I suppose he is hungry also," old Mrs. Wang replied. She began to dislike these men. But then, she had always disliked soldiers.

"I wish you would go away," she said. "What are you doing here? Our village has always been peaceful."

"It certainly looks very peaceful now," one of the men said, grinning, "as peaceful as a grave. Do you know who did that, Old Mother? The Japanese!"

"I suppose so," she agreed. Then she asked. "Why? That's what I don't understand."

"Why? Because they want our land, that's why!"

"Our land!" she repeated. "Why, they can't have our land!"

"Never!" they shouted.

But all this time while they were talking and chewing the bread they had divided among themselves, they were watching the eastern horizon.

"Why do you keep looking east?" old Mrs. Wang now asked.

"The Japanese are coming from there," the man replied who had taken the bread.

"Are you running away from them?" she asked, surprised.

"There are only a handful of us," he said apologetically. "We were left to guard a village — Pao An, in the county of —"

"I know that village," old Mrs. Wang interrupted. "You needn't tell me. I was a girl there. How is the old Pao who keeps the teashop in the main street? He's my brother."

"Everybody is dead there," the man replied. "The Japanese have taken it — a great army of men came with their foreign guns and tanks, so what could we do?"

"Of course, only run," she agreed. Nevertheless she felt dazed and sick. So he was dead, that one brother she had left! She was now the last of her father's family.

But the soldiers were straggling away again leaving her alone.

"They'll be coming, those little black dwarfs," they were saying. "We'd best go on."

Nevertheless, one lingered a moment, the one who had taken the bread, to stare down at the young wounded man, who lay with his eyes shut, not having moved at all.

"Is he dead?" he inquired. Then, before Mrs. Wang could answer, he pulled a short knife out of his belt. "Dead or not, I'll give him a punch or two with this —"

But old Mrs. Wang pushed his arm away.

"No you won't," she said with authority. "If he is dead, then there is no use in sending him into purgatory all in pieces. I am a good Buddhist myself."

The man laughed. "Oh well, he is dead," he answered, and then, seeing his comrades already at a distance, he ran after them.

A Japanese, was he? Old Mrs. Wang, left alone with this inert figure, looked at him tentatively. He was very young, she could see, now that his eyes were closed. His hand, limp in unconsciousness, looked like a boy's hand, unformed and still growing. She felt his wrist but could discern no pulse. She leaned over him and held to his lips the half of her roll which she had not eaten.

"Eat," she said very loudly and distinctly. "Bread!"

But there was no answer. Evidently he was dead. He must have died while she was getting the bread out of the oven.

There was nothing to do then but to finish the bread herself. And when that was done, she wondered if she ought not to follow after Little Pig and his wife and all the villagers. The sun was mounting and it was growing hot. If she were going, she had better go. But first she would climb the dike and see what the direction was. They had gone straight west, and as far as the eye could look westward was a great plain. She might even see a good-sized crowd miles away. Anyway, she could see the next village, and they might all be there.

So she climbed the dike slowly, getting very hot. There was a slight breeze on top of the dike and it felt good. She was shocked to see the river very near the top of the dike. Why, it had risen in the last hour!

"You old demon!" she said severely. Let the river god hear it if he liked. He was evil, that he was — so to threaten flood when there had been all this other trouble.

She stooped and bathed her cheeks and her wrists. The water was quite cold, as though with fresh rains somewhere. Then she stood up and gazed around her. To the west there was nothing except in the far distance the soldiers still half-running, and beyond them the blur of the next village, which stood on a long rise of ground. She had better set out for that village. Doubtless Little Pig and his wife were there waiting for her.

Just as she was about to climb down and start out, she saw something on the eastern horizon. It was at first only an immense cloud of dust. But, as she stared at it, very quickly it became a lot of black dots and shining spots. Then she saw what it was. It was a lot of men — an army. Instantly she knew what army.

"That's the Japanese," she thought. Yes, above them were the buzzing silver planes. They circled about, seeming to search for someone.

"I don't know who you're looking for," she muttered, "unless it's me and Little Pig and his wife. We're the only ones left. You've already killed my brother Pao."

She had almost forgotten that Pao was dead. Now she remembered it acutely. He had such a nice shop — always clean, and the tea good and the best meat dumplings to be had and the price always the same. Pao was a good man. Besides, what about his wife and his seven children? Doubtless they were all killed, too. Now these Japanese were looking for her. It occurred to her that on the dike she could easily be seen. So she clambered hastily down.

It was when she was about halfway down that she thought of the water gate. This old river — it had been a curse to them since time began. Why should it not make up a little now for all the wickedness it had done? It was plotting wickedness again, trying to steal over its banks. Well, why not? She wavered a moment. It was a pity, of course, that the young dead Japanese would be swept into the flood. He was a nice-looking boy, and she had saved him from being stabbed. It was not quite the same thing as saving his life, of course, but still it was a little the same. If he had been alive, he would have been saved. She went over to him and tugged at him until he lay well near the top of the bank. Then she went down again.

She knew perfectly how to open the water gate. Any child knew how to open the sluice for crops. But she knew also how to swing open the whole gate. The question was, could she open it quickly enough to get out of the way?

"I'm only one old woman," she muttered. She hesitated a second more. Well, it would be a pity not to see what sort of a baby Little Pig's wife would have, but one could not see everything. She had seen a great deal in this life. There was an end to what one could see, anyway.

She glanced again to the east. There were the Japanese coming across the plain. They were a long clear line of black, dotted with thousands of glittering points. If she opened this gate, the impetuous water would roar toward them, rushing into the plains, rolling into a wide lake, drowning them, maybe. Certainly they could not keep on marching nearer and nearer to her and to Little Pig and his wife who were waiting for her. Well, Little Pig and his wife — they would wonder about her — but they would never dream of this. It would make a good story — she would have enjoyed telling it.

She turned resolutely to the gate. Well, some people fought with airplanes and some with guns, but you could fight with a river, too, if it were a wicked one like this one. She wrenched out a huge wooden pin. It was slippery with silvery green moss. The rill of water burst into a strong jet. When she wrenched one more pin, the rest would give way themselves. She began pulling at it, and felt it slip a little from its hole.

"I might be able to get myself out of purgatory with this," she thought, "and maybe they'll let me have that old man of mine, too. What's a hand of his to all this? Then we'll —"

The pin slipped away suddenly, and the gate burst flat against her and knocked her breath away. She had only time to gasp, to the river:

"Come on, you old demon!"

Then she felt it seize her and lift her up to the sky. It was beneath her and around her. It rolled her joyfully hither and thither, and then, holding her close and enfolded, it went rushing against the enemy.

ABOUT THE LINES

1 Write a brief character sketch of Mrs. Wang and make specific references to the story to justify your opinions.

2 a. In one sentence, prove that the saying "Like father, like son" holds true for Mr. Wang and Little Pig.

b. Discuss with your partners the similarities between Mrs. Wang and her daughter-in-law.

3 The opening of a short story must catch the attention of the reader and also introduce characters, action, setting, and theme. Make notes on how the author uses the first two paragraphs of "The Old Demon" to achieve these objectives. Now, with your partners, study the opening of any other story in *In Your Own Words* and discuss how effective the introduction is.

BETWEEN THE LINES

1 Discuss with your partners Mrs. Wang's reasons for opening the sluice gate to destroy the approaching Japanese army. Present your material in a paragraph, starting with a sentence such as:
Mrs. Wang's motives for destroying the Japanese are complex.

2 Complete the following unfinished sentences and then, in a small group, discuss and explain your versions:
a. What most angers Mrs. Wang about the Japanese is that . . .
b. Mrs. Wang's treatment of the Japanese airman shows that she . . .
c. Mrs. Wang looks upon the river as . . .

3 Using one or two sentences for each, explain how these excerpts help the reader to understand "The Old Demon." Share your sentences with your partners and revise them where necessary.
a. "She was much more afraid of the river than of the Japanese."
b. "Nothing could break this peace."
c. "That river — it was full of good and evil together."
d. "Is he a Japanese? But he looks like us — his eyes are black, his skin —"

4 The last paragraph of the story deals with the death of Mrs. Wang. With your partners, examine the language used by the authors of "The Forsaken" (see p. 136) and "The Old Demon" to present death in an unusual light. State the attitude of each old woman toward her death.

BEYOND THE LINES

1 Compile an anthology of poems or songs about rivers, such as "Old Man River" or "Morning on the Lièvre." Produce either a written anthology with illustrations and a rationale for each choice, or a taped anthology with a short introduction for each poem or song.

2 Imagine that you are Little Pig's wife, and on your child's tenth birthday tell him or her the story that Mrs. Wang "would have enjoyed telling." With a partner, role play mother and child during this conversation. Remember that children love to ask questions.

3 Write the following newspaper reports of the Japanese attack on Mrs. Wang's village:
a. A press release from the Chinese authorities for publication in a Chinese newspaper.
b. A report filed by a Japanese correspondent covering the war for publication in Japan.
Remember that the point of view will affect the reporting in each case.

THE TOWN DUMP

Wallace Stegner ▮▮▮▮

"If I were a sociologist anxious to study in detail the life of any community I would go very early to its refuse piles."

One aspect of Whitemud's history, and only one, and a fragmentary one, we knew: the town dump. It lay in a draw at the southeast corner of town, just where the river left the Hills and where the old Mounted Police patrol trail (I did not know that that was what it was) made a long, easy, willow-fringed traverse across the bottoms. That stretch of the river was a favourite campsite for passing teamsters, gypsies, sometimes Indians. The very straw scattered around those camps, the ashes of those strangers' campfires, the manure of their teams and saddle horses, were hot with adventurous possibilities. The camps made an extension, a living suburb, of the dump ground itself, and it was for this that we valued them. We scoured them for artifacts of their migrant tenants as if they had been archaeological sites potent with the secrets of ancient civilizations. I remember toting around for weeks a broken harness strap a few inches long. Somehow or other its buckle looked as if it had been fashioned in a far place, a place where they were accustomed to flatten the tongue of buckles for reasons that could only be exciting, and where they had a habit of plating the metal with some valuable alloy, probably silver. In places where the silver was worn away, the buckle underneath shone dull yellow: probably gold.

Excitement liked that end of town better than our end. Old Mrs. Gustafson, deeply religious and a little raddled in the head, went over there once with a buckboard full of trash, and as she was driving home along the river she saw a spent catfish, washed in from the Swift Current or some other part of the watershed in the spring flood. He was two feet long, his whiskers hung down, his fins and tail were limp — a kind of fish no one had seen in the Whitemud in the three or four years of the town's life, and a kind that none of us children had ever seen anywhere. Mrs. Gustafson had never seen one like him, either. She perceived at once that he was the devil, and she whipped up the team and reported him, pretty loudly, at Hoffman's elevator.

We could still hear her screeching as we legged it for the river to see for ourselves. Sure enough, there he was, drifting slowly on the surface. He looked very tired, and he made no great effort to get away when we rushed to get an old rowboat, and rowed it frantically down to where our scouts eased along shore beckoning and ducking willows, and sank the boat under him and brought him ashore in it. When he died we fed him experimentally to two half-wild cats, who seemed to suffer no ill effects.

Upstream from the draw that held the dump, the irrigation flume crossed the river. It always seemed to me giddily high when I hung my chin over its plank edge and looked down, but it probably walked no more than twenty feet

41

above the water on its spidery legs. Ordinarily in summer it carried six or eight inches of smooth water, and under the glassy surface of the little boxed stream the planks were coated with deep sun-warmed moss as slick as frogs' eggs. A boy could sit in the flume with the water walling up against his back, and grab a cross-brace above him, and pull, shooting himself sledlike ahead until he could reach the next cross-brace for another pull, and so on across the river in four scoots.

After ten minutes in the flume he would come out wearing a dozen or more limber black leeches, and could sit in the green shade where darning needles flashed blue, and dragonflies hummed and stopped in the air, and skaters dimpled slack and eddy with their delicate transitory footprints, and there pull the leeches off one by one, while their sucking ends clung and clung, until at last, stretched far out, they let go with a tiny wet *puk* and snapped together like

rubber bands. The smell of the flume and the low bars of that part of the river was the smell of wolf willow.

But nothing else in the east end of town was as good as the dump ground. Through a historical process that went back to the roots of community sanitation, and that in law dated from the Unincorporated Towns Ordinance of the territorial government, passed in 1888, the dump was the very first community enterprise, the town's first institution.

More than that, it contained relics of every individual who had ever lived there. The bedsprings on which Whitemud's first child was begotten might be out there; the skeleton of a boy's pet colt; books soaked with water and chemicals in a house fire, and thrown out to flap their stained eloquence in the prairie wind. Broken dishes, rusty tinware, spoons that had been used to mix paint; once a box of percussion caps, sign and symbol of the carelessness that most of us had in matters of personal or public safety. My brother and I put some of them on the railroad tracks and were anonymously denounced in the *Leader* for nearly derailing the speeder of a section crew. There was also old iron, old brass, for which we hunted assiduously, by night conning junkmen's catalogs to find out how much wartime value there might be in the geared insides of clocks or in a pound of tea lead carefully wrapped in a ball whose weight astonished and delighted us.

Sometimes the unimaginable world reached out and laid a finger on us because of our activities on the dump. I recall that, aged about seven, I wrote a Toronto junk house asking if they preferred their tea lead and tinfoil wrapped in balls, or whether they would rather have it pressed flat in sheets, and I got back a typewritten letter in a window envelope advising me that they would be happy to have it in any way that was convenient to me. They added that they valued my business and were mine very truly. Dazed, I carried that windowed grandeur around in my pocket until I wore it out.

We hunted old bottles in the dump, bottles caked with filth, half buried, full of cobwebs, and we washed them out at the horse trough by the elevators, putting in a handful of shot along with the water to knock the dirt loose; and when we had shaken them until our arms were tired, we hauled them down in somebody's coaster wagon and turned them in at Bill Christenson's pool hall, where the smell of lemon pop was so sweet on the dark pool-hall air that it sometimes awakens me in the night even yet.

Smashed wheels of wagons and buggies, tangles of rusty barbed wire, the collapsed perambulator that the French wife of one of the town's doctors had once pushed proudly up the plank sidewalks and along the ditchbank paths. A welter of foul-smelling feathers and coyote-scattered carrion, that was all that remained of somebody's dream of a chicken ranch. The chickens had all got some mysterious pip at the same time, and died as one, and the dream lay out there with the rest of the town's short history to rustle to the empty sky on the border of the hills.

There was melted glass in curious forms, and the half-melted office safe left from the burning of Joe Knight's hotel. On very lucky days we might find a piece of the lead casing that had enclosed the wires of the town's first telephone system. The casing was just the right size for rings, and so soft that it could be whittled with a jackknife. If we had been Indians of fifty years earlier, that bright soft metal could have enlisted our maximum patience and craft, and come out as ring and medal and amulet inscribed with the symbols of our observed world. Perhaps there were too many ready-made alternatives in the local drug, hardware, and general stores; in any case our artistic response was feeble, and resulted in nothing better than crude seal rings with initials or pierced hearts carved in them. They served a purpose in juvenile courtship, but they stopped a good way short of art.

The dump held very little wood, for in that country anything burnable got burned. But it had plenty of old metal, furniture, papers, mattresses that were the delight of field mice, and jugs and demijohns that were sometimes their bane, for they crawled into the necks and drowned in the rainwater or redeye that was inside.

If the history of Whitemud was not exactly written, it was at least hinted,

44

in the dump. I think I had a pretty sound notion even at eight or nine of how significant was that first institution of our forming Canadian civilization. For rummaging through its foul purlieus I had several times been surprised and shocked to find relics of my own life tossed out there to blow away or rot.

Some of the books were volumes of the set of Shakespeare that my father had bought, or been sold, before I was born. They had been carried from Dakota to Seattle, and Seattle to Bellingham, and Bellingham to Redmond, and Redmond back to Iowa, and Iowa to Saskatchewan. One of the Cratchet girls had borrowed them, a hatchet-faced, thin, eager, transplanted Cockney girl with a frenzy for reading. Stained in a fire, they had somehow found the dump rather than come back to us. The lesson they preached was how much is lost, how much thrown aside, how much carelessly or of necessity given up, in the making of a new country. We had so few books that I knew them all; finding those thrown away was like finding my own name on a gravestone.

And yet not the blow that something else was, something that impressed me even more with how closely the dump reflected the town's intimate life. The colt whose picked skeleton lay out there was mine. He had been incurably crippled when dogs chased our mare Daisy the morning after she foaled. I had worked for months to make him well, had fed him by hand, curried him, talked my father into having iron braces made for his front legs. And I had not known that he would have to be destroyed. One weekend I turned him over to the foreman of one of the ranches, presumably so that he could be better cared for. A few days later I found his skinned body, with the braces still on his crippled front legs, lying on the dump. I think I might eventually have accepted the colt's death, and forgiven his killer, if it had not been for that dirty little two-dollar meanness that skinned him.

Not even finding his body cured me of going to the dump, though our parents all forbade us on pain of cholera or worse to do so. The place fascinated us, as it should have. For this was the kitchen midden of all the civilization we knew. It gave us the most tantalizing glimpses into our neighbours' lives and our own; it provided an aesthetic distance from which to know ourselves.

The town dump was our poetry and our history. We took it home with us by the wagonload, bringing back into town the things the town had used and thrown away. Some little part of what we gathered, mainly bottles, we managed to bring back to usefulness, but most of our gleanings we left lying around barn or attic or cellar until in some renewed fury of spring cleanup our families carted them off to the dump again, to be rescued and briefly treasured by some other boy. Occasionally something we really valued with a passion was snatched from us in horror and returned at once. That happened to the mounted head of a white mountain goat, somebody's trophy from old times and the far Rocky Mountains, that I brought home one day. My mother took one look and discovered that his beard was full of moths.

I remember that goat; I regret him yet. Poetry is seldom useful, but always memorable. If I were a sociologist anxious to study in detail the life of any community I would go very early to its refuse piles. For a community may be as well judged by what it throws away — what it has to throw away and what it chooses to — as by any other evidence. For whole civilizations we sometimes have no more of the poetry and little more of the history than this.

ABOUT THE LINES

1 This is a cloze exercise. Your teacher will give you a worksheet for it.

2 Without reading the article a second time:
   a. On your own, list as many objects in the dump as you can remember;
   b. Combine your list with your partners', and together try to add as many more items as you can;
   c. With your partners, reread the article and check to see how many of the objects you managed to recall and how many were omitted.

3 Adopt the point of view of the narrator and explain to your partners the significance for you, as a child, of:
the buckle;
the catfish;
the irrigation flume;
the colt's skeleton;
the goat's head.
Choose one explanation and write it out in a short paragraph.

BETWEEN THE LINES

1 Write a paragraph using details from this article to prove that: "One person's garbage is another's treasure."

2 Choose any five words the author uses to give the dump an atmosphere of excitement and adventure. Use these words in a sentence or two that conveys the author's enthusiasm for the dump ground.

3 Frame the question that you would most like to ask the author about his perspective on the past. Try your question on your partners and discuss their answers.

THE PEN OF MY AUNT

Josephine Tey

<table>
<tr><td>

Characters

MADAME
SIMONE
STRANGER
CORPORAL

</td><td>

*In a verbal trapeze act, only
quick wits can save the day.*

</td></tr>
</table>

SCENE: *A French country house during the Occupation by German forces in World War II. The lady of the house is seated in her drawing room.*

SIMONE (*approaching*) Madame! Oh, madame! Madame, have you —
MADAME Simone.
SIMONE Madame, have you seen what—
MADAME Simone!
SIMONE But madame —
MADAME Simone, this may be an age of barbarism, but I will have none of it inside the walls of this house.
SIMONE But madame, there is a — there is a —
MADAME (*silencing her*) Simone. France may be an occupied country, a ruined nation, and a conquered race, but we will keep, if you please, the usages of civilization.
SIMONE Yes, madame.
MADAME One thing we still possess, thank God; and that is good manners. The enemy never had it; and it is not something they can take from *us*.
SIMONE No, madame.
MADAME Go out of the room again. Open the door —
SIMONE Oh, *madame!* I wanted to tell you —
MADAME — Open the door, shut it behind you — quietly — take two paces into the room, and say what you came to say. (SIMONE *goes hastily out, shutting the door. She reappears, shuts the door behind her, takes two paces into the room, and waits.*) Yes, Simone?
SIMONE I expect it is too late now; they will be here.
MADAME Who will?
SIMONE The soldiers who were coming up the avenue.
MADAME After the last few months I should not have thought that soldiers coming up the avenue was a remarkable fact. It is no doubt a party with a billeting order.
SIMONE (*crossing to the window*) No, madame, it is two soldiers in one of their little cars, with a civilian between them.
MADAME Which civilian?
SIMONE A stranger, madame.

51

MADAME A stranger? Are the soldiers from the Combatant branch?

SIMONE No, they are those beasts of Administration. Look, they have stopped. They are getting out.

MADAME (*at the window*) Yes, it is a stranger. Do you know him, Simone?

SIMONE I have never set eyes on him before, madame.

MADAME You would know if he belonged to the district?

SIMONE Oh, madame, I know every man between here and St. Estèphe.

MADAME (*dryly*) No doubt.

SIMONE Oh, merciful God, they are coming up the steps.

MADAME My good Simone, that is what the steps were put there for.

SIMONE But they will ring the bell and I shall have to —

MADAME And you will answer it and behave as if you had been trained by a butler and ten upper servants instead of being the charcoal-burner's daughter from over at Les Chênes. (*This is said encouragingly, not in unkindness.*) You will be very calm and correct —

SIMONE Calm! Madame! With my inside turning over and over like a wheel at a fair!

MADAME A good servant does not have an inside, merely an exterior. (*comforting*) Be assured, my child. You have your place here; that is more than those creatures on our doorstep have. Let that hearten you —

SIMONE Madame! They are not going to ring. They are coming straight in.

MADAME (*bitterly*) Yes. They have forgotten long ago what bells are for.

(*Door opens.*)

STRANGER (*in a bright, confident, casual tone*) Ah, there you are, my dear aunt. I am so glad. Come in, my friend, come in. My dear aunt, this gentleman wants you to identify me.

MADAME Identify you?

CORPORAL We found this man wandering in the woods —

STRANGER The corporal found it inexplicable that anyone should wander in a wood.

CORPORAL And he had no papers on him —

STRANGER And I rightly pointed out that if I carry all the papers one is supposed to these days, I am no good to God or man. If I put them in a hip pocket, I can't bend forward; if I put them in a front pocket, I can't bend at all.

CORPORAL He said that he was your nephew, madame, but that did not seem to us very likely, so we brought him here.

(*There is the slightest pause; just one moment of silence.*)

MADAME But of course this is my nephew.

CORPORAL He is?

MADAME Certainly.

CORPORAL He lives here?

MADAME (*assenting*) My nephew lives here.

CORPORAL So! (*recovering*) My apologies, madame. But you will admit that appearances were against the young gentleman.

MADAME Alas, Corporal, my nephew belongs to a generation who delight in flouting appearances. It is what they call "expressing their personality," I understand.

CORPORAL (*with contempt*) No doubt, madame.

MADAME Convention is anathema to them, and there is no sin like conformity. Even a collar is an offence against their liberty, and a discipline not to be borne by free necks.

CORPORAL Ah, yes, madame. A little more discipline among your nephew's generation, and we might not be occupying your country today.

STRANGER You think it was that collar of yours that conquered my country? You flatter yourself, Corporal. The only result of wearing a collar like that is varicose veins in the head.

MADAME (*repressive*) Please! My dear boy. Let us not descend to personalities.

STRANGER The matter is not personal, my good aunt, but scientific. Wearing a collar like that retards the flow of fresh blood to the head, with the most disastrous consequences to the gray matter of the brain. The hypothetical gray matter. In fact, I have a theory —

CORPORAL Monsieur, your theories do not interest me.

STRANGER No? You do not find speculation interesting?

CORPORAL In this world one judges by results.

STRANGER (*after a slight pause of reflection*) I see. The collared conqueror sits in the high places, while the collarless conquered lies about in the woods. And who comes best out of that, would you say? Tell me, Corporal, as man to man, do you never have a mad, secret desire to lie unbuttoned in a wood?

CORPORAL I have only one desire, monsieur, and that is to see your papers.

STRANGER (*taken off guard and filling in time*) My papers?

MADAME But is that necessary, Corporal? I have already told you that —

CORPORAL I know that madame is a very good collaborator and in good standing —

MADAME In that case —

CORPORAL But when we begin an affair we like to finish it. I have asked to see monsieur's papers, and the matter will not be finished until I have seen them.

MADAME You acknowledge that I am in "good standing," Corporal?

CORPORAL So I have heard, madame.

MADAME Then I must consider it a discourtesy on your part to demand my nephew's credentials.

CORPORAL It is no reflection on madame. It is a matter of routine, nothing more.

STRANGER (*murmuring*) The great god Routine.

MADAME To ask for his papers was routine; to insist on their production is discourtesy. I shall say so to your Commanding Officer.

CORPORAL Very good, madame. In the meantime, I shall inspect your nephew's papers.

MADAME And what if I —

STRANGER (*quietly*) You may as well give it up, my dear. You could as easily turn a steamroller. They have only one idea at a time. If the Corporal's heart is set on seeing my papers, he shall see them. (*moving towards the door*) I left them in the pocket of my coat.

SIMONE (*unexpectedly, from the background*) Not in your *linen* coat?

STRANGER (*pausing*) Yes. Why?

SIMONE (*with apparently growing anxiety*) Your *cream* linen coat? The one you were wearing yesterday?

STRANGER Certainly.

SIMONE Merciful Heaven! I sent it to the laundry!

STRANGER To the laundry!

SIMONE Yes, monsieur; this morning; in the basket.

STRANGER (*in incredulous anger*) You sent my coat, *with my papers in the pocket*, to the laundry!

SIMONE (*defensive and combatant*) I didn't know monsieur's papers were in the pocket.

STRANGER You didn't know! You didn't know that a packet of documents weighing half a ton were in the pocket. An identity card, a *laisser passer*, a food card, a drink card, an army discharge, a permission to wear civilian clothes, a permission to go farther than ten miles to the east, a permission to go more than ten miles to the west, a permission to —

SIMONE (*breaking in with spirit*) How was I to know the coat was heavy! I picked it up with the rest of the bundle that was lying on the floor.

STRANGER (*snapping her head off*) My coat was on the back of the chair.

SIMONE It was on the floor.

STRANGER On the back of the chair!

SIMONE It was on the floor with your dirty shirt and your pajamas, and a towel and what not. I put my arms round the whole thing and then — woof! into the basket with them.

STRANGER I tell you that coat was on the back of the chair. It was quite clean and was not going to the laundry for two weeks yet — if then. I hung it there myself, and —

MADAME My dear boy, what does it matter? The damage is done now. In any case, they will find the papers when they unpack the basket, and return them tomorrow.

STRANGER If someone doesn't steal them. There are a lot of people who would like to lay hold of a complete set of papers, believe me.

MADAME (*reassuring*) Oh, no. Old Fleureau is the soul of honesty. You have no need to worry about them. They will be back first thing tomorrow, you shall see; and then we shall have much pleasure in sending them to the Administration Office for the Corporal's inspection. Unless, of course, the Corporal insists on your personal appearance at the office.

CORPORAL (*cold and indignant*) I have seen monsieur. All that I want now is to see his papers.

STRANGER You shall see them, Corporal, you shall see them. The whole half-ton of them. You may inspect them at your leisure. Provided, that is, that they come back from the laundry to which this idiot has consigned them.

MADAME (*again reassuring*) They will come back, never fear. And you must not blame Simone. She is a good child, and does her best.

SIMONE (*with an air of belated virtue*) I am not one to pry into pockets.

MADAME Simone, show the Corporal out, if you please.

SIMONE (*natural feeling overcoming her for a moment*)

He knows the way out. (*recovering*) Yes, madame.

MADAME And Corporal, try to take your duties a little less literally in future. My countrymen appreciate the spirit rather than the letter.

CORPORAL I have my instructions, madame, and I obey them. Good day, madame. Monsieur.

(*He goes, followed by* SIMONE — *the door closes. There is a moment of silence.*)

STRANGER For a good collaborator, that was a remarkably quick adoption.

MADAME Sit down, young man. I will give you something to drink. I expect your knees are none too well.

STRANGER My knees, madame, are pure gelatine. As for my stomach, it seems to have disappeared.

MADAME (*offering him the drink she has poured out*) This will recall it, I hope.

STRANGER You are not drinking, madame.

MADAME Thank you, no.

STRANGER Not with strangers. It is certainly no time to drink with strangers. Nevertheless, I drink the health of a collaborator. (*He drinks.*) Tell me, madame, what will happen tomorrow when they find that you have no nephew?

MADAME (*surprised*) But of course I have a nephew. I tell lies, my friend; but not *silly* lies. My charming nephew has gone to Bonneval for the day. He finds country life dull.

STRANGER Dull? This — this heaven?

MADAME (*dryly*) He likes to talk and here there is no audience. At Headquarters in Bonneval he finds the audience sympathetic.

STRANGER (*understanding the implication*) Ah.

MADAME He believes in the Brotherhood of Man — if you can credit it.

STRANGER After the last six months?

MADAME His mother was American, so he has half the Balkans in his blood. To say nothing of Italy, Russia and the Levant.

STRANGER (*half amused*) I see.

MADAME A silly and worthless creature, but useful.

STRANGER Useful?

MADAME I — borrow his cloak.

STRANGER I see.

MADAME Tonight I shall borrow his identity papers, and tomorrow they will go to the office in St. Estèphe.

STRANGER But — he will have to know.

MADAME (*placidly*) Oh, yes, he will know, of course.

STRANGER And how will you persuade such an enthusiastic collaborator to deceive his friends?

MADAME Oh, that is easy. He is my heir.

STRANGER (*amused*) Ah.

MADAME He is, also, by the mercy of God, not too unlike you, so that his photograph will not startle the Corporal too much tomorrow. Now tell me what you are doing in my wood.

STRANGER Resting my feet — I am practically walking on my bones. And waiting for tonight.

MADAME Where are you making for? (*as he does not answer immediately*) The coast? (*He nods.*) That is four days away — five if your feet are bad.

STRANGER I know it.

MADAME Have you friends on the way?

STRANGER I have friends at the coast, who will get me a boat. But no one between here and the sea.

MADAME (*rising*) I must consult my list of addresses. (*pausing*) What was your service?

STRANGER Army.

MADAME Which Regiment?

STRANGER The 79th.

MADAME (*after the faintest pause*) And your Colonel's name?

STRANGER Delavault was killed in the first week, and Martin took over.

MADAME (*going to her desk*) A "good collaborator" cannot be too careful. Now I can consult my notebook. A charming colour, is it not? A lovely shade of red.

STRANGER Yes — but what has a red quill pen to do with your notebook? — Ah, you write with it of course — stupid of me.

MADAME Certainly I write with it — but it is also my notebook — look — I only need a hairpin — and then — so — out of my quill pen comes my notebook — a tiny piece of paper — but enough for a list of names.

STRANGER You mean that you keep that list on your desk? (*He sounds disapproving.*)

MADAME Where did you expect me to keep it, young man? In my corset? Did you ever try to get something out of your corset in a hurry? What would you advise as the ideal quality in a hiding place for a list of names?

STRANGER That the thing should be difficult to find, of course.

MADAME Not at all. That it should be easily destroyed in emergency. It is too big for me to swallow — I suspect they do that only in books — and we have no fires to consume it, so I had to think of some other way. I did try to memorize the list, but what I could not be sure of remembering were those that — that had to be scored off. It would be fatal to send someone to an address that — that was no longer available. So I had to keep a written record.

STRANGER And if you neither eat it nor burn it when the moment comes, how do you get rid of it?

MADAME I could, of course, put a match to it, but scraps of freshly burned paper on a desk take a great deal of explaining. If I ceased to be looked on with approval my usefulness would end. It is important therefore that there should be no sign of anxiety on my part; no burned paper, no excuses to leave the room, no nods and becks and winks. I just sit here at my desk and go on with my letters. I tilt my nice big inkwell sideways for a moment and dip the pen into the deep ink at the side. The ink flows into the hollow of the quill, and all is blotted out. (*consulting the list*) Let me see. It would be good if you could rest your feet for a day or so.

STRANGER (*ruefully*) It would.

MADAME There is a farm just beyond the Marnay crossroads on the way to St. Estèphe — (*She pauses to consider.*)

STRANGER St. Estèphe is the home of the singleminded Corporal. I don't want to run into him again.

MADAME No, that might be awkward; but that farm of the Cherfils would be ideal. A good hiding-place, and food to spare, and fine people —

STRANGER If your nephew is so friendly with the invader, how is it that the Corporal doesn't know him by sight?

MADAME (*absently*) The unit at St. Estèphe is a noncommissioned one.

STRANGER Does the Brotherhood of Man exclude sergeants, then?

MADAME Oh, definitely. Brotherhood does not really begin under field rank, I understand.

STRANGER But the Corporal may still meet your nephew somewhere.

MADAME That is a risk one must take. It is not a very grave one. They change the personnel every few weeks, to prevent them becoming too acclimatized. And even if he met my nephew, he is unlikely to ask for the papers of so obviously well-to-do a citizen. If you could bear to go *back* a little —

STRANGER Not a step! It would be like — like denying God. I have got so far, against all the odds, and I am not going a yard back. Not even to rest my feet!

MADAME I understand; but it is a pity. It is a long way to the Cherfils farm — two miles east of the Marnay crossroads it is, on a little hill.

STRANGER I'll get there; don't worry. If not tonight then tomorrow night. I am used to sleeping in the open by now.

MADAME I wish we could have you here, but it is too dangerous. We are liable to be billeted on at any moment, without notice. However, we can give you a good meal, and a bath. We have no coal, so it will be one of those flat-tin-saucer baths. And if you want to be very kind to Simone you might have it somewhere in the kitchen regions and so save her carrying water upstairs.

STRANGER But of course.

MADAME Before the war I had a staff of twelve. Now I have Simone. I dust and Simone sweeps, and between us we keep the dirt at bay. She has no manners but a great heart, the child.

STRANGER The heart of a lion.

MADAME Before I put this back you might memorize these: Forty Avenue Foch, in Crest, the back entrance.

STRANGER Forty Avenue Foch, the back entrance.

MADAME You may find it difficult to get into Crest, by the way. It is a closed area. The pot boy at the Red Lion in Mans.

STRANGER The pot boy.

MADAME Denis the blacksmith at Laloupe. And the next night should take you to the sea and your friends. Are they safely in your mind?

STRANGER Forty Avenue Foch in Crest; the pot boy at the Red Lion in Mans; and Denis the blacksmith at Laloupe. And to be careful getting into Crest.

MADAME Good. Then I can close my notebook — or roll it up, I should say — then — it fits neatly, does it not? Now let us see about some food for you. Perhaps I could find you other clothes. Are these all you —

(The CORPORAL's voice is heard mingled in fury with the still more furious tones of SIMONE. She is yelling: "Nothing of the sort, I tell you, nothing of the sort!" but no words are clearly distinguishable in the angry row. The door is flung open, and the CORPORAL bursts in dragging a struggling SIMONE by the arm.)

SIMONE (screaming with rage and terror) Let me go, you foul fiend, you murdering foreigner, let me go. (She tries to kick him.)

CORPORAL (at the same time) Stop struggling, you lying deceitful little bit of no-good.

MADAME Will someone explain this extraordinary —

CORPORAL This creature —

MADAME Take your hand from my servant's arm, Corporal. She is not going to run away.

CORPORAL (reacting to the voice of authority and automatically complying) Your precious servant was overheard telling the gardener that she had never set eyes on this man.

SIMONE I did not! Why should I say anything like that?

CORPORAL With my own ears I heard her, my own two ears. Will you kindly explain that to me if you can.

MADAME You speak our language very well, Corporal, but perhaps you are not so quick to understand.

CORPORAL I understand perfectly.

MADAME What Simone was saying to the gardener, was no doubt what she was announcing to all and sundry at the pitch of her voice this morning.

CORPORAL (unbelieving) And what was that?

MADAME That she wished she had never set eyes on my nephew.

CORPORAL And why should she say that?

MADAME My nephew, Corporal, has many charms, but tidiness is not one of them. As you may have deduced from the episode of the coat. He is apt to leave his room —

SIMONE (on her cue, in a burst of scornful rage) Cigarette ends, pajamas, towels, bedclothes, books, papers — all over the floor like a flood. Every morning I tidy up, and in two hours it is as if a bomb had burst in the room.

STRANGER (testily) I told you already that I was sor —

SIMONE (interrupting) As if I had nothing else to do in this enormous house but wait on you.

STRANGER Haven't I said that I —

SIMONE And when I have climbed all the way up from the kitchen with your shaving water, you let it get cold; but will you shave in cold? Oh, no! I have to bring up another —

STRANGER I didn't ask you to climb the stairs, did I?

SIMONE And do I get a word of thanks for bringing it? Do I indeed? You say: "*Must* you bring it in that hideous jug; it offends my eyes."

STRANGER So it does offend my eyes!

MADAME Enough, enough! We had enough of that this morning. You see, Corporal?

CORPORAL I could have sworn —

MADAME A natural mistake, perhaps. But I think you might have used a little more common sense in the matter. (*coldly*) And a great deal more dignity. I don't like having my servants manhandled.

CORPORAL She refused to come.

SIMONE Accusing me of things I never said!

MADAME However, now that you are here again you can make yourself useful. My nephew wants to go into Crest the day after tomorrow, and that requires a special pass. Perhaps you would make one out for him.

CORPORAL But I —

MADAME You have a little book of permits in your pocket, haven't you?

CORPORAL Yes. I —

MADAME Very well. Better make it valid for two days. He is always changing his mind.

CORPORAL But it is not for me to grant a pass.

MADAME You sign them, don't you?

CORPORAL Yes, but only when someone tells me to.

MADAME Very well, if it will help you, I tell you to.

CORPORAL I mean, permission must be granted before a pass is issued.

MADAME And have you any doubt that a permission will be granted to my nephew?

CORPORAL No, of course not, madame.

MADAME Then don't be absurd, Corporal. To be absurd twice in five minutes is too often. You may use my desk — and my own special pen. Isn't it a beautiful quill, Corporal?

CORPORAL Thank you, madame, no. *We* Germans have come a long way from the geese.

MADAME Yes?

CORPORAL I prefer my fountain pen. It is a more efficient implement. (*He writes.*) "For the 15th and the 16th. Holder of identity card number" — What is the number of your identity, monsieur?

STRANGER I have not the faintest idea.

CORPORAL You do not know?

STRANGER No. The only numbers I take an interest in are lottery numbers.

SIMONE I know the number of monsieur's card.

MADAME (*afraid that she is going to invent one*) I don't think that likely, Simone.

SIMONE (*aware of what is in her mistress's mind, and reassuring her*) But I really *do* know, madame. It is the year I was born, with two "ones" after it. Many a time I have seen it on the outside of the card.

60

CORPORAL It is good that someone knows.

SIMONE It is — 192411.

CORPORAL 192411. (*He fills in the dates.*)

MADAME (*as he nears the end*) Are you going back to St. Estèphe now, Corporal?

CORPORAL Yes, madame.

MADAME Then perhaps you will give my nephew a lift as far as the Marnay crossroads.

CORPORAL It is not permitted to take civilians as passengers.

STRANGER But you took me here as a passenger.

CORPORAL That was different.

MADAME You mean that when you thought he was a miscreant you took him in your car, but now that you know he is my nephew you refuse?

CORPORAL When I brought him here it was on service business.

MADAME (*gently reasonable*) Corporal, I think you owe me something for your general lack of tact this afternoon. Would it be too much to ask you to consider my nephew a miscreant for the next hour while you drive him as far as the Marnay crossroads?

CORPORAL But —

MADAME Take him to the crossroads with you and I shall agree to forget your — your lack of efficiency. I am sure you are actually a very efficient person, and likely to be a sergeant any day now. We won't let a blunder or two stand in your way.

CORPORAL If I am caught giving a lift to a civilian, I shall *never* be a sergeant.

MADAME (*still gentle*) If I report on your conduct this afternoon, tomorrow you will be a private.

CORPORAL (*after a long pause*) Is monsieur ready to come now?

STRANGER Quite ready.

CORPORAL You will need a coat.

MADAME Simone, get monsieur's coat from the cupboard in the hall. And when you have seen him off, come back here.

SIMONE Yes, madame.

(*Exit* SIMONE)

CORPORAL Madame.

MADAME Good day to you, Corporal.

(*Exit* CORPORAL)

STRANGER Your talent for blackmail is remarkable.

MADAME The place has a yellow barn. You had better wait somewhere till evening, when the dogs are chained up.

STRANGER I wish I had an aunt of your calibre. All mine are authorities on crochet.

MADAME I could wish you were my nephew. Good luck, and be careful. Perhaps one day, you will come back, and dine with me, and tell me the rest of the tale.

(*The sound of a running engine comes from outside.*)

STRANGER Two years today, perhaps?

MADAME One year today.

STRANGER (*softly*) Who knows? (*He lifts her hand to his lips.*) Thank you, and *au revoir.* (*turning at the door*) Being sped on my way by the enemy is a

happiness I had not anticipated. I shall never be able to repay you for that.
(*He goes out.*) (*off stage*) Ah, my coat — thank you, Simone.
(*Sound of car driving off.* MADAME *pours out two glasses. As she finishes,*
SIMONE *comes in, shutting the door correctly behind her and taking two paces
into the room.*)
SIMONE You wanted me, madame?
MADAME You will drink a glass of wine with me, Simone.
SIMONE With you, madame!
MADAME You are a good daughter of France and a good servant to me. We shall
    drink a toast together.
SIMONE Yes, madame.
MADAME (*quietly*) To Freedom.
SIMONE (*repeating*) To Freedom. May I add a bit of my own, madame?
MADAME Certainly.
SIMONE (*with immense satisfaction*) And a very bad end to that Corporal!

CURTAIN

ABOUT THE LINES

1 In a short paragraph for each, write character descriptions of two of the
following: Madame, Simone, the Stranger, and the Corporal. Use evidence
from the play to justify your evaluations of the characters.

2 The playwright holds the audience in suspense (see p. 356) throughout this
play. Select two points in the drama where you think the suspense is at
its most intense and explain the effect of these incidents on the audience.

3 Imagine that you are the Corporal and write a report of the events of the play
for your superior officer. Remember that you must stick to the facts.

4 "The Pen of My Aunt" is set in France during World War II. Keeping this
fact in mind:
  a. Design a set for a production of the play;
  b. Make a list of the props that are essential to a production of the play.

BETWEEN THE LINES

1 In one or two sentences, state two reasons why the title is appropriate for this
play. Now, make up at least one other title for the play and defend your
choice in a small group discussion.

2 Imagine that you are Madame, and write two short entries in your diary about your maid, Simone. One entry should have been written before the events of the play, and the other written in the evening after the departure of the Corporal and the Stranger.

3 Within the play "The Pen of My Aunt," the characters Madame, Simone, and the Stranger are, much of the time, acting out roles that are completely new to them and that they had not expected to play. Their audience is the Corporal. In his voice, describe one of the three characters to a friend. Share your description with your partners and see if they agree with your interpretation of the Corporal's point of view.

4 "This play is set in France during World War II, and yet many of the characteristics displayed by the players and the situations in which they find themselves are relevant to any time and any place." Write a paragraph in which you use this sentence as an opening statement.

5 Write an interior monologue in which Madame comes to the conclusion that she would prefer the Stranger to be her nephew.

BEYOND THE LINES

1 Script and dramatize or present in the form of a short story the meeting between Madame and the Stranger "one year today." They would probably discuss the events of the intervening period and experience pleasure when meeting each other again.

2 Imagine that you are the Stranger, and write a letter to Madame in which you thank her for her help in such a way that anybody intercepting the letter would not understand it. You will have to phrase your gratitude in such a way that it means one thing to Madame and something quite different to another reader.

3 Use your librarian or your history teacher as a resource person and research the Fall of France and the French Resistance during World War II. Present to your class any information you find that might be helpful to a greater appreciation of this play.

4 Working in a group of four, either:
   a. Present a performance of this play or part of it for a larger group; or
   b. Tape and present to the class an audio version of the play, or part of it, complete with sound effects and introductory music.

IN THE MIST

Judit Sziráky

"There was some kind of a pit gaping in front of him, a deep, blind-black hole, which was so frightening. . . ."

The little boy was watching Dad, who was standing before the lorry with his head bowed and his trunk slightly bent forward in a strange and unfamiliar posture as if he were tired or sleepy.

The headlights of the truck cast a prickly yellow light on the cobble stones over which the mist floated sticky and wet. In this dense writhing fog occasionally the street disappeared, and so did the open gate and the front wheels of the lorry before which Dad was standing. At times the fog concealed even Daddy.

The little boy grew scared: he took a long deep breath, then he stretched out his arms to push away this denseness, which — by golly, how wonderful! — he was able to do. The yellow light danced again before his eyes, the front wheels of the lorry re-appeared, and so did Dad, who somehow now looked taller and thinner as he just stood there, his shoulders stooped and his eyes peering unseeingly into the mist.

Dad did not look at him. He just took off his glasses, carefully examined them and dried them, then he tipped his hat back on his head and replaced the specs.

The pushing back of his hat was difficult to understand because the wind was not blowing at all; the air was cool and completely motionless and reminded the little boy of the smell of snow.

"Snow," sighed the boy, "snow."

Tiny pin-pricks tickled his nostrils like when Dad pulled the sled in the softly fallen whiteness that reached up to their ankles, and then Dad sometimes became the horse and they ran . . .

The boy would have liked to cry or at least to laugh out loud, but ugly black suitcases were lying around him along with a still uglier dufflebag which was crammed so full that it looked hunchbacked and resembled some kind of a dwarf or gnome.

This was something he would have liked to tell Dad, and also that he was not afraid of them. Why should he be afraid? He was no longer such a little boy, he would be six in the autumn and then he would be going to school; he will hold on to Dad's hand tightly and they will be going together.

But Dad was not looking at him. Dad was gazing ahead at the wheels, and the little boy didn't even know what colour Dad's eyes were because his glasses covered his eyes, and it was dark anyway and one couldn't see in the dark . . .

He would like to have specs, and he will probably get a pair when he grows up. But perhaps he will get them much sooner, at Christmas. But no, he has asked for a magnifying glass for Christmas. Grandfather also had a magnifier. What a pity that Grandfather died and he had not asked for it; Mother says that since then someone has taken it or it has got lost.

The boy feels the pin-pricks again in his nostrils; but this time he does not feel like laughing. Now he is sorry for Grandfather, who was old and thin, walked with a stoop and spoke in such a weak voice that one could barely understand him. And now he is dead and does not exist. But then where is he? And where is Mother?

Mother dressed him in the morning, pulled on his thick-soled boots and his warm navy, wool rompers, and then his winter coat on top of everything. Then the car came and they left. They travelled only for a short while, then they had to stop because other people also wanted to travel in their car. He had asked Mother why. "It will be much better somewhere else," Mother replied, and then Dad said that that wasn't so certain and looked at Mother as if he were angry.

Once long ago they had gone on a journey, but then it was warm, the sun shone, and all three of them were very happy when they got on the train. Then very soon they came to a beautiful blue lake and Dad had said: "This is Lake Balaton!"

The boy had asked that morning, "Are we going to Lake Balaton?" "No," Mother had whispered, "no, to the seacoast."

Dad did not say anything, he left the room.

Even though the little boy was hot in his winter coat he began to tremble as if with cold and cried. Mother put a cap on him and wrapped a soft warm muffler around his neck and then quickly took him by the hand and led him down to the garden.

The boy had never before seen the garden at grey dawn and now he was surprised to see how black it was. The garden looked very small, though it had fine tall trees, and shrubs on which, when the sun was shining, the flowers were white and sweet-smelling. And the steps, the steps which led down to the garden-gate were invisible in the dark. There was some kind of a pit gaping in front of him, a deep, blind-black hole, which was so frightening that he closed his eyes very tightly and sighed. Then Dad came and picked him up in his arms and started to wade through the darkness and took him down to the gate.

The big car was already waiting in front of the gate. The car was large, much larger than any in which the little boy had ridden.

He was glad about this and he was also glad about the headlights which were large and bright, but then he began to feel cold again and soon he was crying with loud sobs. A man, wearing a cap and a short leather jacket, said to father in a very ugly tone of voice: "Come on, now, what are we waiting for? Let's load up. If this little boy keeps on crying, we are going to leave him behind."

But they did not leave him behind because Mother put her arms around him, Dad lifted the suitcases and put them in the car, and very soon they started moving away . . .

And now they are standing.

The little boy does not know why they are standing and he would like to ask Dad. But there is no Dad, now there is again no Dad because he is hidden by that swirling grayness which now seems a little lighter and thinner than it was at dawn when they left.

No, the boy does not understand this journey. For what kind of journey is it when people stop so often and for so long? And why does this hateful little girl keep crying, the one they made sit next to him on the gnome-bag? Perhaps he ought to say something or ask her. When he is crying Mother sets him on her lap, pats him and begins to cradle him in her lap. Mother sometimes even sings to him: Tra-la-la . . .

Couldn't he sing to this little hateful thing here who is crying all the time and has a red ribbon in her hair? Well, no, he won't sing to her, though he likes to sing, and he can also recite poems, he knows a lot of poems by heart, but he won't recite either, let the hateful little girl cry . . .

The boy is holding an apple, he is looking at it, twisting it around and smelling it, and now and again he stares out into the fog looking for Dad. He got the apple from a nice woman. "Do you like apples, little boy?" she had asked him, and he laughed just a very little at this, and then he became suddenly angry and replied, "Of course, I love them, it's funny though . . ."

"Peter," Mother seemed to be scared. "Little Peter!" And then she added: "Be good my dear and behave."

The strange woman began to laugh — she had a sharp and unpleasant laugh — and she turned right away to Mother and whispered to her: "Just leave him, at such times it's best . . . You better forget about teaching him how to behave until we get to the other side . . ."

Mother did not say anything to this, she only adjusted the cap on his head and smoothed the hair from his forehead. Mother was very pale and sad, Mother was quite different from her usual self at home. This was a mother he did not like. He turned from her and hid in a far corner of the lorry.

The strange woman laughed at this too, she laughed at everything as if she were enjoying this trip. "Where are you going?" she asked Mother, and then without waiting for an answer from Mother, she said: "We are going to Sicily. It must be spring already in Sicily, and here it's raining, raining all the time and this horrible thick fog won't lift."

"No, it won't lift, it won't," repeated Mother and she kept looking at the boy, never taking her eyes off him.

This was something that made one smile a little, just a very little, so that only Mother would notice, because now he loved Mother again, but really and so very much that he had to sigh, sigh and cough a little, like long ago when he had a sore throat.

He remembers everything very clearly. He remembers Mother putting him to bed, then lighting the lamp at the head of the bed, and how the dark-green dots of the lampshade started to move somehow and slipped down onto his pillow, and then he put his finger on one of the dots and tried to lift it, but could not although it looked like a marble. Mother laughed and explained about the marble that it was a shadow, and then, when it grew quite dark outside, Oravec came to visit him.

"Are you very ill?" Oravec had asked, and he just nodded that he was ill, very ill, and even closed his eyes to make Oravec see how ill he was, but Oravec did not see, because he drew away, retreating as far back as the door, quite far from him, and there he said, "Then I won't sit next to you because I don't want to catch it . . ." He was just a little angry at Oravec for this, but then Mother came and brought them tea and a jar of preserves and then he sat up in bed very quickly and said good and loud:

"I am not really ill, Mother," and the next morning he and Oravec went to the kindergarten together.

It was always nice and warm in the kindergarten, very light, and a strange smell came from the stove, only it really wasn't a smell, but smoke, and the kindergarten teacher then always opened the windows right away and they had to move to the other room where they cut out ducks from paper, from yellow paper, and from the red paper they cut out stars and made chains . . .

"Oh!" sighed the boy, "oh," and, as if exhausted after a game, he quickly sat down on a bag, which a man had put down next to him in the corner, but the man looked at him sternly and said: "One does not sit on things that belong to other people!" And then he stood up and began to walk up and down in the car, where it was chilly and quite dark, and now again he was very cold and wanted to cry, but he didn't cry, just walked up to Mother and said very loud and with the same sternness that had been on the face of the man who had just spoken to him: "I want to get off and go home with Dad . . ."

Then Mother quickly pulled him onto her lap and began to whisper into his ear, but he could not understand what she was saying because a lot of people were getting on the lorry, and the man in the leather jacket was very angry. A bigger boy, as he passed him, gave him a hard shove with his elbow, and pushed the weepy little girl, too, though she was no longer crying, only sleeping on the bag, but now she had woken up and was wailing, and the big boy turned when he heard her and asked her: "Are you crazy?" then he went further away, lit a cigarette and blew the smoke upwards, making a whirl of smoke rings.

The boy looked at Mother, slowly slipped off her knees and, on unsure feet, a little wobbly, stood up in front of her and breathed fast and panting as if he had been running for a long time or were feverish. "Mother," he whispered leaning close to her, "Mummy, I don't want to . . . let's get off from here . . . I don't want to . . ."

But Mother did not move, she only looked at the boy very strangely, eyes opened wide and round, and he, as if suddenly frightened, shivered and gave a loud piercing scream.

"Hey, what's going on?" someone asked way back in the dark. But Mother did not say anything, only her eyes filled with moisture, because by that time the boy had turned and was pushing his legs forward as if he were planning to run away rapidly. But it was impossible to run away because the car was filled with suitcases and it was also filled with people — this big car which now felt very small, so small that one couldn't do anything in it, only cry and scream.

"Stop that racket!" the older boy yelled at him. "What are you screaming for?" and he even added: "Aw, what an awful brat, screaming to high heaven!"

A cigarette drooped from between the lips of the big boy, but now the smoke was coming out from his nose; and then the little boy pulled out the cigarette and tread on it, and screamed and wailed even more piercingly. And yet he did not want to scream, he would have much rather slept or played, like on other mornings when he was happily playing in the kindergarten by this time; but how strange it was that one just could not stop this screaming, not even for a little time, one could not stop it, though Dad was here, Dad was just getting into the big car, he and the man with the leather jacket . . .

"What's happening here?" the man in the leather jacket asked. He asked Dad who had been standing in the fog in front of the car ever since dawn and was now looking at the boy in fright, he too asking, "What's going on here?"

"I value my life," yelled Leather-jacket now. "How do you think we can make a move like this? You better give a tranquillizer to this boy, but something strong and that's that!"

"What kind of a tranquillizer am I expected to give him?" asks Dad, and looks at Leather-jacket from quite close by, from so close by that the boy breathes faster, then shuts his lids tightly and stops crying.

"Morphine! A shot in his arm and then he'll be quiet like in a crypt . . ."

"Right you are," says the man who so sternly scolded him before. "Nobody wants to risk his life for a bad child!"

"And where am I supposed to get the morphine from?" Dad asks and now he stares at Leather-jacket from very close again. "And who is supposed to administer it? I am no doctor, I work in the office of one of the factories."

The man with the leather jacket laughs loud at this, he laughs at this so hard he screws up his eyes until they look very small, and then when he opens them wide again he whispers to Dad: "What do we need a doctor for? What we need is a good hypodermic, nothing else, and just a little hard cash!"

Maybe he wanted to say more, but then Dad took a deep breath, and then with a very fast and skilful movement, as if he were just playing, he knocked the cap from Leather-jacket's head. Dad was holding the man in the leather jacket tightly and squeezing him, pressing him against the side of the car, and then the sacking which had hidden everything inside was somehow pulled aside, and suddenly one could see the street and also see that it was morning outside and the fog was no longer so thick.

There was a terrible silence, a silence one had to be afraid of. In this silence only Dad's heavy breathing could be heard, and the panting of the man in the leather jacket, who was standing in front of Dad with his eyes closed, as if he had gone to sleep standing. "Get off," he groaned hoarsely. "Get off! What sort of people! One risks his life and then . . . You get out of this truck, for I am not driving you an inch farther, you better find some way of getting to the border . . ."

"No," said father, "Oh, no!"

And he was still saying this when he looked in a funny way at Mother and threw out their suitcases and picked the little boy up in his arms. Dad was still saying this "No" in the street, though at that time the boy was no longer crying, why should he?

It was quite light by then and the sun was weakly shining from behind the clouds.

ABOUT THE LINES

1 This story is written mainly in two tenses: past and present. In point form, make two lists, one of the major events related in the present tense and the other of the major events related in the past tense. Discuss the tense choices with your partners, and together write a note commenting on why you think the author chose to use two different time frames in her story.

2 In the voice of either Mother or Dad, relate your version of this story to a sympathetic relative or neighbour. You might practise your narrative, and when you are satisfied that you can do so naturally, present it to a small group.

3 Complete the following sentences in Peter's voice:
a. I started to cry because . . .
b. I thought my Dad was great when he . . .
c. When I look at Mother, sometimes I feel . . .
Compare your sentences with your partners' and then produce final versions on which you all agree.

BETWEEN THE LINES

1 Reread the section of the story from "Dad did not look at him . . ." to ". . . of the smell of snow" (see p. 64). In the voices of:
a. a little boy; and
b. a watching adult,
state your interpretation of Dad's actions. Compare your statements with your partners', and discuss any differences until you have resolved them or agreed that there are different ways of looking at the situation.

2 The author has written this story from the point of view of the little boy, Peter. Find four instances in the story where this point of view helps the reader to understand and to enjoy the story. Justify each choice in a sentence.

3 Dawn is usually a symbol of hope and life, and in the last sentence of this story, it is used ironically (see p. 352). In the voices of Dad, Mother, and Peter, try to explain what the dawn means to you.

4 You have been asked to make a film version of "In the Mist." Working with your partners, describe the setting, the positioning of the characters, and the sources of light for the scene that you think is the most important in the film. Illustrations would help.

BEYOND THE LINES

1 Research the Hungarian Uprising of 1956, and then give an oral presentation to the class in which you outline the major events of that period.

2 Continue the story from where the author stopped. Your continuation may be positive or negative.

3 Write a short story or a poem based on a child's inability to comprehend a serious situation.

or

Write a children's story illustrating the dangers of not paying sufficient attention to parents. Read your story to a group of younger children and invite their comments.

4 Imagine that you are the adult Peter. Write a memoir of this incident in your life from the adult point of view.

5 Research a group of people who have had to flee their homeland and have come to Canada as refugees.
Examine:
a. the reasons for their move;
b. how they have adapted to their new environment;
c. some ways in which they have affected life in Canada.
Share your findings with a larger group.

EXTENDED ACTIVITIES

1 Choose a historical incident that interests you and retell it in your own words as a short story.

2 Research the life of a famous individual from the past. Using the information from your research, role play the person for a group. Describe the triumphs and troubles of your life and answer any questions the group may pose.

3 Select an area of human endeavour, such as music, military prowess, human rights, exploration, art, etc. Make a list of the ten greatest contributors to that area in your opinion. Summarize the reasons for including each person. Present your material in chart form; illustrations would help.

4 Read a historical novel set in an era that interests you. Give a book talk to your class in which you explain the background to the novel and your reasons for recommending it.

5 Working with a partner, produce a twenty-item historical trivia quiz (do not make the questions too difficult!). Try the quiz on students around the school, and draw conclusions about your questions from the results.

6 Each generation makes its own music, and historical events shape the music of a generation. Choose a period and research its music. Prepare and play to the class a tape of music and songs from the period and explain how the music reflects the times. You might consider: The American Civil War, World War I, the 1920s, the Protest Movements of the 1960s, etc.

EXTENDED ACTIVITIES

7 As times change, so do costumes. Working in a group, research fashion changes for men and women over a period of time. Stage a fashion show, and explain the changes and the reasons for them. You might prefer to produce an illustrated pamphlet.

8 Research eating habits from a previous era in a given culture. Present a typical menu from the period of your choice. You might be able to prepare one or more of the dishes.

9 Produce a series of sketches or cartoons based on a historical event that interests you. Display your drawings in your classroom.

10 Choose a historical figure who was involved in a controversial issue.
a. Speaking as that figure, justify your actions to a small group.

or

b. Make a debatable resolution that focusses on the central issue of the controversy. Working in a group of four, present a formal debate on the resolution to the class.

11 Research your own background. Interview any relatives you can and compile a history of your family and yourself. Using any available photographs, letters, maps, etc., give an oral presentation on your family to a group of classmates. Try to link family history with national and international events.

12 Produce a documentary pamphlet on any interesting feature of your locality. Illustrate your pamphlet and try to include sufficient detail in it so that it could be useful in the school library.

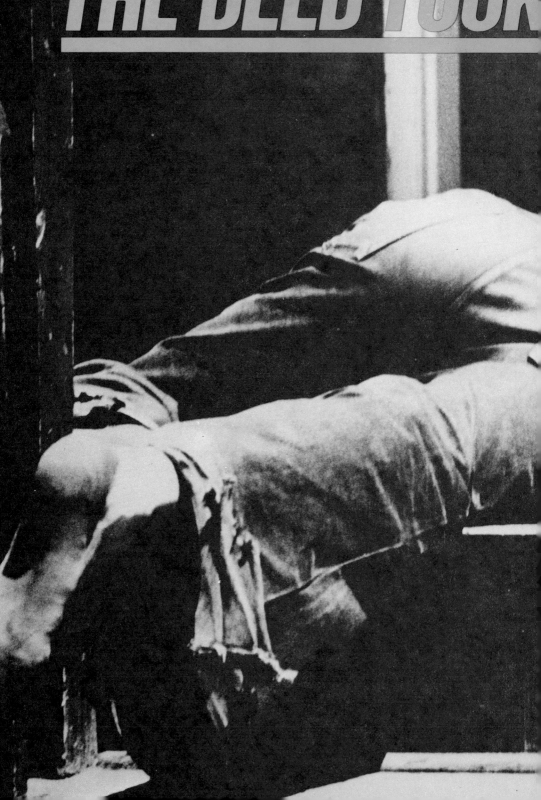

PLACE

Cruelty has a Human Heart,
And jealousy a Human Face;
Terror the Human Form Divine,
And Secrecy the Human Dress.

The Human Dress is forged Iron,
The Human Form a fiery Forge,
The Human Face a Furnace seal'd,
The Human Heart its hungry Gorge.

A Divine Image
William Blake

THE HOBBYIST

Fredric Brown

A crime-fighter with a deadly weapon

"I heard a rumour," Sangstrom said, "to the effect that you —" He turned his head and looked about him to make absolutely sure that he and the druggist were alone in the tiny prescription pharmacy. The druggist was a gnome-like, gnarled little man who could have been any age from fifty to a hundred. They were alone, but Sangstrom dropped his voice just the same. " — to the effect that you have a completely undetectable poison."

The druggist nodded. He came around the counter and locked the front door of the shop, then walked toward a doorway behind the counter. "I was about to take a coffee break," he said. "Come with me and have a cup."

Sangstrom followed him around the counter and through the doorway to a back room ringed by shelves of bottles from floor to ceiling. The druggist plugged in an electric percolator, found two cups and put them on a table that had a chair on either side of it. He motioned Sangstrom to one of the chairs and took the other himself. "Now," he said. "Tell me. Whom do you want to kill, and why?"

"Does it matter?" Sangstrom asked. "Isn't it enough that I pay for — "

The druggist interrupted him with an upraised hand. "Yes, it matters. I must be convinced that you deserve what I can give you. Otherwise — " He shrugged.

"All right," Sangstrom said. "The *whom* is my wife. The *why* — " He started the long story. Before he had quite finished the percolator had completed its task and the druggist briefly interrupted to get the coffee for them. Sangstrom concluded his story.

The little druggist nodded. "Yes, I occasionally dispense an undetectable poison. I do so freely; I do not charge for it, if I think the case is deserving. I have helped many murderers."

"Fine," Sangstrom said. "Please give it to me, then."

The druggist smiled at him. "I already have. By the time the coffee was ready I had decided that you deserved it. It was, as I said, free. But there is a price for the antidote."

Sangstrom turned pale. But he had anticipated — not this, but the possibility of a double cross or some form of blackmail. He pulled a pistol from his pocket.

The little druggist chuckled. "You daren't use that. Can you find the antidote — " he waved at the shelves " — among those thousands of bottles? Or would you find a faster, more virulent poison? Or if you think I'm bluffing, that you are not really poisoned, go ahead and shoot. You'll know the answer within three hours when the poison starts to work."

"How much for the antidote?" Sangstrom growled.

"Quite reasonable, a thousand dollars. After all, a man must live; even if his hobby is preventing murders, there's no reason why he shouldn't make money at it, is there?"

Sangstrom growled and put the pistol down, but within reach, and took out his wallet. Maybe after he had the antidote, he'd still use that pistol. He counted out a thousand dollars in hundred-dollar bills and put them on the table.

The druggist made no immediate move to pick them up. He said, "And one other thing — for your wife's safety and mine. You will write a confession of your intention — your former intention, I trust — to murder your wife. Then you will wait till I go out and mail it to a friend of mine on the homicide detail. He'll keep it as evidence in case you ever *do* decide to kill your wife. Or me, for that matter.

"When that is in the mail it will be safe for me to return here and give you the antidote. I'll get you paper and pen. Oh, one other thing — although I do not absolutely insist on it. Please help spread the word about my undetectable poison, will you? One never knows, Mr. Sangstrom. The life you save, if you have any enemies, just might be your own."

ABOUT THE LINES

1 Read the story through carefully and summarize it in one hundred words. Create a cloze task by deleting every eighth word from your summary. Have a partner work on your cloze task. Discuss any difficulties he/she may find in doing the exercise and rephrase your summary if some parts are not clear.

2 Write a question that you would ask someone if you wanted to see if he/she recognized the turning point in this story. Try out your question on your partners.

3 Write a one- or two-sentence introduction to this story that would arouse the reader's interest but not give away the whole story.

BETWEEN THE LINES

1 Look up the meaning of "irony" in the glossary on page 352. Discuss with your partners what makes each of the following passages from the story ironic. Write your own explanation for two of the passages.
   a. "I must be convinced that you deserve what I can give you."
   b. "Yes, I occasionally dispense an undetectable poison. I do so freely; I do not charge for it, if I think the case is deserving. I have helped many murderers."
   c. "Fine," Sangstrom said. "Please give it to me, then."
   d. "The life you save, if you have any enemies, just might be your own."

2 In a short paragraph, explain why you think the author chose to make the druggist "a gnome-like, gnarled little man who could have been any age from fifty to a hundred."

BEYOND THE LINES

1 Assuming the role of Sangstrom, write the letter of confession that the druggist demanded. Include a believable motive for your "former intention" to kill your wife.

2 Working with a partner, convert this story into a play and include stage directions and prop descriptions. Dramatize your script for a group who has read the story and ask for their constructive criticism. Make any appropriate changes in your presentation and then perform the play for a group who is not familiar with the story.

3 Imagine that you are the druggist. Write an entry in your diary describing the most frightening and evil of all the would-be murderers whom you have met through your strange hobby.

JUST ONE OF THOSE DAYS

Donald E. Westlake

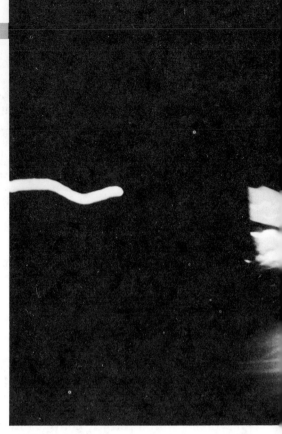

Harry came into the motel room as I was putting my shoulder holster on. "Forget it, Ralph," he said.

I looked at him. "Forget it? What do you mean, forget it?"

He took off his coat and tossed it on the bed. "The bank's closed," he said.

"It can't be closed," I said. "This is Tuesday."

"Wrong," he said. He flipped his automatic out of his holster and tossed it on the bed. "It can be closed," he said. "Everything can be closed. This is Griffin's Day."

"This is *what's* Day?"

"Griffin's," he said. He shrugged out of his shoulder holster and tossed it on the bed. "Kenny Griffin's Day," he said.

"I give up," I said. "What's a Kenny Griffin?"

"Astronaut," he said. He opened his shirt collar and tossed himself onto the bed. "Comes from this burg," he said. "It's his Homecoming Day. They're having a big parade for him."

"By the bank?" I asked.

"What difference?" He moved his automatic out from under his hip, adjusted his pillow, and shut his eyes. "The bank's closed anyway," he said.

I cocked my head, and from far away I heard band music. "Well, if that isn't nice," I said.

"They're gonna give him the key to the city," Harry said.

"That is real nice," I said.

"Speeches, and little kids giving him flowers."

"That's so nice I can't stand it," I said.

"He was in orbit," Harry said.

"He should of stayed in orbit," I said.

"So we'll do it tomorrow," said Harry.

"I know," I said. "But it's just irritating."

It was more irritating to me than to Harry, because, after all, I was the planner. I hated it when a plan went wrong or had to be changed around, no matter how minor the change. Like planning a caper on Tuesday and having to do it on Wednesday instead. A small alteration, an unimportant shift, but we'd have to stay in this town one day longer than expected, which increased the chances of identification at some later date. We'd have to change our airline reservations, which maybe some smart clerk would think about afterward. We'd show up at the Miami hotel a day late, which would tend to make us conspicuous there, too. Nothing vital, sure, nothing desperate, but it only takes a tiny leak to sink a mighty battleship. I remember reading that on a poster once when I was a kid, and it made a big impression on me.

I am the natural planner type. I had cased this bank and this town for three weeks *before* making my plan, and then for another five days *after* it was set. I worked out just the right method, the right time, the right getaway, the right everything.

The one thing I didn't work out was one of those astronauts hailing from this town and deciding on *my* day he'll come on back again. As I later said to Harry, why couldn't he of just phoned?

So we did it on Wednesday. We went to the bank at precisely two fifty-four, flipped the masks up over our faces, and announced, "This is a stickup. Everybody freeze."

Everybody froze. While I watched the people and the door, Harry went behind the counter and started filling the bag.

Actually, Wednesday worked just as well as Tuesday so far as the mechanics of the plan were concerned. On all three mid-week days, Tuesday and Wednesday and Thursday, all but three of the bank employees were at lunch at two fifty-four P.M., having to take a later-than-normal lunch because the bank was at its busiest during usual lunch hours. On the days I had checked it, there had never been any more than three customers here at this time, and the average had been only slightly over one. Today, for instance, there was just one, a small and elderly lady who carried an umbrella despite the bright sun outside.

The rest of the plan would work as well on Wednesday as on Tuesday, too. The traffic lights I'd timed worked the same every day of the week, the plane schedule out at the airport was the same as yesterday, and the traffic we could expect on the Belt Highway was no different, either. Still, I did hate to have things changed on me.

Harry was done filling the bag at one minute to three, which was a full minute ahead of time. We both stood by the door and waited, and when the second hand was done with its sweep once more, Harry put his gun away, flipped his mask off, picked up the bag and went out to where we'd parked the stolen Ford in front of the fire hydrant.

I now had forty seconds. I was looking everywhere at once, at my watch, at the three employees and the little old lady customer and at Harry out front in the Ford. If he didn't manage to get it started in time, we'd have to wait another minute and ten seconds.

But he did. After thirty-one seconds he gave me the sign. I nodded, let nine more seconds go by and dashed out of the bank. Eighteen running paces while I stuffed the gun away and stripped off the mask, and then I was in the car and it was rolling.

There was a traffic light at the corner. "Twenty-two miles an hour," I said, looking at that light, seeing it red down there in front of us.

"I know," said Harry. "Don't worry, I know."

The light turned green just as we reached the intersection. We sailed on through. I looked back, and saw people just erupting from the bank.

Midway down this block there was an alley on the right that led through to the next block. Harry made the turn, smooth and sweet, into a space hardly any wider than our car, and ahead of us was the MG. Harry hit the brakes, I grabbed the bag, and we jumped out of the Ford. Harry opened the Ford's hood and grabbed a handful of wires and yanked. Then he shut the hood and ran to the MG.

I was already in it, putting on the beard and the sunglasses and the cap and the yellow turtleneck sweater. Harry put on his beard and sunglasses and beret and green sports jacket. He started the engine, I stared at the second hand of my watch.

82

"Five," I said. "Four. Three. Two. One. Go!"

We shot out of the alley, turned left, made the light just before it went to red, turned right, made the lights perfectly for three blocks, then hit the Schuyler Avenue ramp to the Belt Highway.

"You watch the signs," Harry said. "I'll watch the traffic."

"Naturally," I said.

Almost every city has one of these by-pass highways now, a belt that makes a complete circuit of the city. Not only can travellers passing through use it to avoid getting involved in city traffic, but local citizens can use it for high-speed routing from one part of the city to the other. This one, called the Belt Highway, was an elevated road all the way around, giving a fine view of the town and the countryside.

But it was neither the town nor the surrounding countryside I was interested in at the moment. Right now my primary concern was the Airport Road exit. As Harry steered us through the light midweek afternoon traffic, I watched the signs.

One thing I have to admit, they did put up plenty of signs. Like for the first exit we came to, which was called Callisto Street Exit. First there was a sign that said, "Callisto Street Exit, $1/4$ Mile." A little after that, there was a sign that said, "Callisto Street Exit, Keep Right." And then finally, at the exit itself, a sign with an arrow pointing to the down-ramp and the words, "Callisto Street Exit."

Of course, all of this was mostly geared for local citizens, so there wasn't any sign telling you where Callisto Street itself might take you, but if you knew it was Callisto Street you wanted, there wasn't a chance in the world that you'd miss it.

Harry buzzed us along in the white MG, just exactly at the fifty-mile-an-hour speed limit, and I watched the exits go by, with the standard three signs for each one: Woodford Road, Eagle Avenue, Griffin Road, Crowell Street, Five Mile Road, Esquire Avenue. . . .

I looked at my watch. I said, "Harry, are you going too slow? You're supposed to go fifty."

Harry was insulted; he prides himself on being one of the best drivers in the business. "I *am* going fifty," he said, and gestured for me to take a look at the speedometer myself.

But I was too intent on watching for signs. Airport Road I wanted; Airport Road. I said, "It shouldn't be taking anywhere near *this* long, I know."

"I'm doing fifty — and I *been* doing fifty."

I looked at my watch, then back out at the highway. "Maybe the speedometer's busted. Maybe you're only doing forty."

"I'm doing fifty," Harry said. "I can *tell*. I know what fifty feels like, and I'm doing fifty."

"If we miss that plane," I said, "we're in trouble."

"We won't miss it," said Harry grimly, and hunched over the wheel.

"The cops will be asking questions all around the neighbourhood back there now," I said. "Sooner or later they'll find somebody that saw this car come out of the alley. Sooner or later they'll be looking for us in *this* car and with *these* descriptions."

"You just watch the signs," said Harry.

So I watched the signs. Remsen Avenue, De Witt Boulevard, Green Meadow Park, Seventeenth Street, Glenwood Road, Powers Street. . . .

Harry said, "You must of missed it."

I said, "Impossible. I've read every sign. Every sign. Your speedometer's off."

"It isn't."

Earhart Street, Willoughby Lane, Firewall Avenue, Broad Street, Marigold Hill Road. . . .

I looked at my watch. "Our plane just took off," I said.

"You keep looking at your watch," Harry said. "That's how come you missed it."

"I did not miss it," I said.

"Here comes Schuyler Avenue again," he said. "Isn't that where we got on?"

"How did I miss it?" I cried. "Hurry, Harry! We'll get it this time! They'll have a plane going *somewhere!*"

Harry crouched over the steering wheel.

They stopped us halfway around the circuit again. Some smart cop had seen us — the description was out by now, of course — and radioed in, and they set up a nice little road block across their elevated highway, and we drove right around to it and stopped, and they put the arm on us.

As I was riding in the back of a police car, going in the opposite direction of the Belt now, I asked the detective I was handcuffed to, "Do you mind telling me what you did with Airport Road?"

He grinned at me and pointed out the window, saying, "There it is."

The sign he pointed at said, "Griffin Road, ¼ Mile."

I said, "Griffin Road? I wanted *Airport* Road."

"That's it," he said. "We changed the name yesterday, in honour of Kenny Griffin. You know, the astronaut. We're all real proud of Kenny around here."

"I better not say anything against him then," I said.

ABOUT THE LINES

1 Complete the following unfinished sentences:
   a. The plan shifted from Tuesday to Wednesday because . . .
   b. The robbers chose two fifty-four p.m. to strike because . . .
   c. To get to the airport, you must take the Belt Highway and cut off at the first exit after . . .

2 Imagine that you are Ralph. Write out all the steps in your getaway. Check your version with a partner's.

3 In one sentence for each one, explain the reasons why Ralph felt that the delay from Tuesday to Wednesday increased the robbers' chances of being caught.

BETWEEN THE LINES

1 Explain in a brief paragraph why "Just One of Those Days" is an appropriate title for this story. Working with your partners, brainstorm a list of alternate titles that would capture the central idea of the story.

2 The townspeople in this story are honouring an astronaut who navigated a rocket ship in orbit outside the Earth's atmosphere. Keeping this fact in mind, discuss with your partners why the robbers' failure to reach a destination in this town is ironic.

3 Imagine that you are Harry. Write a memoir in which you describe your feelings when Ralph is unable to direct you to the exit for Airport Road.

4 Reread the last sentence of the story. Write what Ralph might like to say about Kenny Griffin to express the frustration he and Harry have experienced. (Remember, your statement has to be printable, so have a partner censor it for you if you think you got a little carried away.)

BEYOND THE LINES

1 Interview a local police officer or someone you know who works in crime detection. Ask him/her about any cases in which the crook was captured because of extraordinary bad luck. Prepare a dramatic retelling of one of these cases to share with a group. Be sure to tell your listeners something about the person who told you the story, although you may wish to leave your source unnamed.

2 Phone or visit City Hall or a Municipal Records Office where you live. Investigate situations where streets, public buildings, or towns were named after a particular person. Write an account of one of these cases, explaining why civic authorities chose the name they did. Combine your work with your partners' to make a poster about street and building names and their origins.

3 Call upon your memories of crime shows that you have seen on television or detective stories that you have read, and write a story in which "the perfect crime" was foiled by one small slip-up.

4 Working with your partners, script and dramatize a scene where Harry and Ralph arrive at a federal penetentiary and answer the inevitable question from fellow inmates: "So what are you in for?"

or

Write a shooting script for a scene from this story for film or television.

5 Look up the story of the strange creature from Greek mythology called the "griffin." After you have shared the story with a partner, discuss why it is ironic (see p. 352) that these robbers should be foiled by a Griffin.

THE EXECUTION

Alden Nowlan ▬▬

On the night of the execution
a man at the door
mistook me for the coroner.
"Press," I said.

But he didn't understand. He led me
into the wrong room
where the sheriff greeted me:
"You're late, Padre."

LOOKING IN

1 The narrator of the poem is mistaken for someone else three times. List the identities that were thrust upon him.

2 In one sentence summarize the human failure that led to the final mistake.

3 Write an interior monologue that reflects the panic and rage felt by the victim as he is pushed toward the gallows.

"You're wrong," I told him. "I'm Press."
"Yes, of course, Reverend Press."
We went down the stairway.

"Ah, Mr. Ellis," said the Deputy.
"Press!" I shouted. But he shoved me
through a black curtain.
The lights were so bright
I couldn't see the faces
of the men sitting
opposite. But, thank God, I thought
they can see me!

"Look!" I cried. "Look at my face!
Doesn't anybody know me?"

Then a hood covered my head.
"Don't make it harder for us," the hangman whispered.

LOOKING OUT

1 Imagine that you are the hangman and explain in a written report to your government superior how you feel once you have discovered your mistake. Try to justify your error. You may wish to present this explanation orally by role playing a conversation between the hangman and an official to whom he is responsible.

2 Write a memoir in which you describe an incident when something unfortunate happened to you or someone you know because people weren't listening to each other.

3 Imagine that you are the warden of the prison. Decide what you will do with the real murderer the night that the mistake is made. Give your instructions to the prison officials in a written order.

4 Use this poem as part of an argument against capital punishment.

LAMB TO THE SLAUGHTER

Roald Dahl

A "perfect wife" . . . a perfect crime

The room was warm and clean, the curtains drawn, the two table lamps alight — hers and the one by the empty chair opposite. On the sideboard behind her, two tall glasses. Fresh ice cubes in the ice bucket.

Mary Maloney was waiting for her husband to come home from work.

Now and again she would glance up at the clock, but without anxiety, merely to please herself with the thought that each minute gone by made it nearer the time when he would come. There was a slow smiling air about her, and about everything she did. The drop of the head as she bent over her sewing was curiously tranquil. Her skin — for this was her sixth month with child — had acquired a wonderful translucent quality, the mouth was soft, and the eyes, with their new placid look, seemed larger, darker than before.

When the clock said ten minutes to five, she began to listen, and a few moments later, punctually as always, she heard the tires on the gravel outside, and the car door slamming, the footsteps passing the window, the key turning in the lock. She laid aside her sewing, stood up, and went forward to kiss him as he came in.

"Hullo darling," she said.

"Hullo," he answered.

She took his coat and hung it in the closet. Then she walked over and made the drinks. Soon she was back again in her chair with the sewing, and he was in the other, opposite, holding the tall glass with both his hands, rocking it so the ice cubes tinkled against the side.

For her, this was always a blissful time of day. She knew he didn't want to speak much until the first drink was finished, and she, on her side, was content to sit quietly, enjoying his company after the long hours alone in the house. She loved to luxuriate in the presence of this man, and to feel — almost as a sunbather feels the sun — that warm male glow that came out of him to her when they were alone together. She loved him for the way he sat loosely in a chair, for the way he came in a door, or moved slowly across the room with long strides. She loved the intent, far look in his eyes when they rested on her, the funny shape of the mouth, and especially the way he remained silent about his tiredness, sitting still with himself until some of it went away.

"Tired, darling?"

"Yes," he said. "I'm tired." And as he spoke, he did an unusual thing. He lifted his glass and drained it in one swallow although there was still half of it, at least half of it left. She wasn't really watching him, but she knew what he had done because she heard the ice cubes falling back against the bottom of

the empty glass when
he lowered his arm.
He paused a moment,
leaning forward
in the chair,
then he got up and
went slowly over to
fetch himself another.
"I'll get it!"
she cried, jumping up.
"Sit down," he said.
"Darling, shall I
get your slippers?"
"No."
She watched
him as he began
to sip the drink.
"I think it's a
shame," she said,
"that when a
policeman gets
to be as senior

as you, they keep him walking about on his feet all day long."

He didn't answer, so she bent her head again and went on with her sewing; but each time he lifted the drink to his lips, she heard the ice cubes clinking against the side of the glass.

"Darling," she said. "Would you like me to get you some cheese? I haven't made any supper because it's Thursday."

"No," he said.

"If you're too tired to eat out," she went on, "it's still not too late. There's plenty of meat and stuff in the freezer, and you can have it right here and not even move out of the chair."

Her eyes waited on him for an answer, a smile, a little nod, but he made no sign.

"Anyway," she went on, "I'll get you some cheese and crackers first."

"I don't want it," he said.

She moved uneasily in her chair, the large eyes still watching his face. "But you must have supper. I can easily do it here. I'd like to do it. We can have lamb chops. Or pork. Anything you want. Everything's in the freezer."

"Forget it," he said.

"But darling, you *must* eat! I'll fix it anyway, and then you can have it or not, as you like."

She stood up and placed her sewing on the table by the lamp.

"Sit down," he said. "Just for a minute, sit down."

It wasn't till then that she began to get frightened.

"Go on," he said. "Sit down."

She lowered herself back slowly into the chair, watching him all the time with those large, bewildered eyes. He had finished the second drink and was staring down into the glass, frowning.

"Listen," he said. "I've got something to tell you."

"What is it, darling? What's the matter?"

He had now become absolutely motionless, and he kept his head down so that the light from the lamp beside him fell across the upper part of his face, leaving the chin and mouth in shadow. She noticed there was a little muscle moving near the corner of his left eye.

"This is going to be a bit of a shock to you, I'm afraid," he said. "But I've thought about it a good deal and I've decided the only thing to do is tell you right away. I hope you won't blame me too much."

And he told her. It didn't take long, four or five minutes at most, and she sat very still through it all, watching him with a kind of dazed horror as he went further and further away from her with each word.

"So there it is," he added. "And I know it's kind of a bad time to be telling you, but there simply wasn't any other way. Of course I'll give you money and see you're looked after. But there needn't really be any fuss. I hope not anyway. It wouldn't be very good for my job."

Her first instinct was not to believe any of it, to reject it all. It occurred to her that perhaps he hadn't even spoken, that she herself had imagined the whole thing. Maybe, if she went about her business and acted as though she hadn't been listening, then later, when she sort of woke up again, she might find none of it had ever happened.

"I'll get the supper," she managed to whisper, and this time he didn't stop her.

When she walked across the room she couldn't feel her feet touching the floor. She couldn't feel anything at all — except a slight nausea and a desire to vomit. Everything was automatic now — down the steps to the cellar, the light switch, the deep freeze, the hand inside the cabinet taking hold of the first object it met. She lifted it out, and looked at it. It was wrapped in paper, so she took off the paper and looked at it again.

A leg of lamb.

All right then, they would have lamb for supper. She carried it upstairs, holding the thin bone-end of it with both her hands, and as she went through the living room, she saw him standing over by the window with his back to her, and she stopped.

"For goodness sake," he said, hearing her, but not turning around. "Don't make supper for me. I'm going out."

At that point, Mary Maloney simply walked up behind him and without any pause she swung the big frozen leg of lamb high in the air and brought it down as hard as she could on the back of his head.

She might just as well have hit him with a steel club.

She stepped back a pace, waiting, and the funny thing was that he remained standing there for at least four or five seconds, gently swaying. Then he crashed to the carpet.

The violence of the crash, the noise, the small table overturning, helped bring her out of the shock. She came out slowly, feeling cold and surprised, and she stood for a while blinking at the body, still holding the ridiculous piece of meat tight with both hands.

All right, she told herself. So I've killed him.

It was extraordinary now, how clear her mind became all of a sudden. She began thinking very fast. As the wife of a detective, she knew quite well what the penalty would be. That was fine. It made no difference to her. In fact, it would be a relief. On the other hand, what about the child? What were the laws about murderers with unborn children? Did they kill them both — mother and child? Or did they wait until the tenth month? What did they do?

Mary Maloney didn't know. And she certainly wasn't prepared to take a chance.

She carried the meat into the kitchen, placed it in a pan, turned the oven on high, and shoved it inside. Then she washed her hands and ran upstairs to the bedroom. She sat down before the mirror, tidied her hair, touched up her lips and face. She tried a smile. It came out rather peculiar. She tried again.

"Hullo Sam," she said brightly, aloud.

The voice sounded peculiar too.

"I want some potatoes please, Sam. Yes, and I think a can of peas."

That was better. Both the smile and the voice were coming out better now. She rehearsed it several times more. Then she ran downstairs, took her coat, went out the back door, down the garden, into the street.

It wasn't six o'clock yet and the lights were still on in the grocery shop.

"Hullo Sam," she said brightly, smiling at the man behind the counter.

"Why, good evening, Mrs. Maloney. How're *you?*"

"I want some potatoes please, Sam. Yes, and I think a can of peas."

The man turned and reached up behind him on the shelf for the peas.

"Patrick's decided he's tired and doesn't want to eat out tonight," she told him. "We usually go out Thursdays, you know, and now he's caught me without any vegetables in the house."

"Then how about meat, Mrs. Maloney?"

"No, I've got meat, thanks. I got a nice leg of lamb from the freezer."

"Oh."

"I don't much like cooking it frozen, Sam, but I'm taking a chance on it this time. You think it'll be all right?"

"Personally," the grocer said, "I don't believe it makes any difference. You want these Idaho potatoes?"

"Oh, yes, that'll be fine. Two of those."

"Anything else?" The grocer cocked his head on one side, looking at her pleasantly. "How about afterwards? What are you going to give him for afterwards?"

"Well — what would you suggest, Sam?"

The man glanced around his shop. "How about a nice big slice of cheesecake? I know he likes that."

"Perfect," she said. "He loves it."

And when it was all wrapped and she had paid, she put on her brightest smile and said, "Thank you, Sam. Goodnight."

"Goodnight, Mrs. Maloney. And thank *you*."

And now, she told herself as she hurried back, all she was doing now, she was returning home to her husband and he was waiting for his supper; and she must cook it good, and make it as tasty as possible because the poor man was tired; and if, when she entered into the house, she happened to find anything unusual, or tragic, or terrible, then naturally it would be a shock and she'd become frantic with grief and horror. Mind you, she wasn't *expecting* to find anything. She was just going home with the vegetables. Mrs. Patrick Maloney going home with the vegetables on Thursday evening to cook supper for her husband.

That's the way, she told herself. Do everything right and natural. Keep things absolutely natural and there'll be no need for any acting at all.

Therefore, when she entered the kitchen by the back door, she was humming a little tune to herself and smiling.

"Patrick!" she called. "How are you, darling?"

She put the parcel down on the table and went through into the living room; and when she saw him lying there on the floor with his legs doubled up and one arm twisted back underneath his body, it really was rather a shock. All the old love and longing for him welled up inside her, and she ran over to him, knelt down beside him, and began to cry her heart out. It was easy. No acting was necessary.

A few minutes later she got up and went to the phone. She knew the number of the police station, and when the man at the other end answered, she cried to him, "Quick! Come quick! Patrick's dead!"

"Who's speaking?"

"Mrs. Maloney. Mrs. Patrick Maloney."

"You mean Patrick Maloney's dead?"

92

"I think so," she sobbed. "He's lying on the floor and I think he's dead."

"Be right over," the man said.

The car came very quickly, and when she opened the front door, two policemen walked in. She knew them both — she knew nearly all the men at that precinct — and she fell right into Jack Noonan's arms, weeping hysterically. He put her gently into a chair, then went over to join the other one, who was called O'Malley, kneeling by the body.

"Is he dead?" she cried.

"I'm afraid he is. What happened?"

Briefly, she told her story about going out to the grocer and coming back to find him on the floor. While she was talking, crying and talking, Noonan discovered a small patch of congealed blood on the dead man's head. He showed it to O'Malley who got up at once and hurried to the phone.

Soon, other men began to come into the house. First a doctor, then two detectives, one of whom she knew by name. Later, a police photographer arrived and took pictures, and a man who knew about fingerprints. There was a great deal of whispering and muttering beside the corpse, and the detectives kept asking a lot of questions. But they always treated her kindly. She told her story again, this time right from the beginning, when Patrick had come in, and she was sewing, and he was tired, so tired he hadn't wanted to go out for supper. She told how she'd put the meat in the oven — "it's there now, cooking" — and how she'd slipped out to the grocer for vegetables, and come back to find him lying on the floor.

"Which grocer?" one of the detectives asked.

She told him, and he turned and whispered something to the other detective who immediately went outside into the street.

In fifteen minutes he was back with a page of notes, and there was more whispering, and through her sobbing she heard a few of the whispered phrases — " . . . acted quite normal . . . very cheerful . . . wanted to give him a good supper . . . peas . . . cheesecake . . . impossible that she . . ."

After a while, the photographer and the doctor departed and two other men came in and took the corpse away on a stretcher. Then, the fingerprint man went away. The two detectives remained, and so did the two policemen. They were exceptionally nice to her, and Jack Noonan asked if she wouldn't rather go somewhere else, to her sister's house perhaps, or to his own wife who would take care of her and put her up for the night.

No, she said. She didn't feel she could move even a yard at the moment. Would they mind awfully if she stayed just where she was until she felt better. She didn't feel too good at the moment, she really didn't.

Then hadn't she better lie down on the bed? Jack Noonan asked.

No, she said. She'd like to stay right where she was, in this chair. A little later perhaps, when she felt better, she would move.

So they left her there while they went about their business searching the house. Occasionally one of the detectives asked her another question. Sometimes Jack Noonan spoke to her gently as he passed by. Her husband, he told her, had been killed by a blow on the back of the head administered with a heavy blunt instrument, almost certainly a large piece of metal. They were looking for the weapon. The murderer may have taken it with him, but on the other hand he may've thrown it away or hidden it somewhere on the premises.

"It's the old story," he said. "Get the weapon, and you've got the man."

Later, one of the detectives came up and sat beside her. Did she know, he asked, of anything in the house that could've been used as the weapon? Would she mind having a look around to see if anything was missing — a very big wrench, for example, or a heavy metal vase.

They didn't have any metal vases, she said.

"Or a big wrench?"

She didn't think they had a big wrench. But there might be some things like that in the garage.

The search went on. She knew that there were other policemen in the garden all around the house. She could hear their footsteps on the gravel outside, and sometimes she saw the flash of a flashlight through a chink in the curtains. It began to get late, nearly nine she noticed by the clock on the mantle. The four men searching the rooms seemed to be growing weary, a trifle exasperated.

"Jack," she said, the next time Sergeant Noonan went by. "Would you mind giving me a drink?"

"Sure, I'll give you a drink. Some of this?"

"Yes, please. But just a small one. It might make me feel better."

He handed her the glass.

"Why don't you have one yourself," she said. "You must be awfully tired. Please do. You've been very good to me."

"Well," he answered. "It's not strictly allowed, but I might take just a drop to keep me going."

One by one the others came in and were persuaded to take a little drink. They stood around rather awkwardly with the drinks in their hands, uncomfortable in her presence, trying to say consoling things to her. Sergeant Noonan wandered into the kitchen, came out quickly, and said, "Look, Mrs. Maloney. You know that oven of yours is still on, and the meat still inside."

"Oh, *dear* me!" she cried. "So it is!"

"I better turn it off for you, hadn't I?"

"Will you do that, Jack? Thank you so much."

When the sergeant returned the second time, she looked at him with her large, dark, tearful eyes. "Jack Noonan," she said.

"Yes?"

"Would you do me a small favour — you and these others?"

"We can try, Mrs. Maloney."

"Well," she said. "Here you all are, and good friends of dear Patrick's too, and helping to catch the man who killed him. You must be terribly hungry by now because it's long past your suppertime, and I know Patrick would never forgive me, God bless his soul, if I allowed you to remain in his house without offering you decent hospitality. Why don't you eat up that lamb that's in the oven. It'll be cooked just right by now."

"Wouldn't dream of it," Sergeant Noonan said.

"Please," she begged. "Please eat it. Personally I couldn't touch a thing, certainly not what's been in the house when he was here. But it's all right for you. It'd be a favour to me if you'd eat it up. Then you can go on with your work again afterwards."

There was a good deal of hesitating among the four policemen, but they were clearly hungry, and in the end they were persuaded to go into the kitchen and help themselves. The woman stayed where she was, listening to them through the open door, and she could hear them speaking among themselves, their voices thick and sloppy because their mouths were full of meat.

"Have some more, Charlie?"

"No. Better not finish it."

"She *wants* us to finish it. She said so. Be doing her a favour."

"Okay then. Give me some more."

"That's a big club the guy must've used to hit poor Patrick," one of them was saying. "The doc says his skull was smashed all to pieces just like from a sledge hammer."

"That's why it ought to be easy to find."

"Exactly what I say."

"Whoever done it, they're not going to be carrying a thing like that around with them longer than they need."

One of them belched.

"Personally, I think it's right here on the premises."

"Probably right under our very noses. What do you think, Jack?"

And in the other room, Mary Maloney began to giggle.

ABOUT THE LINES

1 Write a point-form summary of the events of this tale and give it to a partner who has read the story to check for any missing details. Add any points that you may have omitted.

2 Working with your partners, write three questions you would ask a person who has read the story if you wanted to know if he/she had understood it. Try out your questions on someone who has read the story but has not yet discussed it with anyone.

3 List all the details at the beginning of the story that indicate Mary's great devotion to her husband. Then list all the details of her behaviour later in the story that suggest she can hate as strongly as she can love. Compare your lists with your partners'.

BETWEEN THE LINES

1 The characters in this story are a collection of stereotypes and clichés who behave more like puppets than real human beings. Mary is "the little woman," Patrick is "the cheating husband," and the police are "the blundering detectives." List the ways in which these stereotypes are developed through the actions and comments of the characters. Discuss with your partners how Mary uses her "little woman" image as protective covering after the murder.

2 Sometimes when people feel completely rejected and they see no solution to their problems, they turn to violence. Imagine that you are Mary Maloney and write a diary entry describing how you felt when your husband announced that he was going to leave you.

3 Write an interior monologue that reveals Patrick's thoughts when he comes home from work on the night of his murder. Try to capture as much of his motivation and personality as possible. Compare your version with your partners' and make any revisions that seem appropriate.

4 In a group of three, discuss the following questions:
   a. What does Mary sense or notice about her husband that makes her feel uncomfortable about him on the night of the murder?
   b. When does Mary decide to kill her husband?
   c. What are the most difficult parts of her cover-up effort?
Following the discussion, each person in the group should write an answer to one of the questions. The note each group member makes should reflect all the opinions and ideas that were raised in the discussion.

BEYOND THE LINES

1 Using your librarian as a resource person, do some research on other cases of "crimes of passion." Prepare a report on the most interesting case that you come across and share it with the class.

2 Put yourself in Mary's place and try to imagine what you would tell your unborn child about his/her father's death as soon as the child is old enough to understand. Then write a letter to the child to be enclosed with your last will and testament explaining what really happened.

3 When people recall times when they were really angry, they sometimes say that they "were fit to kill someone." Interview three people — a child, a teenager, and an adult. Ask them to:
   a. relate an incident when they were extremely angry;
   b. explain what caused their anger;
   c. describe what they did in response to what angered them.
Choose the story that interested you the most and, in that person's voice, relate the experience to a group. You may present this orally or you may tape it. Compare your account with your partners' to see if there are any common feelings or reactions.

MACAVITY: THE MYSTERY CAT

T.S. Eliot

Macavity's a Mystery Cat: he's called the Hidden Paw —
For he's the master criminal who can defy the Law.
He's the bafflement of Scotland Yard, the Flying Squad's
　　despair:
For when they reach the scene of crime — *Macavity's not
　　there!*

Macavity, Macavity, there's no one like Macavity,
He's broken every human law, he breaks the law of gravity.
His powers of levitation would make a fakir stare,
And when you reach the scene of crime — *Macavity's not there!*
You may seek him in the basement, you may look up in the
　　air —
But I tell you once and once again, *Macavity's not there!*

Macavity's a ginger cat, he's very tall and thin;
You would know him if you saw him, for his eyes are sunken in.
His brow is deeply lined with thought, his head is highly
    domed;
His coat is dusty from neglect, his whiskers are uncombed.
He sways his head from side to side, with movements like a
    snake;
And when you think he's half asleep, he's always wide awake.

Macavity, Macavity, there's no one like Macavity,
For he's a fiend in feline shape, a monster of depravity.
You may meet him in a by-street, you may see him in the
    square —
But when a crime's discovered, then *Macavity's not there!*

He's outwardly respectable. (They say he cheats at cards.)
And his footprints are not found in any file of Scotland Yard's.
And when the larder's looted, or the jewel-case is rifled,
Or when the milk is missing, or another Peke's been stifled,
Or the greenhouse glass is broken, and the trellis past repair —
Ay, there's the wonder of the thing! *Macavity's not there!*

And when the Foreign Office find a Treaty's gone astray,
Or the Admiralty lose some plans and drawings by the way,
There may be a scrap of paper in the hall or on the stair —
But it's useless to investigate — *Macavity's not there!*
And when the loss has been disclosed, the Secret Service say:
"It *must* have been Macavity!" — but he's a mile away.
You'll be sure to find him resting, or a-licking of his thumbs,
Or engaged in doing complicated long division sums.

Macavity, Macavity, there's no one like Macavity,
There never was a Cat of such deceitfulness and suavity.
He always has an alibi, and one or two to spare:
At whatever time the deed took place — MACAVITY WASN'T
    THERE!
And they say that all the Cats whose wicked deeds are widely
    known
(I might mention Mungojerrie, I might mention Griddlebone)
Are nothing more than agents for the Cat who all the time
Just controls their operations: the Napoleon of Crime!

LOOKING IN

1 a. Working with your partners, list all the details in the poem that describe Macavity's appearance and his actions.
Record your information in a chart like the following:

Macavity's Appearance	Macavity's Actions

   b. Without further reference to the poem, in your own words write a brief description of Macavity that could be used in an "All Points Bulletin" about him. Include both his physical characteristics and his infamous behaviour.

2 Discuss with your partners why the poet calls Macavity "the Napoleon of Crime." Brainstorm other names that could be used to describe Macavity as the emperor of criminals.

3 One phrase is repeated several times throughout the poem. Write an explanation of the impression this repetition creates in the reader's mind.

4 Working in a small group, prepare a choral reading of this poem to be shared with the class. (See the glossary, p. 350, for an explanation of choral reading.)

LOOKING OUT

1 With the help of your librarian, research the life and exploits of a famous criminal of your choice. Present a report on your investigations to others interested in criminal masterminds.

2 Read the poem "The Highwayman" by Alfred Noyes. Compose a narrative poem about an infamous criminal you know something about, and present your piece to the class, either in song form or as a dramatic reading. You may wish to imitate the rhyming couplet format of "Macavity: The Mystery Cat."

3 Imagine that you are Macavity's admiring biographer.
Choose one of the suggested adventures in the poem and expand it into a story illustrating Macavity's courage and cunning.

THE DINNER PARTY

Mona Gardner

The hostess has the last word in this dinner party argument.

The country is India. A colonial official and his wife are giving a large dinner party. They are seated with their guests — army officers and government attachés and their wives, and a visiting American naturalist — in their spacious dining room, which has a bare marble floor, open rafters, and wide glass doors opening onto a veranda.

A spirited discussion springs up between a young girl who insists that women have outgrown the jumping-on-a-chair-at-the-sight-of-a-mouse era and a colonel who says that they haven't.

"A woman's unfailing reaction in any crisis," the colonel says, "is to scream. And while a man may feel like it, he has that ounce more of nerve control than a woman has. And that last ounce is what counts."

The American does not join in the argument but watches the other guests. As he looks, he sees a strange expression come over the face of the hostess. She is staring straight ahead, her muscles contracting slightly. With a slight gesture she summons the servant standing behind her chair and whispers to him. The servant's eyes widen, and he quickly leaves the room.

Of the guests, none except the American notices this or sees the servant place a bowl of milk on the veranda just outside the open doors.

The American comes to with a start. In India, milk in a bowl means only one thing — bait for a snake. He realizes there must be a cobra in the room. He looks up at the rafters — the likeliest place — but they are bare. Three corners of the room are empty, and in the fourth the servants are waiting to serve the next course. There is only one place left — under the table.

His first impulse is to jump back and warn the others, but he knows the commotion would frighten the cobra into striking. He speaks quickly, the tone of his voice so arresting that it sobers everyone.

"I want to know just what control everyone at this table has. I will count three hundred — that's five minutes — and not one of you is to move a muscle. Those who move will forfeit fifty rupees. Ready!"

The twenty people sit like stone images while he counts. He is saying ". . . two hundred and eighty . . ." when, out of the corner of his eye, he sees the cobra emerge and make for the bowl of milk. Screams ring out as he jumps to slam the veranda doors safely shut.

"You were right, Colonel!" the host exclaims. "A man has just shown us an example of perfect control."

"Just a minute," the American says, turning to his hostess. "Mrs. Wynnes, how did you know that cobra was in the room?"

A faint smile lights up the woman's face as she replies: "Because it was crawling across my foot."

100

ABOUT THE LINES

1 This is a cloze activity. Your teacher will give you a worksheet for it.

2 Write a point-form summary of the events of this story. Confine yourself to no more than ten points. Share your summary with your partners to check for important details that you may have omitted.

3 In two or three sentences, describe the strategy that the American used to avoid alarming the group and to prevent the snake from striking.

4 In this story, a stereotyped view (an opinion based on a false generalization) of women is presented. Discuss with your partners what the prejudiced attitude is and how it is exposed as untrue through the events of the story. Then each person should write a brief summary reflecting the observations that were raised in the discussion.

BETWEEN THE LINES

1 The author chose to write this story entirely in the present tense, as if it were happening right before the reader's eyes. Rewrite the story by changing all the verbs into the past tense and making any other necessary alterations. Decide with your writing partners which version is more effective and justify your choice.

2 The American realized the whereabouts of the cobra at a definite point in the story. Identify the sentence in the story that indicates that the American knows exactly where the snake is hiding. State when you first realized where the cobra was and explain what was the clue for you. Compare your response to your partners' to see if you agree.

3 Write out one question that you would like to ask Mrs. Wynnes about her experience at the dinner party. Ask someone who has read the story to answer the question. Compare your question and the answer it got to the questions and answers produced by the other students in the class.

BEYOND THE LINES

1 The Colonel in this story makes a prejudiced and stereotyped remark about women that the events of the story prove to be inaccurate: "A woman's unfailing reaction to any crisis is to scream."

a. Working with your partners, outline five examples of sexist statements or attitudes (about either men or women) that enjoy popular support. You may wish to refer to contemporary song lyrics, children's stories, or television commercials for sources.

b. Point out the basic misconception in each stereotyped statement and then rephrase it so that it is free from prejudice.

2 With the help of your librarian, research some biographical accounts of the lives of people who have defeated stereotypes by their own actions and attitudes. Choose one person whose story particularly interested you and share it with a group in an oral presentation.

3 After discussing some possibilities with your partners, write a short story involving:

a. a group situation;

b. an argument;

c. an atmosphere of suspense;

d. an unexpected event that supports one side of the argument and refutes the other.

TWO-MINUTE MYSTERIES

Donald J. Sobol

Whodunit?

THE CASE OF THE HAUNTED HOUSE

"You can't rent more for your money than this house," said Tilford, the real estate agent. "It has charm, fancy brickwork, half-timbering, casement windows, three terraces, and a lady ghost."

"Ghost?" inquired Dr. Haledjian, pushing open a bedroom window. He gazed upon the flagstone terrace two stories below.

"The ghost is Jennifer Godley," explained Tilford. "This was her house. On March 28, 1979, she was hurled from this very window. Her body was found on the stones below."

"At first the police thought she was a suicide, or had accidentally fallen," continued Tilford. They then realized that this window was closed when she was found.

"Henry Godley, her husband, admitted entering the bedroom and closing the window himself. It was a chilly day, and he claimed that he didn't know his wife lay dead on the stones below. Of course, he was sentenced to life —"

"Whoa!" cried Haledjian. "On what evidence?"

"Ben Taylor, a school teacher, saw the whole thing. He was out bird-watching. The Godleys lived like hermits — never had visitors, didn't allow anyone within a mile of the place. But Ben Taylor had binoculars, and at the trial he testified that he saw Henry Godley slide up the window and throw poor Jennifer head first to the terrace."

Haledjian pursed his lips in thought. The next day he telephoned Tilford. "I've decided not to rent the house for the summer," he said. "But I'm going to see that Henry Godley is given a new trial!"

Why?

THE CASE OF THE MISSING BUTTON

Marty Linden, a husky tenth-grade student, scowled at Inspector Winters. "You must be some kind of nut. I didn't slug Ms. Casey, and I didn't steal her purse!"

"No? Unfortunately for you, a ninth-grade girl happened to enter the corridor where Ms. Casey lay. The girl saw a boy in a dark cardigan sweater and brown pants leaving by the door at the far end."

The inspector paused and then demanded, "Do you always wear your sweater buttoned?"

"Sure," replied Marty. "Why?"

"Because you might have noticed the third button from the top is missing," snapped the inspector. He held up the missing button. "The girl who spotted you found the button clasped in Ms. Casey's hand."

"I lost that button two days ago," retorted Marty. "This girl — how could she be sure it was me in that long corridor?"

"She isn't positive — she saw only your back. But this missing button proves you did it. Lucky Ms. Casey isn't badly hurt. Now, where is her purse?"

"Marty kept insisting he didn't know a thing about the slugging and theft," the inspector told Dr. Haledjian later.

"No doubt," said Haledjian, "the boy had some silly alibi about where he was when Ms. Casey was slugged and robbed?"

"Right. He claims he got a note to be in the school boiler room at ten — fifteen minutes before Ms. Casey was assaulted. He waited half an hour, but nobody showed up."

"I trust you made an arrest?" asked Haledjian.

What was the guilty student's error?

---

1 Working in a small group, script and dramatize one of the foregoing mini-mysteries. Make sure you include all the details described in the story, but do not give away the solution directly. After your presentation, ask your audience to suggest possible solutions to the mystery.

2 Work with your partners and write your own two-minute mystery. Ask another group to solve it.

BEALE'S TREASURE

John Picton   *Try cracking the code.*

Thomas Beale was a born leader. A tall, unusually strong man with dark hair and penetrating eyes to match, he was a figure to admire as he strode through the countryside of Virginia in the early 1800s. Sitting around the open fire in the local tavern at night, everyone would listen when he talked about the mysterious, unknown country beyond the frontier, which then extended to Missouri. But, for all his magnetism, he seemed an unlikely person to create one of the most intriguing treasure mysteries of all time — he devised a code to hidden riches that remains unsolved by cryptographers to this day. Awaiting the person who can crack the code is a huge cache of gold, silver, and gems that could be worth millions of dollars.

Life in Virginia was good, but it was too quiet for men with spirit. The local youth yearned for adventure. They thought of the West with its unknown dangers — as they worked with their scythes and hand plows. At night, the group in the tavern grew as word of the discussions spread. By the time their dream became a plan, thirty young men had agreed to head West to seek their fortunes. Packing clay pipes and tricorn hats, the merry band marched into the countryside on an April day in 1817, to the envy of those left behind.

What would they find? Would they ever return? The answer to the first question is known. The answer to the second question remains a mystery.

From St. Louis, the jumping off point for adventurers, the group trekked west, into the hills around the largely Indian settlement known as Santa Fe. They stayed all winter, bored with the barren hills and thinking of the lush greenery back home, of the townfolk sitting around their fires and preparing turkey and cranberry sauce for Christmas.

"Nothing of interest occurred during the winter, and of this little town we soon became heartily tired," Beale wrote. "We longed for the advent of weather which would enable us to resume our wanderings and our exhilarating pursuits."

In March, 1818, Beale selected a party to go north and scout the land. They planned to return in a few days. But time went quickly. Game was plentiful, and days turned into weeks. Chasing herds of buffalo took them farther away from Santa Fe — into what is now Colorado.

It was there that they struck it rich. Sitting one night beside the camp fire, one of the men noticed something glimmering in the rock. It was gold.

Some of the advance party went back to Santa Fe to tell Beale and the rest. "Upon reaching the locality," Beale wrote later, "I found all as it had been reported and the excitement intense. Everyone was diligently at work with such tools and appliances as they had improvised, and quite a little pile had already accumulated." Working on an equal-shares basis, they picked and hacked at the ground for another year, building up such a pile of gold that it became time to move it from this lawless, desolate land. They all agreed the precious

metal should be moved to Virginia, since that was where they all planned to settle in comfort.

They chose a cave near Buford's Tavern, in Bedford County, since it was a place they all knew. In the summer of 1819, Beale and some of the men escorted the treasure back east — to find that farmers were storing crops in the cave they had chosen. Somewhere in the Blue Ridge Mountains, they built another cave and hid the gold. Then they rode back to their mine.

In December, 1821, Beale rode east with a second shipment. The following month, he booked a room at the Washington Hotel in nearby Lynchburg where he knew the proprietor, a man named Robert Morriss. Over a few tankards of ale beside the roaring fire, Beale asked Morriss if he could leave a box at the hotel for safekeeping. "Of course," Morriss said. "I'll put it in my safe." And so began one of the greatest treasure mysteries of all time.

Unknown to the tavern keeper, the box contained the secret to a fortune. In the box, Beale had put three separate pieces of paper, each written in a separate code. Explaining simply that it contained "important papers," he said that someone would be calling for the box.

It is known that Beale arrived back in St. Louis in early May, 1822, and that he left a letter with a friend there. The friend was never traced.

On May 16, Morriss got a letter from Beale saying that if, after ten years, he or his agent had not retrieved the box, Morriss was to open it. Beale added that the papers inside would not mean anything without a secret code — and that the code was held by a friend who would deliver it in June, 1832.

Morriss never heard from anyone about the box again. He forgot about it until 1845 — thirteen years after the appointed date — when he had the box broken open. Inside, he found the three coded messages — to him, just a jumble of figures — and a letter dated January 4, 1822, which ended: "As ten years must elapse before you see this letter, you can conclude by that time that none of us will be alive. You will then go to the depository and divide its contents into thirty-one equal parts. One of these parts you will keep for your services. The other shares are to be distributed to the parties named in No. 3."

But there were no clues. Who were the other thirty? What was the treasure? Who was the mysterious friend in St. Louis? Mystified, Morriss returned the box to his safe — for another seventeen years. It was not until 1862, at the height of the Civil War — and he was eighty-four years old — that he told someone about it.

He gave the papers to a younger man, James Ward, on condition that if he could solve the puzzle, he was to share Morriss's half. The other thirty shares would be put in trust. If, after twenty years, the treasure was still unclaimed, Ward was to get the lot.

Ward realized that there was little chance of anyone claiming the treasure after forty years, and he worked on it day and night. It proved to be a curse, for it so consumed him that his family life suffered and his income dropped. It was twenty years before, poverty stricken, he gave up. But he thought he would recoup something for his long efforts.

He had the codes printed in a pamphlet, which he planned to sell for fifty cents each. He had managed to crack Code No. 2, which he included in the pamphlet. He explained:

"My first impression was that each number represented a letter. But the different numbers used exceeded the letters of the alphabet. I wondered then if some document had been used, with each word assigned a different number. With this idea in mind, a test was made, using every book I could produce. By numbering the letters and comparing their numbers with those of the manuscript, I hoped to find the answer. It wasn't until I used the Declaration of Independence that the code began to crack."

Ward said he had numbered each word of the document from one to 1322. The first letter of each numbered word spelled out the extent of the treasure:

"The first deposit consisted of ten hundred and fourteen pounds of gold and thirty-eight hundred and twelve pounds of silver deposited November, 1819. The second was made December, 1821, and consisted of nineteen hundred and seven pounds of gold and twelve hundred and eighty-eight of silver, also jewels obtained in St. Louis in exchange to save transportation and valued at thirteen thousand dollars (a king's ransom in those days)."

The code said the treasure was buried in a vault six feet below ground, "about four miles from Buford's." It ended: "Paper No. 1 describes the exact locality of the vault so that no difficulty will be had in finding it." But Codes 1 and 3 obviously were based on different documents, which Ward was not able to discover. Neither did he make anything from his pamphlets. A fire at the printing shop destroyed almost all of them.

But one did fall into the hands of a stenographer named Clayton Hart. With his brother George, Hart worked unsuccessfully for ten years on trying to decipher the Beale codes. Finally, in 1924, George wrote to code expert Colonel George Fabyan asking for help. The Colonel replied: "A code of this character could not be deciphered without the key, regardless of whether one put twenty or forty years on it." Clayton Hart continued to work on them, unsuccessfully, until his death in 1949.

Did Thomas Beale return alone and make off with the treasure? If so, what happened to the men who had buried it with him? In any case, the records indicate that Beale was a man of character and unlikely to steal the treasure.

But what happened to his colleagues? Is it likely that thirty of them would have perished without claiming their hoard?

In his book *Treasure Seeker's Treasury,* Roy Norvill says that the village of Montvale now stands on the site of Buford's Tavern. The mystery of Beale's codes will not be cleared up until someone finds the treasure four miles away — or finds the place where it was.

ABOUT THE LINES

1 In your own words, retell this story of buried treasure to someone who has read the article and have him/her check that you have included all the important details. Make any necessary adjustments to your story and then share it with an audience which knows nothing about it. You could imagine that you are an old-fashioned storyteller entertaining people with your yarns around a campfire. You may wish to tape your account for other people to hear.

2 Write a point-form summary of the instructions that Beale left with Robert Morriss when the box containing the codes was deposited in Morriss's safe at the Washington Hotel.

3 List all the people whose lives were touched by this discovery of silver and gold. In one or two sentences for each person, indicate how he was affected by the experience.

BETWEEN THE LINES

1 In a few sentences, explain why you think Beale and his men did not fight among themselves over the treasure.

2 Discuss with your partners how the treasure could have become a "curse" to James Ward and his family. List the negative things that you think could have happened to him because of his obsession with the mystery.

3 Working in a small group, brainstorm the reasons that could explain why Beale's agent never arrived at Morriss's hotel with the key to the code. Order your list, beginning with the most likely explanation and ending with the least probable.

BEYOND THE LINES

1 Working with your partners, write stories accounting for some of the thirty men of Beale's party. Did they meet a tragic fate? Did they return to the treasure site only to find that the treasure had disappeared? Did they return with Beale to reclaim the treasure?

2 a. Write a mystery story that remains unsolved at the end.
  b. Devise a word code that, when unscrambled, would reveal the solution to your mystery.
  c. Try your story and code on a small group and see if they can find the solution.

3 In the voice of James Ward's wife, write a diary entry in which you reveal your anger and frustration at your husband's obsession with Beale's buried treasure.

4 Imagine that you are Beale and that you and your party returned for the treasure. Write a memoir describing the changes in your life after you became rich.

THE PATIENT

Agatha Christie

Characters

LANSEN   EMMELINE ROSS
NURSE   WILLIAM ROSS
DR. GINSBERG   BRENDA JACKSON
INSPECTOR CRAY   THE PATIENT
BRYAN WINGFIELD

SCENE: *A private room in a nursing home. An autumn afternoon.*

The room is square, plain and hygienic-looking. In the right wall are two sets of double doors. Across the back is a large window covered by Venetian blinds which are at present down but not "closed". Up left, and extending across half the window is a curtained alcove, the curtains drawn back. Inside the alcove is a cabinet. An electrical apparatus, with dials, red light, etc., is down left centre. A hospital trolley is up right centre in the window, and a wall telephone down right. Down right centre is a small table, with an elbow chair to right of it and four small chairs in a rough semicircle to left of it. These have the appearance of having been brought into the room for a purpose and not really belonging to it. On the trolley is a sterilizer with boiling water.

When the curtain rises, the lights fade up from a blackout. LANSEN, a tall gangling young man with spectacles, wearing a long white hospital overall, is fiddling with an electrical apparatus on castors. The NURSE, a tall, good-looking woman, competent and correct, slightly inhuman and completely submissive to everything the doctor says, is at the trolley. She lifts the lid of the sterilizer, removes a needle with a forceps, places it in a tray, crosses to the cabinet, takes out a towel, and crosses back to put it on the trolley. A buzzer sounds.

DR. GINSBERG enters and goes to the telephone. He is a dark, clever-looking man in his middle forties.

GINSBERG All right, Nurse, I'll answer it. (*at the telephone*) Yes? . . . Oh, Inspector Cray, good. Ask him to come up to Room Fourteen, will you? (*He crosses to the electrical apparatus.*) How are you doing, Lansen? Got it fixed up?

LANSEN Yes, everything's in order. I'll plug in here, Dr. Ginsberg.

GINSBERG You're quite sure about this, now? We can't afford to have a slip up.

LANSEN Quite sure, Doctor. It'll work a treat.

GINSBERG Good. (*He turns and looks at the chairs.*) Oh, a little less formal, I think, Nurse. Let's move these chairs a bit. (*He moves one.*) Er — that one over there against the wall.

(GINSBERG *exits.*)

NURSE Yes, Doctor. (*She comes down and lifts the chair.*)

LANSEN Careful! (*He takes it and places it against the wall.*)

NURSE (*indicating the apparatus, with slight curiosity*) What is this thing?

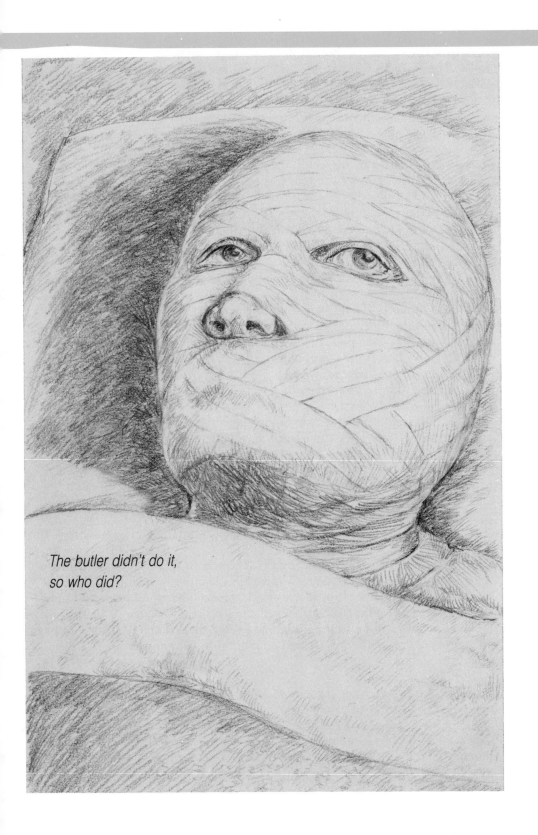

The butler didn't do it,
so who did?

LANSEN (*grinning*) New electrical gadget.

NURSE (*bored*) Oh, one of those. (*She moves up to the trolley.*)

LANSEN Trouble with you people is you've no respect for science.

(INSPECTOR CRAY *enters. He is a middle-aged man of delusively mild appearance.* GINSBERG *enters with him.*)

INSPECTOR Good afternoon.

GINSBERG Everything's ready.

INSPECTOR (*indicating the electrical apparatus*) Is this the contraption?

LANSEN Good afternoon, Inspector.

GINSBERG Yes. It's been well tested, Inspector.

LANSEN It works perfectly. The least touch will make a connection. I guarantee there will be no hitch.

GINSBERG All right, Lansen. We'll call you when we need you.

(LANSEN *exits. To* NURSE) Has Nurse Cartwright got the patient ready?

NURSE Yes, Doctor. Quite ready.

GINSBERG (*to the* INSPECTOR) Nurse Bond here is going to stay and assist me during the experiment.

INSPECTOR Oh, good. That's very kind of you.

NURSE Not at all, Inspector. I'll do anything I can to help. I'd never have gone off duty, if I'd thought that Mrs. Wingfield was unduly depressed.

GINSBERG Nobody's blaming you, Nurse. (*The* NURSE *moves to the trolley.*) You say the others have arrived?

INSPECTOR Yes, they're downstairs.

GINSBERG All four of them?

INSPECTOR All four of them. Bryan Wingfield, Emmeline Ross, William Ross and Brenda Jackson. They can't leave. I've posted my men.

GINSBERG (*formally*) You must understand, Inspector, that the well-being of my patient comes before anything else. At the first sign of collapse or undue excitement — any indication that the experiment is having an adverse effect — I shall stop the proceedings. (*to* NURSE) You understand that, Nurse?

NURSE Yes, Doctor.

INSPECTOR Quite so, quite so — I shouldn't expect anything else. (*uneasily*) You don't think it's too risky?

GINSBERG (*sitting in the elbow chair; coldly*) If I thought it was too risky I should not permit the experiment. Mrs. Wingfield's condition is mainly psychological — the result of severe shock. Her temperature, heart and pulse are now normal. (*to the* NURSE) Nurse, you are already acquainted with the family. Go down to the waiting room and bring them up here. If they ask you any questions, please be strictly non-committal in your answers.

NURSE Yes, Doctor.

(*The* NURSE *exits.*)

INSPECTOR Well, here we go.

GINSBERG Yes.

INSPECTOR Let's hope we have luck. Have any of them been allowed to see her?

GINSBERG Her husband, naturally. And also her brother and sister for a few minutes. The nurse assigned to look after her here, Nurse Cartwright, was present all the time. (*He pauses.*) Miss Jackson has not visited Mrs. Wingfield, nor asked to do so.

114

INSPECTOR Quite so. You'll give them a little preliminary talk, will you? Put them in the picture.

GINSBERG Certainly, if you wish. (*The* INSPECTOR *strolls up to the window.*) I see that Mrs. Wingfield fell from the second-storey balcony.

INSPECTOR Yes. Yes, she did.

GINSBERG (*rising*) Remarkable, really, that she wasn't killed. Head contusions, dislocated shoulder and fracture of the left leg.

(*The* NURSE *opens the door.* BRYAN WINGFIELD, WILLIAM ROSS *and* EMMELINE ROSS *enter.* WINGFIELD *is a short, stocky man of about thirty-five, attractive, with a quiet manner normally and rather a poker-face.* ROSS *is a man of the same age, also short, but dark-haired, rather mercurial in temperament.* EMMELINE, *his sister, is a tall, grim-faced woman of forty. They are all in a state of emotional disturbance. The* NURSE *exits.*)

GINSBERG (*shaking hands with* EMMELINE) Good afternoon, Miss Ross, will you sit down? (*He shakes hands with* ROSS.) Mr. Ross! Good afternoon, Mr. Wingfield. (*He shakes hands with* WINGFIELD.)

WINGFIELD You sent for us — it's not — my wife? There's not bad news?

GINSBERG No, Mr. Wingfield. No bad news.

WINGFIELD Thank God. When you sent for us I thought there might be a change for the worse.

GINSBERG There is no change of any kind — neither for the worse, nor — alas — for the better.

EMMELINE Is my sister *still* unconscious?

GINSBERG She is still completely paralysed. She cannot move or speak.

EMMELINE (*sitting*) It's terrible! Simply terrible!

INSPECTOR Was Miss Jackson with you?

WINGFIELD She was following us. (BRENDA JACKSON *enters. She is a tall, extremely pretty young woman of twenty-five.*) Dr. Ginsberg, my secretary, Miss Jackson.

GINSBERG Good afternoon.

(*She turns and looks at the electrical apparatus.*)

ROSS Poor Jenny, what an awful thing to happen to anyone. Sometimes I feel it would have been better if she'd been killed outright by the fall.

WINGFIELD No. Anything but that.

ROSS I know what you feel, Bryan. But this — I mean, it's a living death, isn't it, Doctor?

GINSBERG There's still some hope for your sister, Mr. Ross.

BRENDA But she won't stay like this? I mean — she'll get better, won't she?

GINSBERG In cases of this kind — it is very difficult to forecast the progress of a patient. Her injuries will heal, yes. The bones will knit, the dislocation has already been reduced, the wounds in the head are nearly healed.

WINGFIELD Then why shouldn't she get well? Why shouldn't she be herself again in every way?

GINSBERG You are touching there on a field in which we are still ignorant. Mrs. Wingfield's state of paralysis is due to shock.

EMMELINE The result of her accident?

GINSBERG Her accident was the ostensible cause.

ROSS Just what do you mean by ostensible?

GINSBERG Mrs. Wingfield must have suffered unusual fears as she fell from the balcony. It is not so much her *physical* injuries but something in her *mind* that has produced this state of complete paralysis.

(*Brenda sits.*)

WINGFIELD You're not trying to say — (GINSBERG *sits behind the table.*) — you're not thinking what I'm sure the Inspector has been more or less suggesting — that my wife tried to commit suicide? That I don't believe for a moment.

INSPECTOR I haven't *said* I thought it was suicide, Mr. Wingfield.

WINGFIELD (*sitting*) You must think something of the kind or you and your people wouldn't keep hanging round like vultures.

INSPECTOR We have to be quite clear as to the cause of this — accident.

ROSS My God, isn't it simple enough? She's been ill for months. She'd been feeling weak, up for the first time, or practically the first time. Goes over to the window, out on to the balcony — leans over, is suddenly taken giddy and falls to the ground. That balcony's very low.

EMMELINE Don't get so excited, William, don't shout.

ROSS (*turning to* EMMELINE) It's all very well, Bunny, but it makes me mad, all this business. (*to* GINSBERG) Do you think it's pleasant for us having the police mixing themselves up in our family affairs?

WINGFIELD Now, Bill, if anyone should complain it's myself, and I don't.

(ROSS *moves to the window.*)

BRENDA What have we been asked to come here for?

INSPECTOR One moment, Miss Jackson. (*to* EMMELINE) Miss Ross, I wish you could tell me a little more about your sister. Was she at all subject to fits of melancholy — depression?

ROSS Oh, I wouldn't say that at all.

EMMELINE Men don't realize these things. I know what I'm talking about. I think it is quite possible, Inspector, that her illness had left her particularly low and depressed, and that with other things she had to worry and distress her . . .

(BRENDA *rises and moves towards the door. The* INSPECTOR *moves towards her.* GINSBERG *and* WINGFIELD *rise.*)

INSPECTOR Where are you going, Miss Jackson?

BRENDA I'm leaving. I'm not one of the family, I'm only Mr. Wingfield's secretary. I don't see the point of all this. I was asked to come with the others, but if all you're going to do is to go over and over again about the accident — whether it was accident or attempted suicide — well, I don't see why I should stay.

INSPECTOR But it's not going to be the same thing over and over again, Miss Jackson. We are about to make an experiment.

BRENDA An experiment? What kind of experiment?

INSPECTOR Dr. Ginsberg will explain. Sit down, Miss Jackson. (BRENDA *moves back to her chair and sits.* WINGFIELD *and* GINSBERG *sit.*) Dr. Ginsberg!

GINSBERG I had better perhaps recapitulate what I know or have been told. Mrs. Wingfield has been suffering in the last two months from an illness somewhat mysterious in nature which was puzzling the doctor in attendance on her, Dr. Horsefield. This I have on the authority of Dr. Horsefield himself. She was, however, showing decided signs of improvement and was convalescent, though there was still a nurse in the house. On the day in question, exactly ten days ago, Mrs. Wingfield got up from bed after lunch and was settled by Nurse Bond in an easy chair near the open window, it being a fine, mild afternoon. She had books beside her, and a small radio. After seeing her patient had all she needed, nurse went out for her afternoon walk as usual. What happened during the course of the afternoon is a matter of conjecture.

(*The* INSPECTOR *moves to above* WINGFIELD.)

But at half past three a cry was heard. Miss Ross, who was sitting in the room below, saw a falling body cross the window. It was the body of Mrs. Wingfield, who had fallen from the balcony of her room. There was no one with her at the time when she fell, but there were *four* people in the house, the four people who are assembled here now.

INSPECTOR Perhaps, Mr. Wingfield, you would like to tell us in your own words just what happened then?

WINGFIELD I should have thought I'd told it often enough already. I was correcting proofs in my study. I heard a scream, a noise from outside. I rushed to the side door, went out on the terrace and found — and found poor Jenny. (*He rises.*) Emmeline joined me a moment later, and then William and Miss Jackson. We telephoned for the doctor and . . . (*His voice breaks.*)

GINSBERG I — I . . .

INSPECTOR Yes, yes, Mr. Wingfield, there's no need to go into any more. (*He turns to* BRENDA.) Miss Jackson, will you tell us again your side of the story?

BRENDA I had been asked to look up a reference in the encyclopaedia for Mr. Wingfield. I was in the library when I heard a commotion and people running. I dropped the book and came out and joined them on the terrace.

INSPECTOR (*turning to* ROSS) Mr. Ross?

ROSS What? Oh — I'd been playing golf all the morning — always play golf on a Saturday. I'd come in, eaten a hearty lunch and was feeling whacked. I lay down on my bed upstairs. It was Jenny's scream that woke me up. I thought for a moment I must have been dreaming. Then I heard the row down below and I looked out of my window. There she was on the terrace with the others gathered round. (*fiercely, facing the* INSPECTOR) Oh, God, have we got to go over this again and again?

INSPECTOR I only wanted to stress the point that nobody who was in the house can tell us exactly what happened that afternoon. (*He pauses.*) Nobody, that is, except Mrs. Wingfield herself.

ROSS It's all perfectly simple, as I've said all along. Poor Jenny thought she was stronger than she was. She went out on the balcony, leaned over, and that's that. (*He sits on the chair, takes off his spectacles and wipes them.*) Perfectly simple accident — might have happened to anybody.

WINGFIELD Somebody ought to have been with her. (*He moves up to the window.*) I blame myself for leaving her alone.

EMMELINE But she was supposed to rest in the afternoon, Bryan, that was part of the doctor's orders. We were all going to join her at half past four for tea, but she was supposed to rest every afternoon from three o'clock until then.

INSPECTOR Miss Ross — the accident seems a little difficult to explain. The railings of the balcony did not give way.

ROSS No, no. She got giddy and overbalanced. I leaned over myself to test it afterwards and it could easily happen.

INSPECTOR Mrs. Wingfield is a very small woman. It wouldn't be so easy for her to overbalance even if she was taken giddy.

EMMELINE I hate to say it, but I think you're right in what you suspect. I think poor Jenny was worried and troubled in her mind. I think a fit of depression came over her . . .

WINGFIELD (*moving to* EMMELINE) You keep saying she tried to commit suicide. I don't believe it. I won't believe it!

EMMELINE (*with meaning*) She had plenty to make her depressed.

WINGFIELD What do you mean by that?

EMMELINE (*rising*) I think you know quite well what I mean. I'm not blind, Bryan.

WINGFIELD Jenny wasn't depressed. She'd nothing to be depressed about. You've got an evil mind, Emmeline, and you just imagine things.

ROSS Leave my sister alone.

BRENDA (*rising and facing* EMMELINE) It was an accident. Of course it was an accident. Miss Ross is just trying to — trying to . . .

EMMELINE (*facing* BRENDA) Yes, what am I trying to do?

BRENDA It's people like you that write anonymous letters — poison pen letters. Just because no man has ever looked at you . . .

EMMELINE How dare you!

ROSS (*rising*) Oh, my God! Cut it out, both of you.

WINGFIELD I think we're all rather overexcited, you know. We're talking about things that are quite beside the point. What we really want to get at is, what was Jenny's state of mind on the day she fell? Well, I'm her husband, I know her pretty well, and I don't think for a moment she meant to commit suicide.

EMMELINE Because you don't want to think so — you don't want to feel responsible!

WINGFIELD Responsible? What do you mean by responsible?

EMMELINE ⎫ ⎧Driving her to do what she did!
ROSS ⎬ (*together*) ⎨What do you mean by that?
WINGFIELD ⎭ ⎩How dare you!

BRENDA It's not true!

GINSBERG (*rising*) Please — please! When I asked you to come here, it was not my object to provoke recriminations.

ROSS (*angrily*) Wasn't it? I'm not so sure. (*He wheels round and looks suspiciously at the* INSPECTOR.)

GINSBERG No, what I had in mind was to conduct an experiment.

BRENDA We've already been told that, but you still haven't told us what kind of experiment.

GINSBERG As Inspector Cray said just now — only one person knows what happened that afternoon — Mrs. Wingfield herself.

WINGFIELD (*sighing*) And she can't tell us. It's too bad.

EMMELINE She will when she's better.

GINSBERG I don't think you quite appreciate the medical position, Miss Ross. (*He crosses to the electrical apparatus.* BRENDA *sits.*) It may be months — it may even be years before Mrs. Wingfield comes out of this state.

WINGFIELD Surely not!

GINSBERG Yes, Mr. Wingfield. I won't go into a lot of medical details, but there are people who have gone blind as a result of shock and have not recovered their sight for fifteen or twenty years. There have been those paralysed and unable to walk for the same periods of time. Sometimes another shock precipitates recovery. But there's no fixed rule. (*to the* INSPECTOR) Ring the bell, please.

(*The* INSPECTOR *crosses and rings the bell below the doors.*)

WINGFIELD I don't quite understand what you are driving at, Doctor. (*He looks from* GINSBERG *to the* INSPECTOR.)

INSPECTOR You're about to find out, Mr. Wingfield.

GINSBERG Miss Jackson . . .

(BRENDA *rises.* GINSBERG *moves the chair left of the table close to it, lifting* EMMELINE's *handbag, which he hands to her.*)

EMMELINE Thank you.

(GINSBERG *crosses to the window and closes up the Venetian blinds. The lights dim.* GINSBERG *switches on the upstage lights.*)

GINSBERG Inspector, do you mind?

(*The* INSPECTOR *switches on the downstage lights.*

LANSEN *opens the doors up right and pulls the* PATIENT *on the trolley, the* NURSE *following. They place the trolley downstage, parallel to the footlights, with the* PATIENT's *head to right. The* PATIENT's *head is heavily bandaged so that nothing of the features show but the eyes and nose. She is quite motionless. Her eyes are open but she does not move.*

The NURSE *stands about two feet from the* PATIENT's *head.* LANSEN *moves the electrical apparatus round and nearer to the* PATIENT. GINSBERG *moves above the trolley.*)

WINGFIELD Jenny, darling!

(EMMELINE *advances but does not speak.*)

BRENDA What's going on? What are you trying to do?

GINSBERG Mrs. Wingfield, as I have told you, is completely paralysed. She cannot move or speak. But we are all agreed that she knows what happened to her on that day.

BRENDA She's unconscious. She may be unconscious — oh — for years, you said.

GINSBERG I did not say *unconscious*. Mrs. Wingfield cannot move and cannot speak, but she *can* see and hear; and I think it highly probable that her mind is as keen as ever it was. She knows what happened. She would like to communicate it to us, but unfortunately she can't do so.

WINGFIELD You think she can hear us? You think she does know what we are saying to her, what we're feeling?

GINSBERG I think she knows.

WINGFIELD (*moving to the head of the* PATIENT) Jenny! Jenny, darling! Can you hear me? It's been terrible for you, I know, but everything's going to be all right.

GINSBERG Lansen!

LANSEN (*adjusting the electrical apparatus*) I'm ready, sir, when you are.

GINSBERG I said Mrs. Wingfield could not communicate with us, but it is possible that a way has been found. Doctor Zalzbergen, who has been attending her, and who is a specialist on this form of paralysis, became aware of a very slight power of movement in the fingers of the right hand. It is very slight — hardly noticeable. She could not raise her arm or lift anything, but she can very slightly move the two fingers and thumb on her right hand. Mr. Lansen here has fixed up a certain apparatus of an electrical nature. You see, there is a small rubber bulb. When that bulb is pressed, a red light appears on the top of the apparatus. The slightest pressure will operate it. If you please, Lansen! (LANSEN *presses the bulb twice. The red light on the apparatus goes up twice.*) Nurse, uncover the patient's right arm. (*The* NURSE *lays the* PATIENT's *arm on the coverlet.*) Lansen, between the thumb and two fingers. Gently. (LANSEN *places the bulb in the* PATIENT's *right hand and crosses to the electrical apparatus.*) Now I'm going to ask Mrs. Wingfield some questions.

ROSS Ask her questions? What do you mean? Questions about what?

GINSBERG Questions about what happened on that Saturday afternoon.

ROSS (*moving to face the* INSPECTOR) This is *your* doing!

GINSBERG The experiment was suggested by Mr. Lansen and myself.

WINGFIELD But you can't possibly put any reliance on what might be purely muscular spasms.

GINSBERG I think we can soon find out whether Mrs. Wingfield can answer questions or not.

WINGFIELD I won't have it! It's dangerous for her. It'll set her recovery back. I won't allow this! I won't agree to it.

BRENDA (*warningly*) Bryan! (*She turns to face* WINGFIELD, *then senses the* INSPECTOR *watching her, crosses to a chair and sits.*)

GINSBERG Mrs. Wingfield's health will be fully safeguarded, I assure you. Nurse! (WINGFIELD *moves away. The* NURSE *moves over and takes up her position by the* PATIENT *with her fingers on the* PATIENT's *wrist. To the* NURSE) At the least sign of collapse, you know what to do.

NURSE Yes, Doctor. (*She takes the* PATIENT's *pulse.*)

(*The* INSPECTOR *moves in to right of the* NURSE.)

BRENDA (*almost under her breath*) I don't like this — I don't like it.

EMMELINE I'm sure you don't like it.

BRENDA Do you?

EMMELINE I think it might be interesting. (*She goes and sits on chair.*)

ROSS ⎱ (*together*) ⎰ I don't believe for a . . .
WINGFIELD ⎰   ⎱ Inspector, I hope . . .

INSPECTOR Quiet, please! We must have absolute quiet. The doctor is about to begin.

(WINGFIELD *sits.* ROSS *moves down right. There is a pause.*)

GINSBERG Mrs. Wingfield, you have had a very narrow escape from death and are now on the way to recovery. Your physical injuries are healing. We know that you are paralysed and that you cannot speak or move. What I want is this —

(WINGFIELD *rises.*)

— if you understand what I am saying to you, try and move your fingers so that you press the bulb. Will you do so?

(*There is a pause, then the* PATIENT's *fingers move slightly and the red light comes on. There is a gasp from all the four people. The* INSPECTOR *is now closely watching, not the* PATIENT *but the four visitors.* GINSBERG, *on the other hand, is intent on the*

121

PATIENT. LANSEN *is intent on his apparatus, and beams with pleasure every time the light goes on.*)

You have heard and understood what we have been saying, Mrs. Wingfield? (*one red light*)

Thank you. Now what I propose is this: when the answer to a question is "yes" you press the bulb once; if the answer is "no" you will press it twice. Do you understand?

(*one red light*)

Now, Mrs. Wingfield, what is the signal for "no"?

(*two red lights in rapid succession*)

I think, then, it must be clear to all of you that Mrs. Wingfield can understand what I'm saying and can reply to my questions. I'm going back to the afternoon of Saturday the fourteenth. Have you a clear recollection of what happened that afternoon?

(*one red light*)

As far as possible, I will ask you questions that will save you too much fatigue. I am assuming, therefore, that you had lunch, got up, and that Nurse here settled you in a chair by the window. You were alone in your room with the window open and were supposed to rest until four-thirty. Am I correct?

(*one red light*)

Did you, in fact, sleep a little?

(*one red light*)

And then you woke up . . .

(*one red light*)

Went out on to the balcony?

(*one red light*)

You leaned over?

(*one red light*)

You lost your balance and fell?

(*There is a pause.* LANSEN *bends over to adjust the electrical apparatus.*)

Just a minute, LANSEN! You fell?

(*one red light*)

But you did not lose your balance.

(*Two red lights. A gasp from everyone*)

You were giddy — felt faint?

(*two red lights*)

WINGFIELD Inspector, I . . .

INSPECTOR Sssh!

(WINGFIELD *turns away.*)

GINSBERG Mrs. Wingfield, we have come to the point where you have to tell us what happened. I am going to say over the letters of the alphabet. When I come to the letter of the word you want, will you press the bulb. I'll begin. A, B, C, D, E, F, G, H, I, J, K, L, M, N, O, P.

(*one red light*)

You have given me the letter "P". I'm going to hazard a guess — I want you to tell me if I am right. Is the word in your mind "pushed"?

(*One red light. There is a general sensation.* BRENDA *shrinks away, her face in her hands.* ROSS *swears.* EMMELINE *is still.*)

122

BRENDA No, it can't be true!

ROSS What the hell!

WINGFIELD This is iniquitous!

GINSBERG Quiet, please. I cannot have the patient agitated. Mrs. Wingfield, you obviously have more to tell us. I'm going to spell again. A, B, C, D, E, F, G, H, I, J, K, L, M.

(one red light)

M? The letter "M" is probably followed by a vowel. Which vowel, Mrs. Wingfield? A, E, I, O, U.

(One red light. The INSPECTOR moves to left of LANSEN above the electrical apparatus.)

M-U?

(one red light)

Is the next letter "R"?

(One red light. The INSPECTOR and GINSBERG exchange a look.)

M-U-R- . . . Mrs. Wingfield, are you trying to tell us that what happened that afternoon was not an accident; are you trying to tell us that it was attempted murder?

(One red light. There is an immediate reaction.)

BRYAN — It's incredible! Absolutely incredible. It's impossible, I tell you, impossible!

BRENDA — It's not true. She doesn't know what she's saying.

EMMELINE (together) — (rising) This is nonsense! Poor Jenny doesn't know what she's doing.

ROSS — Murder! Murder! It can't be murder! D'you mean someone got in?

GINSBERG Please. Quiet, please!

EMMELINE She doesn't know what she's saying.

INSPECTOR I think she does.

GINSBERG Mrs. Wingfield, did some unknown person come in from outside and attack you?

(two red lights sharply)

Was it someone in the house who pushed you?

(a pause, then one red light)

WINGFIELD My God!

(The red light flashes several times.)

NURSE Doctor, her pulse is quickening.

INSPECTOR (crossing close to GINSBERG) Not much further. We must have the name.

GINSBERG Mrs. Wingfield, do you know who pushed you?

(one red light)

I'm going to spell out the name. Do you understand?

(one red light)

Good. A, B.

(one red light)

B. Is that right?

(several red lights)

NURSE Doctor! She's collapsed.

GINSBERG It's no good. I daren't go on, Nurse! (*The* NURSE *moves to the trolley upstage for the hypodermic and comes down to the* PATIENT, *handing the syringe to* GINSBERG. BRENDA *sits.*) Thank you, Lansen. (*He breaks the ampule head, fills the syringe and injects it in the* PATIENT's *arm.*)

(LANSEN *switches off the electrical apparatus, removes the bulb from the* PATIENT *and the plug from the wall. He wheels the electrical apparatus into the curtained recess, and exits. The* NURSE *returns the syringe to the trolley upstage. The* INSPECTOR *moves below the* PATIENT.)

GINSBERG Nurse, would you unplug the sterilizer?

NURSE Yes, Doctor.

(*The* NURSE *unplugs the sterilizer.* GINSBERG *moves to the small trolley, and with the* NURSE *wheels it to the left wall.*)

WINGFIELD Is she all right?

GINSBERG The strain and excitement have been too much for her. She'll be all right. She must rest for a while. We should be able to resume in about half an hour.

WINGFIELD I forbid you to go on with it! It's dangerous.

GINSBERG I think you must allow me to be the best judge of that. We'll move Mrs. Wingfield up nearer the window. She'll be all right there.

(GINSBERG *and the* NURSE *move the* PATIENT *upstage, with her head near the doors up right, the* NURSE *at the head.*)

EMMELINE There's not much doubt is there, who she meant? "B." (*She looks at* WINGFIELD.) Not much doubt about that, is there, Bryan?

WINGFIELD You always hated me, Emmeline. You always had it in for me. I tell you here and now, I didn't try to kill my wife.

EMMELINE Do you deny that you were having an affair with that woman there? (*She points at* BRENDA.)

BRENDA (*rising*) It's not true.

EMMELINE Don't tell me that. You were head over ears in love with him.

BRENDA (*facing the others*) All right, then. I *was* in love with him. But that was all over ages ago. He didn't really care for me. It's all over, I tell you. All *over!*

EMMELINE In that case it seems odd you stayed on as his secretary!

BRENDA I didn't want to go. I — oh, all right, then! (*passionately*) I still wanted to be near him. (*She sits.*)

EMMELINE And perhaps you thought that if Jenny were out of the way, you'd console him very nicely, and be Mrs. Wingfield Number Two . . .

WINGFIELD Emmeline, for heaven's sake!

EMMELINE Perhaps it's "B" for Brenda.

BRENDA You horrible woman! I hate you. It's not true.

ROSS (*rising*) Bryan — and Brenda. It seems to narrow it down to one of you two all right.

WINGFIELD I wouldn't say that. It could be "B" for brother, couldn't it? Or Bill?

ROSS She always called me William.

WINGFIELD After all, who stands to gain by poor Jenny's death? Not me. It's you. You and Emmeline. It's you two who get her money.

GINSBERG Please — please! I can't have all this argument. Nurse, will you take them down to the waiting room.

124

NURSE Yes, Doctor.

ROSS (*turning to* GINSBERG) We can't stay cooped up in a little room with all of us slanging each other.

INSPECTOR You can go where you please on the hospital premises, but none of you is actually to leave the place. (*sharply*) Is that understood?

WINGFIELD All right.

ROSS Yes.

EMMELINE I have no wish to leave. My conscience is clear.

BRENDA (*going up to her*) I think — *you* did it.

EMMELINE (*sharply*) What do you mean?

BRENDA You hate her — you've always hated her. And you get the money — you and your brother.

EMMELINE My name does *not* begin with a "B," I'm thankful to say.

BRENDA (*excitedly*) No — but it needn't. (*She turns to the* INSPECTOR.) Supposing that, after all, Mrs. Wingfield *didn't* see who it was who pushed her off the balcony.

EMMELINE She has told us that she did.

BRENDA But supposing that she didn't. (*crosses to the* INSPECTOR) Don't you see what a temptation it might be to her? She was jealous of me and Bryan — oh, yes, she knew about us — and she was jealous. And when that machine there —(*She gestures towards the electrical apparatus.*) gave her a chance to get back at us — at me — don't you see how tempting it was to say "Brenda pushed me . . ." It could have been like that, it could!

INSPECTOR A little far-fetched.

BRENDA No, it isn't. Not to a jealous woman. You don't know what people are like when they're jealous. And she'd been cooped up there in her room — thinking — suspecting — wondering if Bryan and I were still carrying on together. It isn't far-fetched, I tell you. It could easily be true. (*She looks at* WINGFIELD.)

WINGFIELD (*thoughtfully*) It is quite possible, you know, Inspector.

BRENDA (*to* EMMELINE) And you *do* hate her.

EMMELINE Me? My own sister?

BRENDA I've seen you looking at her often. You were in love with Bryan — he was half engaged to you — and then Jenny came home from abroad and cut you out. (*facing* EMMELINE) Oh, she told me the whole story one day. You've never forgiven her. I think you've hated her ever since. I think that you came into her room that day, and you saw her leaning over the balcony, and it was too good a chance to be missed — you came up behind her and — (*with a gesture*) pushed her over . . .

EMMELINE Inspector! Can't you stop this kind of thing?

INSPECTOR I don't know that I want to, Miss Ross. I find it all very informative.

GINSBERG I'm afraid I must insist on your leaving now. The patient must rest. We should be able to resume in twenty minutes. (*He moves to the upstage light switch and turns off part of the lights.*) Nurse will take you downstairs.

NURSE Yes, Doctor. (*She opens the door.*)

(ROSS, EMMELINE, WINGFIELD *and* BRENDA *move to exit.*)

INSPECTOR Miss Ross, would you mind waiting a moment?

(*They pause, then* BRENDA *exits, followed by* ROSS, *the* NURSE *and* WINGFIELD.)

EMMELINE Well, what is it?

(*The* INSPECTOR *eases the chair left of the table a little farther.* EMMELINE *sits on it. The* INSPECTOR *moves to behind the table.*)

INSPECTOR There are one or two questions I should like to put to you. I didn't want to embarrass your brother . . .

EMMELINE (*interrupting sharply*) Embarrass William? You don't know him. He has no self-respect at all. Never ashamed to admit that he doesn't know where to turn for the next penny!

INSPECTOR (*politely*) That's very interesting — but it was your brother-in-law that I thought might be embarrassed by the questions I am about to ask you.

EMMELINE (*a little taken aback*) Oh, Bryan. What do you want to know?

INSPECTOR Miss Ross, you know the family very well. A person of your — intelligence — would not be deceived as to what went on in it. You know the lives of your sister and your brother-in-law, and what the relations were between them. It is reasonable that, up to now, you would say as little as you could. But now that you know what our suspicions are — and the way they have been confirmed only a minute or two ago — well, that alters matters, doesn't it?

EMMELINE Yes, I suppose it does. (*She puts her bag on the floor.*) What do you want me to tell you?

INSPECTOR This affair between Mr. Wingfield and Miss Jackson, was it serious?

EMMELINE Not on his part. His affairs never are.

INSPECTOR There actually *was* an affair.

EMMELINE Of course. You heard her. She as good as admitted it.

INSPECTOR You know it of your own knowledge?

EMMELINE I could tell you various details to prove it, but I do not propose to do so. You will have to accept my word for it.

INSPECTOR It started — when?

EMMELINE Nearly a year ago.

INSPECTOR And Mrs. Wingfield found out about it?

EMMELINE Yes.

INSPECTOR And what was her attitude?

EMMELINE She taxed Bryan with it.

INSPECTOR And he?

EMMELINE He denied it, of course. Told her she was imagining things. You know what men are! Lie their way out of anything! (*The* INSPECTOR *and* GINSBERG *exchange a look.*) She wanted him to send the girl away, but he wouldn't — said she was far too good a secretary to lose.

INSPECTOR But Mrs. Wingfield was very unhappy about it?

EMMELINE Very.

INSPECTOR Unhappy enough to want to take her own life?

EMMELINE Not if she'd been well and strong. But her illness got her down. And she got all kinds of fancies.

GINSBERG (*showing interest*) What kinds of fancies, Miss Ross?

EMMELINE Just fancies.

INSPECTOR Why was Mrs. Wingfield left alone that afternoon?

EMMELINE She preferred it. One of us always offered to sit with her, but she had her books and her radio. For some reason she preferred to be alone.

INSPECTOR Whose idea was it to send the nurse off duty?

GINSBERG In private nursing that's standard practice. She would have two hours off every afternoon.

INSPECTOR Miss Jackson has told us that "it was all over ages ago," referring to her affair with Mr. Wingfield. Do you say that that was not so?

EMMELINE I think they broke with each other for a while. Or possibly they were very careful. But at the time of the accident, it was on again all right. Oh, yes!

INSPECTOR You seem very sure of that.

EMMELINE I lived in the house, didn't I? (*She pauses.*) And I'll show you something. (*She reaches for her bag, takes out a piece of notepaper and hands it to the* INSPECTOR.) I found it in the big Ming vase on the hall table. They used it as a postbox, it seems.

INSPECTOR (*reading*) "Darling, we must be careful. I think she suspects. B." (*He looks at* GINSBERG.)

EMMELINE It's Bryan's writing all right. So, you see!

GINSBERG Do you mind if I ask a question or two?

INSPECTOR No, Doctor, please do.

GINSBERG I'm interested in those "fancies" you mentioned, Miss Ross. You had some particular fancy in mind, I think.

EMMELINE Just a sick woman's imaginings. She was ill, you see, and she felt she wasn't making the progress she should have done.

GINSBERG And she thought there was a reason for that?

EMMELINE She was — just upset.

INSPECTOR (*leaning on the table and stressing his words*) She thought there was a reason for it.

EMMELINE (*uneasily*) Well — yes.

GINSBERG (*quietly*) She thought those two were poisoning her? That's it, isn't it?

(*There is a pause. The* INSPECTOR *sits on the table.*)

EMMELINE (*reluctantly*) Yes.

GINSBERG She said so to you?

EMMELINE Yes.

GINSBERG And what did you say?

EMMELINE I told her it was all nonsense of course.

GINSBERG Did you take any steps yourself?

EMMELINE Bryan couldn't — he just couldn't.

GINSBERG Did you discuss it with the doctor attending her? Take any samples of food?

EMMELINE (*shocked*) Of course not. It was just a sick woman's fancy.

GINSBERG Well, it happens, you know. Far more often than is known. The symptoms of arsenic poisoning, it's almost always arsenic, are practically indistinguishable from gastric disorders.

EMMELINE Bryan couldn't — he just couldn't.

GINSBERG It might have been the girl.

EMMELINE Yes! Yes, I suppose so. (*She sighs.*) Well, we shall never know now.

GINSBERG You're quite wrong there, Miss Ross. There are ways of telling. Traces of arsenic can be found in the hair, you know, and in the fingernails . . .

EMMELINE (*rising*) I can't believe it! I can't believe it of Bryan! (*turning to the*

INSPECTOR *agitatedly*) Do you want me any longer, Inspector?

INSPECTOR No, Miss Ross. (EMMELINE *moves towards the table to take the paper, but the* INSPECTOR *rises and picks it up first.*) I'll keep this. It's evidence.

EMMELINE Yes, of course.

(EMMELINE *exits.*)

GINSBERG (*rubbing his hands*) Well, we got something.

INSPECTOR (*sitting in the elbow chair*) Yes. (*He looks at the piece of paper.*) From the Ming vase in the hall. Interesting.

GINSBERG It's his writing?

INSPECTOR Oh, yes, it's Bryan Wingfield's writing all right. You know, he was quite a one for the ladies. Bowled them over like ninepins. Unfortunately they always took him seriously.

GINSBERG Doesn't strike me as the Casanova type. Writes all those historical novels. Very erudite.

INSPECTOR There's quite a lot of dirt in history. Oh . . . (*He notices he is in* GINSBERG's *chair; rises.*)

GINSBERG Thank you. (*He sits in the elbow chair.*) So it wasn't all over!

INSPECTOR Get four people all het up and accusing each other, get an embittered and malicious woman on her own and invite her to spill the beans — it gives one some material to work on, doesn't it?

GINSBERG In addition to what you had already. What did you have?

INSPECTOR (*smiling*) Just some good solid facts. (*He sits.*) I went into the financial angle. Bryan Wingfield's a poor man, his wife's a rich woman. Her life's insured in favour of him — not for a very large sum, but it would enable him to marry again, if he wanted to. Her money came to her in trust. If she dies childless, it's divided between her brother and sister. The brother's a wastrel, always trying to get money out of his rich sister. According to Bryan, she told her brother she wasn't going to pay for him any more. (*thoughtfully*) But I dare say she would have done — in the end.

GINSBERG So which is it? B for Bryan? B for Brenda? B for Brother Bill? Or Emmeline without a B?

INSPECTOR (*rising*) Emmeline without the — Emmeline? Wait a minute — something I heard this afternoon, while they were all here . . . No, it's gone.

GINSBERG Could it be B for burglar?

INSPECTOR No, that's definitely out. We've got conclusive evidence on that point. The road was up in front of the house and there was a constable on duty there. But the side and the front gate were directly under his eye. Nobody entered or left the house, that afternoon.

GINSBERG You know, you asked me to co-operate, but you were very careful not to put all your cards on the table. Come on! What *do* you think?

INSPECTOR It's not a question of thinking. I know.

GINSBERG What?

INSPECTOR I may be wrong, but I don't think so. You think it over. (GINSBERG *enumerates on his fingers.*) You've got seven minutes.

GINSBERG Huh! Oh, yes. (*He rises and moves to the* PATIENT. *The* INSPECTOR *joins him.*) Mrs. Wingfield. Thank you for your help, Mrs. Wingfield. We come now to the crucial moment in the experiment.

INSPECTOR Mrs. Wingfield, we are about to leave you here, apparently unguarded. None of the suspects knows that you regained your powers of speech yesterday. They don't know that you did not in fact see who pushed you off that balcony. You realize what that means?

PATIENT One of them will — will try to . . .

INSPECTOR Someone will almost certainly enter this room.

GINSBERG Are you sure you want to go through with this, Mrs. Wingfield?

PATIENT Yes, yes. I must know — I must know who . . .

INSPECTOR Don't be afraid. We shall be close at hand. If anyone approaches you or touches you . . .

PATIENT I know what to do.

INSPECTOR Thank you, Mrs. Wingfield, you're a wonderful woman. Just be brave for a few moments longer and we shall trap our killer. Trust me. Trust both of us, eh?

GINSBERG Ready?

(*They move the trolley downstage.*)

INSPECTOR Right.

GINSBERG Why don't you come into my office? (*holding the door open*) In view of this poisoning suggestion, you might like to look over the files.

INSPECTOR Yes, I'd like another look at those X-ray plates too, if I may. (*He switches off the downstage lights.*)

(GINSBERG *and the* INSPECTOR *exit. When off, they switch off the light in the passage. In the blackout, the* NURSE *enters upstage, with a small syringe, and crosses left to behind the curtain.*)

PATIENT Help! Help!

(*The* INSPECTOR *enters.*)

INSPECTOR All right, Mrs. Wingfield, we're here!

(GINSBERG *enters and switches on the lights by the upstage switch. He rushes straight to the* PATIENT.)

PATIENT Help! Murder! (*pointing to the curtains*) There!

(*The* INSPECTOR *crosses to the* PATIENT.)

INSPECTOR Is she all right?

GINSBERG She's all right. You've been very brave, Mrs. Wingfield.

INSPECTOR Thank you, Mrs. Wingfield. The killer has played right into our hands. (*He faces* GINSBERG.) That note in the Ming vase was all I needed. Bryan Wingfield would hardly need to write secret notes to a secretary he sees every day. He wrote that note to someone else. And that constable on duty. He swears that nobody entered or left the house that afternoon. (*He faces the curtain.*) So it seems you didn't take your off-duty walk that day. (*He moves towards the curtain.*) You may come out from behind that curtain now, Nurse Bond.

(NURSE BOND *comes out from behind the curtain and takes a pace downstage. The lights black out and —*)

THE CURTAIN FALLS

ABOUT THE LINES

1 Draw a sketch depicting the details of the scene of the crime, or the room in which the experiment was conducted.

2 Using one sentence for each of the suspects, describe a possible motive for attempting to kill Mrs. Wingfield that each of them might have had. Compare your assessments of motivation with your partners' to see if you agree.

3 Working with a partner, write a set of instructions that would clearly explain to Mrs. Wingfield what she was to do during the experiment.

4 Imagine that you are the Inspector. Write a report to your supervisory officer in Scotland Yard describing the trap that you set for the criminal.

BETWEEN THE LINES

1 Reread the play. List any clues that suggest Nurse Bond was the guilty person. Compare your list with a partner's and discuss any differences.

2 "The title of the play describes Mrs. Wingfield in two ways." Discuss this statement with your partners and write an explanation of the playwright's title choice.

3 Imagine that you are Brenda Jackson. Make an entry in your diary describing how you feel when Nurse Bond is discovered to be the culprit.

4 In Dr. Ginsberg's voice, explain why you are so willing to become involved in solving this case. Present your reasons to a small group.

BEYOND THE LINES

1 Working in a group, prepare and present a performance or a dramatic reading of this play for your class and other students in the school who like murder-mysteries. To get ideas, read the production notes included at the beginning and throughout the play.

2 Rewrite the ending of the play, replacing Nurse Bond with one of the other suspects as the discovered would-be murderer.

3 Imagine that you are the prosecutor for the Crown in its case against Nurse Bond. Present your argument to convince the judge and jury of her guilt. Be sure to include her motivation. You may wish to try out your presentation on a small group first. Invite people to offer suggestions that would strengthen your argument, and then present your case to a larger group who have read the play. (Someone else in the class may wish to act as Defence Counsel for Nurse Bond.)

beware: do not read this poem

Ishmael Reed

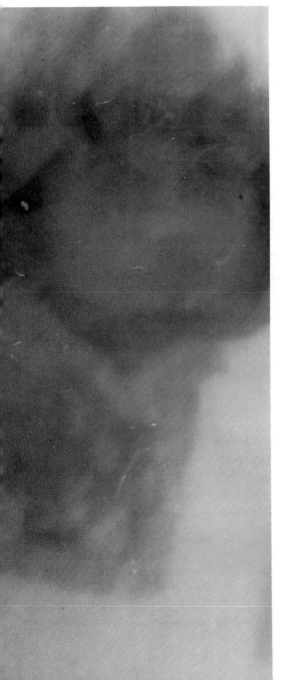

tonite   ,   thriller was
abt an ol woman   , so vain she
surrounded herself w/
     many mirrors

it got so bad that finally she
locked herself indoors & her
whole life became the
     mirrors

one day the villagers broke
into her house   ,   but she was too
swift for them   .   she disappeared
     into a mirror

each tenant who bought the house
after that   ,   lost a loved one to
     the ol woman in the mirror   :
     first a little girl
     then a young woman
     then the young woman/s husband

the hunger of this poem is legendary
it has taken in many victims
back off from this poem
it has drawn in yr feet
back off from this poem
it has drawn in yr legs

back off from this poem
it is a greedy mirror
you are into this poem .   from
     the waist down

nobody can hear you can they   ?
this poem has had you up to here
     belch
this poem aint got no manners
you cant call out frm this poem

relax now & go w/ this poem
move & roll on to this poem
do not resist this poem
this poem has yr eyes
this poem has his head
this poem has his arms
this poem has his fingers
this poem has his fingertips

this poem is the reader & the
reader this poem

statistic   :   the us bureau of missing persons reports
                that in 1968 over 100 000 people disappeared
                leaving no solid clues
                      nor trace   only
a space   in the lives of their friends

LOOKING IN

1 This poem has two sections. Retell the story of the first four stanzas in three sentences. Then write a statement explaining how these stanzas create a mysterious link with the rest of the poem.

2 Imagine that you are the poet, and write a footnote for this poem explaining why you chose to use abbreviations of words in the poem.

3 In a small group, discuss how the title, "beware: do not read this poem," contributes to the atmosphere of this poem. Brainstorm other titles that would capture the threatening force the poet has created.

LOOKING OUT

1 The last two stanzas of the poem suggest a sinister and imaginary absorption of the reader into the poem. List other ways in which people can disappear from their family and friends; for example, when they join cults.

2 Working with a small group, prepare a choral reading (see p. 350) of this poem. Choose appropriate music to create an eerie background for your performance.

3 Write an additional verse for this poem in which two people reading the poem together disappear into it.

4 Research accounts of real-life mysterious disappearances. Choose one case that particularly interests you and retell the story for the class.

EXTENDED ACTIVITIES

1 Read a mystery novel of your choice. Prepare an enticing book talk about your novel to present to the class. Remember to supply enough information to catch your audience's interest *without* unravelling the mystery entirely.

2 Design a book jacket that could be used for one of the stories in this unit if it were extended to a full-length novel.

3 Research the life and adventures of a famous detective. You may choose a fictional character like Sherlock Holmes or a real-life detective. Prepare an oral presentation for the class. Highlight the most interesting things you discovered about the person whom you "investigated."

4 Working with a partner, write a ballad that captures the story of a crime, a criminal, the victim of the crime, and a detective who traps the guilty party. Choose appropriate musical accompaniment to present your ballad to a group in song form or with the music as background for a dramatic reading.

5 Write a story about "a perfect, non-violent crime" in which the criminals get away with it and remain free to enjoy their spoils.

or

Write a story about a crime that had one small flaw in the plan that led to the criminal's capture.

6 Using your librarian as a resource person, investigate mysterious events that have yet to be explained, like the story recounted in "Beale's Treasure." Select one case and share the information that you have "uncovered" with a group.

7 Imagine that you are a reporter on your local newspaper. Write a newspaper account covering one of the crimes described in this unit, or any other crime that you have read about or seen depicted on television. Remember to include an attention-getting headline for your report.

8 Write a letter to the editor of your local newspaper, either supporting or arguing against the following statement:
"Our courts should impose much harsher penalties on those who commit violent crimes."
Use specific examples from cases you know about to reinforce your position. (You may wish to do some research on court decisions in Canada in the last ten years.)

THE SHIFTING

ladders
park   then
play
high   slide
climb
slowly   laughing
they
while   down
nervously
wave   swift
Children   years

QUALITY

The Philosophers
R. G. Everson

THE FORSAKEN

Duncan Campbell Scott

I

Once in the winter
Out on a lake
In the heart of the north-land,
Far from the Fort
And far from the hunters,
A Chippewa woman
With her sick baby,
Crouched in the last hours
Of a great storm.
Frozen and hungry,
She fished through the ice
With a line of the twisted
Bark of the cedar,
And a rabbit-bone hook
Polished and barbed;
Fished with the bare hook
All through the wild day,
Fished and caught nothing;
While the young chieftain
Tugged at her breasts,
Or slept in the lacings
Of the warm *tikanagan*.
All the lake surface
Steamed with the hissing
Of millions of iceflakes
Hurled by the wind;
Behind her the round
Of a lonely island
Roared like a fire
With the voice of the storm
In the deeps of the cedars.
Valiant, unshaken,
She took of her own flesh,
Baited the fish-hook,
Drew in a grey-trout,
Drew in his fellows,
Heaped them beside her,
Dead in the snow.

Valiant, unshaken,
She faced the long distance,
Wolf-haunted and lonely,
Sure of her goal
And the life of her dear one:
Tramped for two days,
On the third in the morning,
Saw the strong bulk
Of the Fort by the river,
Saw the wood-smoke
Hang soft in the spruces,
Heard the keen yelp
Of the ravenous huskies
Fighting for whitefish:
Then she had rest.

II

Years and years after,
When she was old and withered,
When her son was an old man
And his children filled with vigour,
They came in their northern tour on the verge of winter,
To an island in a lonely lake.
There one night they camped, and on the morrow
Gathered their kettles and birch-bark,
Their rabbit-skin robes and their mink-wraps,
Launched their canoes and slunk away through the islands,
Left her alone forever,
Without a word of farewell,
Because she was old and useless,
Like a paddle broken and warped,
Or a pole that was splintered.

Then, without a sigh,
Valiant, unshaken,
She smoothed her dark locks under her kerchief,
Composed her shawl in state,
Then folded her hands ridged with sinews and corded with veins,
Folded them across her breasts spent with the nourishing of children,
Gazed at the sky past the tops of the cedars,
Saw two spangled nights arise out of the twilight,
Saw two days go by filled with the tranquil sunshine,
Saw, without pain, or dread, or even a moment of longing:
Then on the third great night there came thronging and thronging
Millions of snowflakes out of a windless cloud;
They covered her close with a beautiful crystal shroud,
Covered her deep and silent.
But in the frost of the dawn,
Up from the life below,
Rose a column of breath
Through a tiny cleft in the snow,
Fragile, delicately drawn,
Wavering with its own weakness,
In the wilderness a sign of the spirit,
Persisting still in the sight of the sun
Till day was done.
Then all light was gathered up by the hand of God and hid
    in His breast,
Then there was born a silence deeper than silence,
Then she had rest.

LOOKING IN

1 a. In the voice of an observer, write an account of the young Chippewa woman's struggle to save her child.

   b. Imagine that you are the young Chippewa woman, and write a memoir that captures your feelings as you fought to make it safely to the fort.

Working with a partner, compare the two versions that each of you have written. Note the similarities and the differences in the two perspectives. Discuss which one was more interesting and consider the reasons for your choice.

2 Read the poem aloud with a partner, with one person reading Part I and the other person reading Part II. After discussing the poem:
  a. List the features in the poet's style that link the two parts of the poem; and
  b. Note the differences in the way that the two sections were written.
  You may wish to prepare a polished reading of the poem to share with the class or another group.

3 a. List all the words or phrases in the first part of the poem that suggest the young woman's strength and vigour.
  b. List all the words and phrases in the second part of the poem that suggest the old woman's mental strength and physical weakness.
  c. In a paragraph, describe the woman in both stages of her life.

4 a. In one sentence, describe the feelings evoked in you by the first section of the poem.
  b. In one sentence, describe how you felt as you read the second section of the poem.
  c. Compare your sentences with your partners' to see if you reacted in the same way to the two situations.

5 The title "The Forsaken" implies a judgment of the actions of the Chippewa tribe. Suggest another title that reflects this custom as part of the natural order of things.

6 Design and produce a mural that depicts the actions of the young Chippewa woman as she fights for her child's life.

or

Draw a sketch of the old Chippewa woman that captures all the details described in the last twenty-five lines of the poem.

LOOKING OUT

1 Working in a group, discuss ways in which our society deals with the aged. Compare the Chippewa way with the approaches taken by people you know. After the discussion, write an argument defending or rejecting the following statement:
The Chippewa way of dealing with their old people is really very cruel.
Discuss your point of view with someone who holds the opposite opinion.

2 Script a conversation between the old Chippewa woman's grandson and his child in which the father explains "the forsaking" of Great Grandmother. With a partner, dramatize or tape the conversation for a larger group. You may wish to combine this with a polished reading of the poem.

3 Using material from your resource centre or local library, research some aspect of the Chippewa tribe in Canada. Present your findings to the class. You may wish to include pictures or reproductions of Chippewa art of the past and the present.

C.D. Minni

Mario dreamed — of running barefoot across a beach to tell his grandfather, to tell him they were going to Canada. The old man sat in the lee of a red-brick church that stood half on the paving, half on the shore. He was mending his fishing nets, removing the weakened outer edges. The harbour shone like an oil green mirror; the town shone with whitewash and the bright awnings of shops. . . .

He dreamed — of baggage piled in the street, green trunks and bulging suitcases fastened with rope. He sat on one of the trunks, waiting. The house was crowded with relatives, friends and neighbours, but they did not miss him until later. "Mario? Where's Mario?" He was embraced, kissed, crushed, tears on his cheeks. It was time to go. The bus to Naples pulled out of the village square, down a street of vine-hung balconies and out along the rocky coast, north. Oleanders flowered blood-red in crags; below, the sea flashed an incredible blue. The bus passed nondescript towns like his own, olive groves, twisted railroad tracks, scars of war. . . .

He dreamed — of the ship, a Greek liner, and of how passengers in native costumes squatted in a circle on deck, clapping hands rhythmically, yelling, as one of them danced in their centre. He was learning new words, passports, emigration, disembarkation. . . . But then it seemed that he was, with the shifting quality of dreams, on a train rattling across frozen prairies where snow drifted, and he was celebrating his ninth birthday with his parents in the restaurant car. . . .

He dreamed, but he woke to the shrill cry of gulls in a room surrounded by green trunks, and he remembered: the bus, the ship, the train. All of them now unreal as if he had indeed dreamed them. But he was here. Destination; one of his new words. He smelled coffee and heard voices downstairs.

One of the suitcases was open, and he saw that his mother had already laid out clean clothes for him. He dressed: knee trousers with stockings and a blue shirt, for today he was to sign up at school.

He went to the window and pushed up the sash. It was drizzling, and the wind blew from the Ocean. The Pacific, his teacher had called it on the last day. She had suspended the regular lesson and asked the class to take out their geography books and look up where Mario was going. Everyone was awed that he was going so far away.

Now, gulls circled against the grey sky, crying ruefully, sped seaward or alighted on warehouses and men's bunkhouses built on pilings over the shore. There was, he saw, scarcely space for a town on this inlet. The rain-beaten houses climbed the mountainside in haphazard rows up to the forest's edge. Across the inlet was the pulp mill, where his father worked, its chimney belching out smoke. Men, carrying black lunchbuckets, were crossing over the wooden bridge. They reminded him of ants, each burdened with a grain of wheat.

ANADIAN MOSAIC

A new country, new people, new ways, and Mario became Mike. . . .

In the street below, his small brother was already exploring the neighbourhood.

Mario went into the bathroom and drew water to wash. His mother came in and made him scrub his ears until they squeaked. She had prepared a big Canadian breakfast; these were their first real home meals, and they had sat down to it when his small brother ran inside in bewilderment.

"Hey, no one knows how to talk in this place!"

He looked so funny standing there that they could not help but laugh — at his turned-up nose, at his child's logic, at their own strangeness.

"Mario is going to school to learn," his father said and fetched their coats.

Only three weeks ago, in his native village, it was spring. Orange trees and roses bloomed in gardens behind stone houses. Now, here, in a yard daffodils pushed bravely through leftover snow, but the wind was cold. Mario turned up his coat collar as he followed his father through unfamiliar streets, past strange wood-frame houses, work of carpenters with hammer and nails.

Up ahead surrounded by a steel fence was the schoolyard. He heard shouting and the whack of a bat, but only weeks later knew the game was called baseball.

In the principal's office he waited, sitting, while registration papers were filled. The principal was a tall man with a polished dome of a head, and he motioned for the boy to follow him. Down a corridor. Up some stairs. Knocked on a door. Room no. 6. A teacher with silver hair.

She introduced him to the class, a new student — from Italy. Some giggled, and for the first time he became conscious of his clothes. But he took an empty seat and received workbooks and pencils.

Some subjects he could do even on that first day — arithmetic, art, gym. Others puzzled him. At recess another boy showed him where the washroom was, then left. He was alone until the bell rang. He walked home alone. The teacher began to keep him in after school to learn English. By the time he left, the schoolyard was almost empty, except for a few boys. Usually the same boys.

Three of them came up to him one day, shouting — "Hey dummy! Cat got your tongue?" When he tried to run, they blocked his way, surrounding him. "Where'd ya get the funny getup, eh?" They began to pull at his clothes, and he heard his blue shirt rip. Then he was pushed, knocked down, kicked. He swore at them. "What say?"

"Aw, leave him alone," one said. He had red hair and blue jeans.

In that moment of distraction Mario stood up. The three were laughing at him as if at a joke, and this hurt him most. He threw his arithmetic book. It caught one of the boys in the face; blood gushed from his nose. The others seized him, one holding back his arms, another raising his fist. Mario saw the arm arch, the fist like a hammer, and before knowing it he had kicked with force, connecting with genitals. There was a yelp of pain as the boy buckled and clutched his pants. Mario, having twisted free, ran, his breath like a hot wire in his throat. When he looked back, they were staring at him.

The next morning they were waiting for him. He brandished his arithmetic book as they surrounded him. One of them had red hair and blue jeans, and his face cracked into a grin as he extended a hand.

"Friends?" he said.

Were they his friends?

142

But they shook.

"Bruce," he said.

"Mario."

"Friends. OK?"

"OK."

His exploit had won him respect in the schoolyard. But on Saturday his father took him to the Bay store and bought him Canadian clothes, his first blue jeans. He wore them when he danced around the May pole and when he signed up for Little League baseball.

With his friend Bruce he explored the woods above the town, saw a black bear, competed and lost in the marbles championships, and fished off the wharf. He told Bruce that his grandfather was a fisherman.

"Ya? What'd he catch?"

"Everything. Octopus even."

"Really?" — with sudden interest.

"Sure. You eat octopus with bread and olives."

"Yetch!"

He asked Bruce where his grandparents lived.

"In the city," his friend said. "In a home."

"Home?"

"You know, for old folks."

He did not know. In his native village families were large, embracing uncles, cousins and especially grandparents. It puzzled him that there should be no old people in this town.

He had also made other discoveries. One: the pulp mill was the pulse of the town which adjusted to — or complained about — the rhythm of its changing work shifts. Two: his friends seemed to live on hot dogs, potato chips, peanut butter and Cokes. Three: though he was changing, his parents remained foreign. His mother especially needed protection. He became her companion and interpreter — at the store, the post office, the bank, even the church.

The school holidays had begun. The weather turned fine. Bruce asked him if they wanted to be best friends, and together they planned new adventures. They went cycling. They built a treehouse where on the wings of imagination anything was possible. They made a raft and sailed it down the Mississippi. They never missed the Saturday twenty-cent matinee where they bought crackerjacks and candy bars, and they collected and traded comics — especially Superman and Batman — with the treasured DC sign.

His coach had told him that he had a good pitching arm, and he spent hours in the schoolyard developing his technique. The Giants were going to win the Little League trophy that year, and he was drawn into the excitement. The fans cheered when he walked to the pitcher's mount. They cheered Mike.

He did not know at what point he had become Mike. One day looking for a suitable translation of his name and finding none, he decided that Mike was the closest. By the end of summer, he was Mario at home and Mike in the streets.

It was Mike who pitched a five-hitter for the Giants, Mike who in August watched the salmon run upstream to spawn and Mike who returned to school in September. At Christmas he received his first pair of skates and toque on his head, planned to learn hockey. When he dreamed, it was of Rocket Richard or three-speed bikes or a girl named Gwendolyn who sat behind him in Grade Five. . . .

. . . It is by luck that I find a parking place. There is a crowd. Children are running everywhere. Some line up at a truck which is dispensing free ice cream. Dignitaries, from the provincial and municipal governments, are shaking hands with leaders of the Italian-Canadian Community. Speeches are made. Cameras click.

The sun is warm, and the park's sunken gardens are a riot of colours. There is music, accordians and mandolins, and a troupe in gay folk costumes is performing, twirling in a dance, linking arms, breaking and reforming. A kaleidoscope of colours and patterns.

The music, a sea-song, draws me like a hooked fish. It plays on the stereo of my memory. And I — Mike — Mario — am again running barefoot across the beach to the red-brick church where Grandfather is mending his nets.

He hooks his toes into the net, anchoring it to the ground, lifts a section with his left bronzed hand until the edge pulls tight and with his right hand rips away the line of cable and cork floats. Next, he cuts about a foot of the mesh behind the ripped edge, drops the net, lifts his foot, brings up another section of the edge and starts all over again. The strip of discarded mesh settles in a neat pile near his idle foot.

ABOUT THE LINES

1 This is a cloze task. Your teacher will give you a worksheet for it.

2 Speaking in the voice of the adult Mike/Mario, retell the story of your childhood experience as a new Canadian onto a tape to be shared with other students. Ask someone else who has read the story to listen to your tape and make suggestions on how you could improve the presentation. You may wish to use background music to help dramatize the story.

3 Read the following statements and note true or false after each one. Then, using information from the text, write a short explanation supporting your choice.
   a. Mario's last day in school in Italy was just like any other day, with classes as usual.
   b. The students in Mario's new class in Canada tried to make him feel welcome.
   c. Once he proved himself, Mario won Bruce's friendship and respect.
   d. Mario soon became an active member of his new community.

4 Note in point form the cultural differences or challenges that Mario and his family had to face as new Canadians.

BETWEEN THE LINES

1 Write three questions that Mario probably asked or wanted to ask a Canadian friend about the customs of his new country when he first arrived in Canada. Working with a partner, role play a conversation in which you act as Mario and seek answers to your questions from your partner, who assumes the role of a Canadian child.

2 Write a brief explanation of the author's choice of title for this story. Suggest another title that would capture the essence of the story. Compare and discuss your choice with other students who have also retitled the story.

3 In two or three sentences, explain why Mario felt that "his mother especially needed a protector."

4 Mario/Mike's Italian fisherman grandfather is a very important figure in his life. Discuss this statement with a partner by examining references Mario makes to his grandfather throughout his story. Then in the grownup Mario's voice, describe your grandfather to your own child, who was born in Canada. You may write or tape your description.

BEYOND THE LINES

1 Imagine that you are the adult Mario/Mike, and write a letter to a relative in Italy announcing your intention to return for a visit. Explain why you wish to go back to your roots with your own family.

2 Assume the role of Mario's mother or father and write a memoir describing the difficulties and triumphs you experienced when you immigrated to Canada.

3 Interview someone you know who was born and spent a significant part of his/her life in another country before coming to live in Canada. Work with a partner to prepare appropriate questions before you conduct your interview. Write a newspaper article based on the information you gathered in the interview. Revise your work with help from your partner, and submit it to your local newspaper for possible publication.

4 Mario and his family experienced a significant transition in their lives when they immigrated to Canada. Change often helps us to grow and to develop. Write an autobiographical piece in which you relate an important change that occurred in your life. Describe its impact on you at the time and later on. Share your account with someone with whom you feel comfortable.

THIS ABOVE ALL

Fatherly advice, centuries apart

LETTER FROM F. SCOTT FITZGERALD TO HIS DAUGHTER

La Paix, Rodger's Forge
Towson, Maryland

August 8, 1933

Dear Pie:

I feel very strongly about you doing [your] duty. Would you give me a little more documentation about your reading in French? I am glad you are happy — but I never believe much in happiness. I never believe in misery either. Those are things you see on the stage or the screen or the printed page, they never really happen to you in life.

All I believe in in life is the rewards for virtue (according to your talents) and the *punishments* for not fulfilling your duties, which are doubly costly. If there is such a volume in the camp library, will you ask Mrs. Tyson to let you look up a sonnet of Shakespeare's in which the line occurs *"Lilies that fester smell far worse than weeds."*

Have had no thoughts today, life seems composed of getting up a *Saturday Evening Post* story. I think of you, and always pleasantly; but if you call me "Pappy" again I am going to take the White Cat out and beat his bottom *hard, six times for every time you are impertinent.* Do you react to that?

I will arrange the camp bill.

Halfwit, I will conclude.

Things to worry about:
    Worry about courage
    Worry about cleanliness
    Worry about efficiency
    Worry about horsemanship
    Worry about . . .
Things not to worry about:
    Don't worry about popular opinion
    Don't worry about dolls
    Don't worry about the past
    Don't worry about the future
    Don't worry about growing up
    Don't worry about anybody getting ahead of you
    Don't worry about triumph
    Don't worry about failure unless it comes through your own fault
    Don't worry about mosquitoes
    Don't worry about flies
    Don't worry about insects in general
    Don't worry about parents
    Don't worry about boys
    Don't worry about disappointments
    Don't worry about pleasures
    Don't worry about satisfactions

Things to think about:
    What am I really aiming at?
    How good am I really in comparison to my contemporaries in regard to:
    (a) Scholarship
    (b) Do I really understand about people and am I able to get along with them?
    (c) Am I trying to make my body a useful instrument or am I neglecting it?
                                    With dearest love,
                                        [Daddy]

P.S. My come-back to your calling me Pappy is christening you by the word Egg, which implies that you belong to a very rudimentary state of life and that I could break you up and crack you open at my will and I think it would be a word that would hang on if I ever told it to your contemporaries. "Egg Fitzgerald." How would you like that to go through life with — "Eggie Fitzgerald" or "Bad Egg Fitzgerald" or any form that might occur to fertile minds? Try it once more and I swear to God I will hang it on you and it will be up to you to shake it off. Why borrow trouble?
                            Love anyhow.

SPEECH BY POLONIUS TO HIS SON
(From Hamlet, Act I, Scene III)
William Shakespeare

POLONIUS Yet here, Laertes? Aboard, aboard, for shame!
The wind sits in the shoulder of your sail,
And you are stay'd for. There; my blessing with thee!
And these few precepts in thy memory
Look thou charácter.[1] Give thy thoughts no tongue,
Nor any unproportion'd[2] thought his act;
Be thou familiar, but by no means vulgar;
Those friends thou hast, and their adoption tried,
Grapple them unto thy soul with hoops of steel;
But do not dull thy palm with entertainment
Of each new-hatch'd, unfledg'd comrade. Beware
Of entrance to a quarrel; but being in,
Bear 't that th' opposed may beware of thee.
Give every man thy ear, but few thy voice;
Take each man's censure,[3] but reserve thy judgement.
Costly thy habit as thy purse can buy,
But not express'd in fancy; rich, not gaudy;
For the apparel oft proclaims the man,
And they in France of the best rank and station
Are most select and generous, chief in that.
Neither a borrower nor a lender be;
For loan oft loses both itself and friend,
And borrowing dulleth edge of husbandry;[4]
This above all: to thine own self be true,
And it must follow, as the night the day,
Thou canst not then be false to any man.
Farewell; my blessing season[5] this in thee!

---

[1] *Character:* inscribe.
[2] *Unproportioned:* unsuitable.
[3] *Censure:* opinion.
[4] *Husbandry:* thrift.
[5] *Season:* bring to fruition.

LOOKING IN

1 Both F. Scott Fitzgerald and Polonius are giving advice to their children as they move from childhood to independence. In chart form, like the following example, list the do's and don'ts identified by each father. Paraphrase ideas where appropriate.

F. Scott Fitzgerald to His Daughter		Polonius to His Son	
Do's	Don'ts	Do's	Don'ts

2 In a brief paragraph for each, comment on similarities and differences between the two parental admonitions. Compare your analysis with your partners', and together produce polished notes after your discussion.

3 Working with your partners, discuss the following questions:
   a. If you were F. Scott Fitzgerald's daughter, what would you say is the most significant point your father made in his letter?
   b. If you were Polonius's son, what would you consider to be the central message of your father's blessing?
   After the discussion, write out in your own words the message that was chosen as most significant in each case.

4 Read the two parental messages carefully. Write two questions that you would ask each parent if you were his child receiving this advice. Share your questions with your partners to see if you reacted to the same or different issues.

5 From Fitzgerald's letter, we learn a lot about the nature of the relationship between him and his daughter. Imagine that you are Fitzgerald's biographer, and list observations that you can make about his feelings for and attitude toward his daughter by reading this letter.

LOOKING OUT

1 Write a letter, poem, or monologue in which you give some advice on growing up to a younger brother, sister, or friend. Try your message out on a younger person and ask for his/her opinion of your suggestions. Rewrite any parts that your listener has trouble understanding.

2 Write a memoir recounting a lesson that you learned about life when you chose to ignore or to follow advice that was given to you.

3 Working with your partners, come up with three suggestions that you would make to a grade eight student coming into high school to help make the transition easier. Write out the suggestions and send them to a grade eight class. Ask for their reaction to your advice.

SONG FOR NAOMI

Irving Layton

Who is that in the tall grasses singing
By herself, near the water?
I can not see her
But can it be her
Than whom the grasses so tall
Are taller,
My daughter,
My lovely daughter?

Who is that in the tall grasses running
Beside her, near the water?
She can not see there
Time that pursued her
In the deep grasses so fast
And faster
And caught her,
My foolish daughter.

What is the wind in the fair grass saying
Like a verse, near the water?
Saviours that over
All things have power
Make Time himself grow kind
And kinder
That sought her,
My little daughter.

Who is that at the close of the summer
Near the deep lake? Who wrought her
Comely and slender?
Time but attends and befriends her
Than whom the grasses though tall
Are not taller,
My daughter,
My gentle daughter.

LOOKING IN

1 A rhetorical question is asked when the answer is already known or when no answer is expected. List the questions that are rhetorical in this poem and then list the questions that indicate a genuine desire to know more. Working with your partners, speculate on what the answers might be to the latter category of questions.

2 The title of this poem indicates this is a "song." In two or three sentences, identify the characteristics of the poem that make it lyrical.

3 Working with your partners, discuss and write an interpretation of the following lines from the poem:
"Saviours that over
All things have power
Make Time himself grow kind
And kinder . . ."

LOOKING OUT

1 Write a memoir of an experience you have had where you watched something or someone grow or change over a period of time. You may wish to accompany your account with sketches or drawings. Share your material with your partners.

2 Assuming the role of your mother or father, write an account describing your growing years. Highlight events that particularly impressed you, the parent, as exciting or frightening.

THE SATELLITES

Gabrielle Roy

TRANSLATED BY JOYCE MARSHALL

I

In the transparent night of the Arctic summer, beside a little lake far away in the immense naked land, glimmered the fire lit to guide the seaplane that was expected at any moment. Stocky shadows all around fed the flames with handfuls of reindeer moss torn from the soil.

Nearby, at the end of a plank fastened to two empty oil-drums and placed on the water to serve as a gangway, there were a few cabins, one of them faintly illuminated. A little farther away were seven or eight other rickety houses, quite enough, in these parts, to constitute a village. From all sides rose the lament of the always famished dogs which no one ever heard any more.

Near the fire the men chatted calmly. They spoke in that smooth and gentle Eskimo voice with its occasional rises, a voice much like the summer night and punctuated only by brief bursts of laughter about everything and nothing. With them such laughter was very often just a way of concluding a sentence, providing a full stop, perhaps a sort of commentary of fate.

They had begun to make little wagers among themselves. They wagered that the seaplane was going to come, that it would not come, that it had set out but would never arrive, and even that it had not set out at all.

Fort Chimo had spoken, however. The radio had told them to be in readiness; the seaplane would stop on its way back from Frobisher Bay that evening to pick up the patient. The patient was Deborah, and it was for her that light had been left in the hut.

The men went on wagering for their own entertainment. For instance, they said that Deborah would have died before the seaplane arrived, as the Eskimos used to die in former times, without fuss. Or the seaplane would carry her a long way off and no one would ever see her again, living or dead. They wagered also that she would return by the road of the sky cured and looking twenty years younger. At this notion they all laughed heartily, especially Jonathan, Deborah's husband, as if he were once more the butt of the joking of his wedding night. They even went so far as to wager that the white men might soon find a remedy against death. No one would die any more. They would live forever — multitudes of old people. At this prospect they fell silent, but impressed even so. There were about ten of them around the fire: old men like Isaac, Deborah's father, reared in the old harsh way; middle-aged men like Jonathan, divided between two influences, the ancient and the modern; and finally young men, more erect of body than their elders, slimmer too, and these were definitely inclined towards the life of today.

Old Isaac, standing slightly to one side, perpetually rolling a round pebble between his fingers, said that nothing now was as it had been in the old days.

152

Deborah lives in two worlds and belongs to neither.

"In the old days," he declared with pride, "no one would have taken all this trouble to prevent a woman from dying when her hour had come. Nor even a man, for that matter. What sense is it," he asked, "to prevent at such great expense someone from dying today who in any event is going to die tomorrow? What is the sense of it?"

No one knew what the sense of it was, so they began to search for it together with touching good will.

Isaac, for his part, continued to gaze attentively at the fire. His eyes filled with memories, and what seemed a sort of compassion mingled with hardness. They knew then what he was going to speak of and even the youngest moved closer, for the subject was fascinating.

"That night you know of," the old man began, "was not as cold as some have said. It was a seasonal night, that's all. Nor did we abandon the Old One on the pack-ice as they have also said. We spoke to her first. We said good-bye to her. In short, we behaved as good sons should. We wrapped her in caribou skins. We even left her one that was brand new. Find me any white men," he asked all in general, "who would do as much for one of their old people, for all their fine words. We didn't abandon her," he repeated with a curious stubbornness.

"And isn't it true," asked one of the young men, "that you left her something to eat?"

"Yes," said Benjamin, Isaac's younger brother. "We left her something to eat — a big piece of fresh seal-meat."

"That's right," said Isaac with a sort of disdain, head high, "but to my thinking she didn't eat."

"How could we know?" said one of the men. "She might have wished to hold on for a day, perhaps two . . . to watch for. . . ."

"Not to my thinking," Isaac repeated. "She could no longer walk alone. She could scarcely swallow. She was almost blind. Why would she want to hold on for a few days more? And why do they all want to hold on now?"

They were silent, looking at the flames. There was in their eyes a sort of beauty about the death of the Old One in the shadow, wind, and silence; they were still not sure how it had come to pass, whether by water, by the cold, or from shock.

"Didn't they at least find something? The new skin, perhaps?" asked one of the young Eskimos.

"No," said Isaac. "Not a trace. The Old One had departed as she came into the world. There wouldn't even have been a scrap of her to bury."

Jonathan rose then and announced that he would go to see whether Deborah needed anything.

He stood for a moment on the doorsill, looking at a human form that lay stretched upon two old automobile seats placed end to end.

"Are you there?"

"I'm here," she said weakly.

"You're not worse?"

"I'm not worse."

"Be patient," said Jonathan then and went at once to rejoin the others around the fire.

154

What else could she do but be patient? Emaciated and short of breath, she had been lying there for weeks, victim of a swiftly progressing illness. She was only forty-two, and yet she considered this old enough to die. From the moment one was no longer good for anything, one was always old enough for death.

But then their pastor, the Reverend Hugh Paterson, had passed that way last week. Seated on the ground near Deborah's "bed," he had begged her not to let herself die.

"Come, Deborah! At least make an effort!"

Feeble as she was, she had managed to draw from herself something like a grieving laugh.

"What, don't want . . . but when the body isn't good any more . . . "

"But yours *is* still good — strong and sturdy. You're too young to leave life. Come, a little courage!"

Courage? She was willing, but what was the use? How did you manage to stop death once it was on its way? Was there a means?

There was a means, and it was very simple: arrange for the seaplane to come. Deborah would be put on board. She would be taken to a hospital in the South. And there, almost certainly, she would be cured.

Of all this she chiefly retained a word that for her held magic: South. She had dreamed of it, just as the people of the South — if she had known this, her astonishment would have been boundless — dream of the North at times. Simply for the pleasure of the journey, to see at last what this famous South was like, she might have made up her mind. But she was too weary now.

"As long as there is life," the pastor continued, "we must hope, we must try to hold on to it."

Deborah then turned her head towards the pastor to examine him in her turn, at length. She had already observed that the white men cling to their lives more than the Eskimos.

"Why?" she asked. "Is it because your lives are better than ours?"

This very simple question seemed to plunge into utter perplexity a man who until then had been able to answer some very perplexing questions.

"It is true," he replied, "that the white men fear dying more than you Eskimos do, but why this is so I would find it hard to say. It is very strange when you think of it, for we haven't learned to live in peace with one another or, for that matter, with ourselves. We haven't learned what is most essential, yet it's true that we are bent upon living longer and longer."

The illogic of this drew from Deborah another rather sad little laugh.

Still, the pastor pointed out a short time later, charity and mutual love had made great progress among the Eskimos since they had accepted the Word.

She knew then that he was going to refer once more to that old story of the grandmother abandoned on the pack-ice — a story he had had from them and had later reworked to his own liking and recalled to them on every occasion; he had even made it the theme of his principal sermon, drawing from it the conclusion that the Eskimos of today were more compassionate than those of past times.

It wasn't that there was no truth in the story as he recounted it, for there was. But he omitted certain illuminating details, for instance that the grandmother had asked to be left on the pack-ice because she could not manage to keep up with the others; she had asked it with her eyes, if not in words. At any rate, this is what her sons had believed they read in her gaze, and why should they have been mistaken?

For several minutes Jonathan, who had returned to the cabin, listened to Deborah thinking aloud and repeating the words of encouragement the pastor had addressed to her before he left.

"The plane still isn't here," said Jonathan. "It may come any minute. How are you?"

She said she was not too bad.

"Good," he said then, and added that he would go and wait with the others.

Next it was Deborah's daughter-in-law, who came from the neighbouring cabin and stopped for a moment on the threshold:

"Do you need anything?"

"No, nothing. Thanks just the same, Mary."

Alone once more, Deborah dragged herself to the door and leaned her weary back against the frame, her face raised towards the sky. Thus she too would see the arrival of this famous seaplane that was coming to save her.

What had eventually decided her was not the love of life as such. Simply to live did not mean at all that much to her. No, what had decided her was the wish to recover the years that were past. To walk for hours after the men, laden with bundles, over the broken soil of the tundra, camp here, hunt there, fish a little farther along, build fires, mend the clothes — it was this good life she wanted to have once more.

"I don't see why you shouldn't recover sufficiently to do what you used to do," the pastor had somewhat imprudently promised her.

She had believed him. Had he not spoken the truth so many times before? For instance, when he said that he loved his children of Iguvik with all his heart. This was certainly true, for to remain here one must either become rich or love; and the pastor had not become rich.

He said also that times were changing and that there was good in all these changes. Today the government took better care of its Eskimo children. It spent a great deal of money on them. And the Eskimos themselves had greatly changed.

"You wouldn't any longer — admit it, Deborah — abandon the Old One to the cold and the night."

This, it was true, might never happen again. In a sense this was precisely what was troubling Deborah. For what would they do now with their poor old people? They would look after them, this was understood, but for what purpose?

She had reached the point now of searching her mind to find imaginary solutions to hypothetical or possible evils, without the least idea, as yet, that it is through this door that sorrow enters a life.

"Good," she had agreed finally. "Get your plane to come."

Just when she had reached that stage in her reflections Jonathan came running.

156

"We can hear a noise behind the clouds. It must be the seaplane."

Immediately afterwards, the noise swelled and drowned out his voice. The dogs joined in. There was an indescribable din, a huge splash in the water, then almost silence again.

The cabin of the seaplane opened. The nurse descended first, a tiny bit of a woman with a decided air.

"Where is the patient?" she asked.

She was holding an electric lamp with a handle as long as a rifle, directing its powerful rays all around. From the night emerged objects which seemed to amaze even the Eskimos, who had never beheld them before in this unusual light: for example, the old washbasin Jonathan had found a little while ago, which had remained stranded ever since on the mossy ground without the arrival or outflow of any water but rain; sometimes, when enough had gathered, Jonathan took it into his head when he passed to wash his hands. There were also hundreds of discarded rusted oildrums; scrap-iron of every sort; and, between two posts, some laundry hung up to dry.

Behind the nurse came the Reverend Hugh Paterson and the pilot. They all walked down the gangway, the young woman in the lead. With white men this wasn't surprising, it was quite often the woman who commanded.

They arrived at the shack. They took Deborah from between skins and old gnawed blankets and thrust aside almost everything that was hers to wrap her in new clean whiteness. They loaded her upon a sort of plank, despite her protests. Only yesterday, after all, she had got up to prepare meals for her household. They ignored everything she said and hoisted her aboard as if she were a parcel. They then climbed in themselves, slammed the doors, and rose into the air. A moment or so later there was no more trace of them.

Below, returned to the fire, the stupefied men did not quite know what to say about all this. At last they went back to wagering among themselves — what else was there to do? She would not return; she would perhaps return.

"Not to my thinking," cut in Isaac. "Not with the wind there is this evening."

II

With daybreak Deborah began to see her country. They had tried to keep her lying down, but she had resisted and been granted permission finally to sit up, and now she could see her strange and enormous country from one end to the other. What had she ever been able to see of it before today, always more or less on the move across the barren expanse? It is true. But in winter, pricked and blinded by the winds and the snow, in summer by the mosquitoes, burdened in all weather up to the forehead with bundles, and always preoccupied with something that must be done — hunting, fishing, meals? Only today, at last, was she discovering it. She found it beautiful, much better even than she would have believed from the scraps she had had till then in her head.

She herself, now that the nurse had washed, combed and tidied her, was far from plain. She possessed, in any case, the lively and readily sparkling eyes of her race; but hers, as well — perhaps because of some melancholy of spirit — lingered upon everything they encountered with loving insistence. What astonished and even fascinated her was the lakes — their often peculiar shapes, their unbelievable profusion. Yet she must have known these little lakes, almost all of them stoppered with no visible communication between them, from wandering and toiling entire days with Jonathan in their maze, packs on back, seeking a dry path, skirting this one, turning back on their steps, searching elsewhere — but always ahead of them, hollowed in the rock, there would be yet another basin brimming with water. Yet nothing, perhaps, had more appeal for her now than this curious region she had always found so difficult.

The movement and stir of the journey had done her good, had revived her, unless it was the medicine the nurse had given her. Nothing escaped her watchful attention. In the desert of water and rock stretching far into the distance, she recognized the fur-trading post where they used to trade, the people of her village, and of other villages too. How small it was, scarcely bigger than a die laid on the empty land, the post that since their birth had dominated almost all their journeys, on foot, by sleigh, by kayak — the goal, so to speak, of their lives. There was just time to catch sight of it beside an immense river flowing towards the ocean, with nothing else around it but clouds, and then you could see it no longer.

As she passed, she had taken time even so to say good-day in her heart to the factor, a widower whose life there alone, cut off from his own kind, seemed even to the Eskimos most pitiable.

In the distance she could distinguish the meeting, seemingly quite gentle, of earth and sea. Often, however, in Deborah's country, these two forces met as enemies, amidst piled-up ice, with blows and tumult, as in a savage struggle.

On the other side were the mountains. She contemplated them at length and saw finally just what they were like — old, round mountains, worn away by time. She saw their colours and their summits, how they ended and how they stood one beside the other along the horizon, like an endless encampment of tents of almost equal height. Perhaps really to see mountains one must have the good fortune, as she had at this moment, to be seated calmly in the clouds.

At this thought Deborah's sick face brightened with something very like a gentle desire to laugh.

At Fort Chimo she had to change planes and take a much larger one departing for the South.

While she was waiting, wrapped in a blanket on a stretcher, left by herself for a moment in the midst of cans and bales of all sorts, she noticed something fascinating on the edge of the runway a short distance away. This was a species of small creatures that bowed with the wind, quivering almost without cessation. Doubtless these were what she had heard called trees. She had heard that they came from the South, in an incalculable number first, and very tall when they set out. It was also said that, little by little, as they climbed towards the cold, their ranks dwindled; the survivors, like exhausted humans who had undergone too severe a test, stooped and sagged and could scarcely hold themselves erect.

Deborah glanced quickly around to make sure no one was there to prevent her doing as she wished. She was still feeling very well, probably because of her good medicine, and she had an irresistible impulse to take a closer look at those tiny trees in a row along the tarmac. With some difficulty she managed to

158

extricate herself from the blanket and began to walk towards the midget birches. She tried to unroll their fragile leaves, whose very touch told her they were living things that left a little of their moisture in the hollow of her hand. Then stealthily, as if she were committing a robbery, she filled her pockets quickly with little leaves. These would be for the children of Iguvik when she returned, so that they would have some notion of the foliage of a tree.

After several hours' flight, when the aircraft came out of the clouds and dipped close to earth, it was the white men's country that she began to discover. Luckily she had seen those first spindly trees; otherwise would she ever have believed her eyes when tall spruce-trees and the first big maples appeared. Even from high in the air it was clear that these were creatures of surprising vitality, with numerous branches, some of them reaching higher than the rooftops. Yet all the houses here seemed at least as big as the factor's imposing residence in Deborah's country. In addition, they had windows on all their surfaces, so that they appeared to be looking from every side at once. There must be firewood here in abundance, since there was no fear of losing heat through all those openings.

Deborah began to wonder why, when their pastor was trying to show them the happiness of a future life, he had not simply described this green land unfolding pleasantly in the sun, all ablaze with the lights cast by windows, roofs, and steeples. Handsome animals seemed also to share in life's sweetness here; they could be seen browsing in very green grass or simply lying in the sun with nothing to do but switch their tails.

As companions among the animals, the Eskimos had only their dogs, and their life now seemed to her very cruel. It was perhaps by contrasting their lean-flanked huskies with these pampered beasts, which even from a distance looked plump and placid, that she began to grasp the impassable distance between the North and the South.

For as long as it was visible, she could not take her eyes from a little white horse that was standing at the end of a meadow beside water — probably in the wind too, to refresh himself. Such a pretty little animal — but for what could anything so slender and delicate be used?

The plane lost more altitude and a great many other details appeared. For instance those walls that cut the land into slices of all shapes and dimensions — what were they?

She was told that they were fences, something in the nature of a marker, a boundary used to separate the fields.

Separate! Cut!

Suddenly she was almost eager to be on her way back to her own people so she could share with them such an extraordinary piece of news. Just think, down there they've actually come to the point of cutting up the land into little pieces surrounded by strands of iron or planks.

"Planks!" they would say. "Planks wasted like that!"

They perhaps wouldn't believe her, the only one of them who had ever gone to the South.

Now the aircraft was searching out a place to touch down, and Deborah's eyes could not capture all the unexpected things offered. At length the nurse came over to find out what so amazed her patient. There was nothing, however, in the least out of the ordinary. It was simply the approaches to a little city like hundreds in the country, with houses surrounded by massed roses and phlox — here a swing where children played at rising and falling, there a swimming pool into which people plunged; finally great beds of multicoloured flowers and also trees, some with fine white bark, others with foliage as pliant as hair. What would Deborah have felt if she could have understood that, to people living farther in the South, the gracious land beneath her was still the North, with its harsh climate and unrewarding soil?

Suddenly she was afraid, however, and overwhelmed by the sense that the earth was coming straight up to meet her. She clung to the seat. Rising into the air had seemed quite natural. Returning to earth was alarming. She closed her eyes. So it had been no use trying to escape from her death in the North. It had come on ahead to wait for her in the South.

At last she opened her eyes and saw to her great astonishment that the plane had landed without her knowledge and was now rolling quietly. Smiling with embarrassment, she glanced quickly at the other passengers, as if to discover whether she had been caught out in her fear.

She felt stiff with emotion and fatigue. The good medicine no longer seemed to be working so well. Once more she was taken in hand, but now she had no strength to resist. And what was the use, anyway? She was beginning to realize that she had been placed in powerful hands and these hands were already so intent upon curing her that now there was no time or thought for anything else.

She was put once more upon a stretcher; then inside a vehicle that set off at great speed. Other vehicles passed or overtook them. Their occupants, as they glanced towards Deborah, seemed to her to look preoccupied and dispirited, and she wondered whether some crushing event had occurred here today.

But when she looked towards the horizon she felt a sudden, very quiet delight. Travelling along the rim of the sky were several small black sleighs on wheels, attached to one another and drawn by a larger sleigh that gave forth smoke, and from time to time brief peculiar cries, as if they were summoning people to leave what they were doing and come on board. Deborah felt a sort of summons from far back in her life, from her first years. All the children in the world are perhaps summoned in this way; in the north by dog sleighs and here, probably, by this other sort of sleigh.

"It's a train," she was told. "Nothing but a train."

She raised her head and let her eyes follow to the curve of the horizon the magic sleigh, which glided without bounds or jolts, as if there was a road for it along the sky that was as smooth as the air. The team seemingly went of its own accord without strokes of the whip on its spine and without any fatigue. Perhaps to Deborah it looked as if the team went only where it wished.

Later, when she was asked whether there were anything that would particularly please her, her eyes would shine and she would invariably answer, "Train. Deborah very much like to ride in train."

III

After a week of examination, sometimes in the dark with the aid of a powerful roaring machine and at other times in floods of blinding light, she received

160

a visit from the government in the person of an interpreter, who sat down unceremoniously beside the fine bed Deborah occupied all by herself in the hospital.

"Well now," said the government, "you have a tumour, a nasty lump that's eating you up inside. It must be removed. Do you give your consent?"

Deborah scarcely hesitated. Always the knife had seemed to her the best way to eradicate evil when that was indicated.

"Cut," she decided, and went off, perfectly calm, almost without fear, to the operation.

Soon afterwards she seemed to be recovering. She was to be seen, in a long dressing-gown lent by the hospital but shod in her mukluks, wandering persistently about the corridors, without asking anything of anyone, until she had found the way out to the garden. It was planted with a few handsome trees. From the windows above they could watch her as she moved with her still slightly shuffling steps along the gravel walks. She approached one of the maples warily, rather as one might a living creature, so as not to startle it. She stretched forth her hand and touched it delicately with her fingertips. It was as if she were trying to tame it. Then she looked at it with delight, listening to it rustle. Finally she put her arm around its trunk and, leaning her cheek there, stood motionless, contemplating the great mass of leaves high in the sky as the wind stirred them gently.

She also made friends among humans. First, among her own people. There was a fair number of them in the hospital, several of whom could once have been considered neighbours, since they all lived only three or four hundred miles from each other; at times, no doubt, by some accident of stopping-point or itinerary — small groups of travellers going towards or away from the trading-post — they had passed very close to one another; perhaps engulfed in blizzards, they had missed one another only by a hair. So their meeting at last today seemed to them a miracle. They visted back and forth continually, always with great signs of delight.

Among the whites she also made friends, and of these several died. When she saw that they were no better off than the Eskimos, that they were attacked by the same bodily afflictions, she felt amazement, first, and later almost as much grief for them as for the sick Eskimos. Then the vague hope she had maintained till then, though half hiding it from herself — that the white men would eventually manage to stretch life out forever — was extinguished once for all. Because she had almost come to believe this for a moment, she now found the truth harder to bear.

Happily she still had two excellent distractions to help her pass the time. First the shower. From the moment she first discovered this seemingly inexhaustible fountain of hot water and soap, it became with her a sort of passion. Perhaps this passion always existed in a latent state, frustrated for centuries among all those of her race. For close to a half-hour at a time, without noticing that people came now and then to try to turn the door-knob, Deborah would soap and then rinse the magnificant dark hair that draped her like a shawl to her knees.

When she returned to her bed, she would brush and brush it with the idea,

161

perhaps, of making it shine like the gentle glow of the seal-oil lamp in the little snow-house of old, the memory of which had suddenly returned to her. After this, she would go back and wash her hair again.

"You'll end by rubbing so hard it will fall out," the Sister reprimanded her gently.

Deborah's little smile was at once timid and a shade mischievous. For it was the poor Sister, actually, who was rather short of hair.

Her second and always equally unbridled passion was for smoking cigarettes. When she was not busy tending her hair, she was almost always to be found squatting in the middle of her bed as if it were the ground, shrouded in heavy smoke. Her expression would then be a little less melancholy. It was as if all this smoke managed to obscure, at least slightly, the thought that was now trying to present itself at every instant to Deborah's mind. After the manner of her people, she had thus managed to take from civilization two things that seemed almost incompatible: soap for cleanliness and clarity, tobacco to blur the thoughts and soil the fingers.

The Sister reproached her one day. This was a nun who had been delegated for a long time to visit the sick Eskimos. She knew their language.

"Really, Deborah, I don't understand you."

Deborah's big astonished eyes seemed to say: Well, do I understand you? But no matter, I love you anyway.

"On the one hand," the Sister continued, "you are cleanliness itself, forever washing yourself. On the other hand, you scatter cigarette ashes almost everywhere, you dirty everything. You're like an old bush camp all by yourself. What can this do for you, all this smoke?"

It didn't perhaps do very much. Just gave her some little fragments of a dream, pictures she had believed lost. But still it brought the great savage and distant North to some extent into this skimpy room. That was what it did.

One day, through the smoke, Deborah managed to recover almost everything she had ever possessed. The camp appeared before her half-closed eyes. It was all there, down to the wash-basin Jonathan had salvaged after the departure of the troops, which might be full of water at this very moment, down to her washing that no one perhaps had thought of bringing in. She saw the narrow walkway joined to the empty oil-drums, rising and falling with the slight movements of the water, like a creature that breathed; she saw her shack, its door wide open, and all around the pure and naked sky. She felt upon her cheeks what might have been drops of lukewarm rain. She put her fingers to her face and gathered a tear, which she examined with amazement and a trace of shame. What was this now? Except for those drawn from her by the extreme cold or, in summer, by the smoke from the fires lit to drive away the mosquitoes, she had no recollection of ever shedding tears.

In her surprise, the tears for a moment stopped flowing. Then they resumed in a storm. So that she would at least not be seen or heard, she hid herself under the sheet.

Quite often after that, she was found in a motionless little round heap in the middle of the bed.

The Sister began almost to plead with her, "Smoke, Deborah, or go and wash your lovely hair."

But this did not mean very much to her now. However, they discovered her from time to time eating oranges, with tears streaming down her face. She had thought of saving those she was given in her drawer or under the mattress to take to the children of her country. Until the day when the smell warned the nurse.

"Now look, Deborah. Oranges don't keep indefinitely."

"Ah!"

Her face showed that this was a very cruel disappointment. So there was no hope of trying to take them back with her. Well in that case, she would do her best to eat them. However, her heart was not in it. She looked as if she were eating the most bitter of fruit. Many of the fine good things of the South lost interest in her eyes as soon as she learned they could not bear the journey. It was as if she were now refusing to become attached to them. Perhaps she even held it obscurely against them.

From then on she grew sadder from day to day. The idea seemed to have come to her that like the oranges, like the tender leaves on the branches of the trees, like the flowers plucked from the garden, she herself would not last long enough to make the journey back to her country.

She stopped washing herself. She no longer sat leafing through magazines while giving the impression that she was reading the text here and there. She gave up everything except the little cloud of blue smoke in which she enclosed herself more often than ever now, as if inside a precarious wall that defined her modest place in the world.

Then one day the government came back to her again and said, "So you're as lonesome as that! Come, this isn't reasonable, Deborah."

So that's what it was — lonesomeness. She had needed to be surrounded with attention, showered with oranges and visits, loved as never before and treated like a queen to know lonesomeness. What a curious illness it was!

"Yes, it must be that I'm lonesome," Deborah admitted.

"You think about your own country all the time, eh?"

"Yes, I do."

"Well, in that case," said the government, "we're going to let you go. Of course it would have been better for you to stay with us a little longer. Your illness may return. We don't know yet whether it's been rooted out completely and for good. But if you're dying of lonesomeness . . . "

So she could go if she wanted to. She wouldn't be kept against her will. She had permission? She was free?

Tears flowed from the dark eyes, and this was stranger than ever. For now they did not come from the pain of lonesomeness but because this pain had been removed.

IV

Once more she saw the tender aspect of the world with its trees, all laden these days with gold, and its pleasant valleys in which rivers, winding from one island of greenness to another, seemed to be visiting each in turn.

But she loved the earth beneath her more when there were no longer any trees. Most appealing of all to her were the arid knolls and bald hummocks of the naked land, between which gleamed the icy water of solitary lakes. So many, many lakes, and so remote as well that very few of them have been given a name. Her eyes devoured this singular network of water and rock where she had so often roamed in former days with Jonathan, packs on her back, sometimes with a child in her womb, her face so bathed in sweat that she could scarcely see before her, and now this period of her life seemed to have been of moving tenderness. So one had to go very far in order to judge one's life, and it was perhaps on its most arduous days that the best memories were being prepared.

She remained seated this time, too, to make the crossing of the sky, though she could no longer manage to hold her head erect.

For rather a long time the land disappeared from their sight. Even Deborah closed her eyes and dozed a little, while they were in the clouds, and there was nothing to look at but their masses of snow — very soft snow, it was true, but a little too similar to everlasting pack-ice.

Suddenly she sat up. Her eyes, so heavy with fatigue, blazed with interest. Below, once again, was the big river flowing towards the sea, with the little fur-trading post beside it, alone in the infinite barren land.

Now she was nearly home. Almost at once, in fact, she recognized the place in the world which belonged to her and to which she belonged; and finding it again, returning from so far away, must have seemed to her a sort of miracle, for the worn face, so long spiritless, was suddenly radiant.

The seaplane was about to touch water. The various objects of the camp grew closer. There was the wash-basin, which was beginning to fill with moss and rust; there were the discarded oil-drums and, where her washing had been, some skins that had been cleaned and stretched to dry in the sun. And there was Jonathan.

He was standing beside the lake, in almost the same spot where he had watched her leave and in almost the same attitude. With the years he had become a heavy little man, almost as broad as he was high. His head thrown up and his neck drawn back between his shoulders, he followed the movement of the seaplane in the bright sun. Deborah could even distinguish the thick fringe of his hair and the handsome dark colour of his skin. She herself had had time in the hospital to become as pale and ugly as a white woman. At one point he raised his hands above his head. Perhaps in greeting. But it looked, quite truthfully, as if he were saying to the aircraft, "Hi there, be a bit careful." Then, without waiting any longer, he went into the cabin. This was perhaps to tidy up a little, at least to conceal the worst of the litter that had lain strewn about for weeks. Even though this meant that they had to go and fetch him to help carry Deborah, at least to lend a hand at the reception of his own wife. And not until then did he let it be clear that he knew who was arriving.

After the event, at least for some time, he seemed fairly pleased to see her back. He even went one day to a lake that was very hard to reach, eight knolls away, and caught her a fine fish with delicate flesh. She scarcely touched it; everything disagreed with her nowadays. He spent some time tinkering with the two automobile seats she used as a bed and finally attached them together so they no longer parted at every moment, leaving a space into which she slipped.

But when he saw that despite all this attention Deborah was still without appetite, nauseated by odours, as if she no longer knew what an Eskimo house was like — hadn't she gone as far as to ask him to remove some animal guts that were only a week old? — and that she lay stretched out in her corner just as before, he lost patience and went to complain to the other men.

"She shouldn't have gone," he said and then, in the same level tone, "She shouldn't have come back either."

"That was my thinking, as I told you," Isaac reminded him. "When it's time to die, one doesn't make all this fuss. One dies."

But Jonathan was irritable these days, and although the old man had essentially just supported his own argument, he turned on him suddenly.

"You're a fine one to talk, old man," he said. "Here you are, seventy years old, fat and well fed. What do you do to deserve that? Nothing. You live on the government with your pension. You have nothing to do but you have all you need: your lard, your flour, your tobacco, your sugar, your tea. . . ."

"It's not the same thing," Isaac defended himself. "I at least still have my strength. I don't need anyone to help me walk or do what I want to do."

"Even so, you don't do anything either from morning till night but you still have your lard, your flour, your sugar. . . ."

More than anything, perhaps, the tedium of the enumeration wearied Isaac. He departed, grumbling, to seek refuge in the shack. It was impossible to have peace anywhere now. He sat down in a corner on a wooden crate that bore on one side the warning, *This side up*, and on the other, *Haut*. He looked all around him for something with which to busy himself. It was true that for quite some time he had done nothing. But what was there to do? Hunt? There were no more caribou to speak of. Fish then, perhaps? Yes, but from the moment one had the old-age pension and was no longer pressed from behind, what was the use of all that trouble? Something broke in man, perhaps, when he received without giving as much in return. The perplexed old man, sitting on his crate, looked as if he were glimpsing a little of the misfortune that had befallen the population of the North, not long ago so industrious. He shook himself and picked up an old fishing net which he began to examine to see whether it was worth the trouble of mending.

He caught the eye of his daughter, who had been lying in her own little corner watching him think.

To tell the truth, he scarcely recognized her since she had been in the South. This was not only because she had grown thin and pale. Even the expression of her face seemed to him completely changed. One might have said that she no longer thought quite as they did now, or even that they could not quite guess what she was thinking.

"Do you want me to tell you?" he said. "I should go off of my own accord and put myself on the pack-ice as we put the Old One in the good time."

He mused a little.

"It was a beautiful cold night. There were spirits in white tunics dancing and circling all around the sky."

He was becoming more and more fond of remembering that time.

"Since the wind was from the right direction," he said, "the ice must have gone very quickly. It certainly didn't take long. The ice broke loose with a little snap. Then off with it! It was far away."

In contrast to what he had always said until now, that the Old One had totally disappeared, he now maintained that she must have been preserved by the frost.

"The cold is good and compassionate," he claimed.

And he began to describe the Old One as he now pictured her, intact, seated in the centre of her column of ice — a tiny white island on the raging black sea — turning and turning continually at the end of the world in the last free waters of the earth, just like those satellites of today, those curious objects, he said, that they were going to hang high in the air so that they would never come down again.

"That's what she has become," he said dreamily. "I'd stake my life on it. A satellite."

He lowered his gaze once more to Deborah's emaciated face, which was marked with suffering and anxieties of the spirit that one did not often find in the old days on Eskimo faces. But it was true that in the old days one did not often see Eskimos grown thin and pale. They had died before that.

Isaac grumbled on, "Ha, that's all nonsense! Eh, my poor Deborah? What do you think? When do we show more kindness to people? When we keep them from dying? Or when we help them just a little? . . . Eh?"

V

Then, with the first snows, the Reverend Hugh Paterson chanced to pass that way again on his early-winter rounds. The voices of the dogs were heard resounding sharply in air that had been scoured by the already icy winds. A few moments later in came the pastor, a long lean silhouette beside the Eskimos, most of them round and short. He seated himself on the corner of one of the old automobile seats that weather and perhaps ocean-salt had pitted. He had often wondered how they could have reached this place, by what curious journey, who or what could have brought them — the sea, a plane, or perhaps some old trapper on his back?

"So, my poor Deborah," he said, "you're no better?"

He met the gaze of soft and sorrowful eyes that seemed to reproach him for preventing death from striking in its hour.

Dying, Deborah appeared to be thinking, is easier the first time than the second. Who knows, it may even become harder the longer it is deferred.

Sad enough to make one weep and yet in their depths still a little mocking, doubtless from force of habit, Deborah's great dark eyes seemed to appeal for understanding across the silence.

And then, as if he understood perfectly, he stretched out his hands to join Deborah's together, and then draw them towards him, keeping them pressed between his own.

"My poor child, all you have learned, loved, and understood in these few more months you've lived is yours forever. Nothing can take any of it from you. Even a single additional step in life and you are enhanced forever."

The dark eyes reflected. They seemed to grasp these fine words and take them into herself to keep for the day when she might make something from them. Does one ever know with thoughts?

"Still, you ought to have stayed in the hospital where you'd have been better looked after," he said without logic but with tender affection.

167

"Why want so much to look after?" she asked and, powerless to understand, sank into a sort of silent misery.

It was this that disconcerted her most among civilized people, this terrible determination, even when death was close and certain, to defy it still. This absurd preference also, when they must finally die, that it should be in a bed.

"Dear Mr. Paterson," she said, "Deborah much prefers for dying to be here than there."

"Who's talking about dying?" Once again he tried to deceive her with false lightness.

Then he remembered to give her the little present of drugs that the government had entrusted to him for her. The government was very concerned about her, he said, and would be anxious to hear whether the operation had been a complete success.

"Say thank you," she said simply.

Finally the pastor went on to point out that death was not an evil. In fact it was death now, and no longer life, that he described as the best friend of human beings. It was the deliverance from all our ills. At last one was free. We departed with shoulders, hands, and hearts finally unburdened.

These were fine things to hear, though seemingly quite the opposite to what he had said when he had been encouraging Deborah to live. They were none the less convincing in their fashion. Even Deborah knew now that one ought to say those things that best fitted the affair of the moment, otherwise there would be nothing left to say, it would no longer be worth the trouble of opening one's mouth, and no one would ever speak again.

"Deborah would like to be free right away," she said.

"Deborah will perhaps not have very long to wait," he replied tenderly, as if this were his wish for her. "A few steps more, a little patience still, and she will be in complete happiness."

Happiness. Another incomprehensible expression. If happiness simply lived somewhere on earth, where was that? When she arrived in the South, she had been able to believe it might be here in the midst of favour and wealth. But soon she had come to feel that there was even less happiness here than in her home. Now, she never stopped puzzling about this.

"When all's said and done," the pastor was forced to admit, "we can encounter happiness in all its radiance only on the other side of life."

She agreed wholeheartedly, her eyes eager, as if hungry for the unknown. And for what else could she hunger now?

"On that side," he said again, "all that has been obscure to us will be understood. Clarity will reign. No one will lack again for anything."

VI

The nights are long in that latitude, as winter approaches, even for those who sleep well. For Deborah they were interminable. Her short life, which had been devoured by needs that left little time for thinking, was coming to an end, paradoxically, in an infinity of time in which there was nothing else to do. So it seemed as if her short life were being prolonged for some reason that Deborah was trying to comprehend.

She lay resting on the automobile seats while the others around her, wrapped in whatever old blankets they still possessed, slept directly on the floor.

The air in the hut was fouled, both by the unpleasant odour her diseased body was beginning to give off and by the Eskimos' own odour of oil and fish, which she now found sickening. With the coming of winter they had reached the point, in this rickety shack which the fierce cold obliged them to keep tightly closed, of restricting one another cruelly. One could cough, spit, turn over, and everyone would stir, cough, turn over.

Deborah had taken it into her head to try to picture that place after death, so different from life, where no one would lack again for anything. She needed all her confidence in the pastor to have faith in such words. For at the present time she lacked almost everything. What she most lacked, moreover, was all she had so recently learned to know, those comforts of life in the South: hot water and soap, the clear and abundant light, always ready to flash on, of electricity; a little space all to herself; but especially, perhaps, that sort of friendliness — or show of friendliness — between people in the South. She had thought this uncalled-for, but now, even though still not entirely convinced it was real affection, she would have liked to feel its warmth around her.

As she now saw it, the better life became, the more needs it satisfied and the more new needs arose. So that it seemed to her quite unlikely that there ever could be a life or a place where one would lack for nothing.

The others around her too were, on her account, in want and deprivation, Isaac of the warm blanket he had "lent" her — just for a time and not for the whole winter — and Jonathan of love, for to Deborah love had become torture.

The nights therefore were increasingly long and uncomfortable for them all.

Outside the complaining of the dogs would diminish for a moment only to swell again. In the old days she had not heard this. It existed, inevitable as the frost that overtakes the water or as the click of the trap on a prey. It existed, that was all. Now she heard it continually and the sound harassed her. Couldn't they give the dogs just once enough to eat? Jonathan looked at her sidelong. Was she crazy? Satisfy the dogs? You might as well try to satisfy the animals of the tundra, the whole of famished creation.

She came close to suffocating one evening in the tightly closed cabin. Who would have believed that in this frigid land, so full of wind, she would find herself wishing, more than anything in the world, for a single breath of fresh air. It was in the South too, with its wide-open windows, that she had acquired this taste for the movement of air in the house. If only, this night again, they could have left the door open just a crack. But the others were freezing. While she was burning.

More and more, also, she was impatient to be on that other side of life where no one would be sad any more. And for what else now could she be impatient?

She threw off her blankets, then took the warmest and spread it over old Isaac, who lay curled up on the floor. He had coughed a good deal latterly, though without yet making up his mind to ask her for his blanket. She put on her mukluks and pulled open the door. The cutting air seemed to strengthen her.

The night was clear and cold. Snow had fallen. In this fresh but shallow snow Deborah left very clean imprints of her steps.

So it was that they were able to follow next day the journey she had made.

She had first struggled painfully to the top of the nearest knoll. To hear the beating of the surf? Or because she remembered climbing up there often with other children to try to glimpse the ocean, which was not very far away? Whatever her reason had been, she went on. To the next hummock, then to yet another. Moving from knoll to knoll, she finally reached the pack-ice.

There before her eyes, probably revealed to her in the pale glimmer from the snow, lay the most broken terrain on earth, an uneven buckling expanse of ice-floes, roughly hinged to one another.

No doubt the wind on that tormented coast had been blowing with utmost fury.

Yet she had entered it. Here and there, on the crust of snow a few more tracks could be picked out. They showed that Deborah had fallen on several occasions and that at last she had crawled more than she had walked. The tracks continued a little farther. They were to be found right to the edge of the open water.

When they examined the contour of the pack-ice from the ocean side, they saw that a portion of it had recently broken loose.

But though they peered long and searchingly through the dark and tumultuous landscape of black water, it was useless; they could distinguish nothing within it that bore any relation to a human shape. Or hear anything but the shrieking of the wind.

ABOUT THE LINES

1 a. Summarize in point form the old Eskimo men's argument against fighting death.
   b. Summarize in point form the Pastor's argument for struggling for prolonged life.
   c. Write a dramatic monologue (based on the points summarized above) on the subject of death in the voice of either Isaac or the Pastor. Prepare a polished performance and share it with a group who have read the story.

2 List all the new experiences involving both nature and technology that fascinated Deborah on her trip South. For each experience, write a statement that captures Deborah's reaction to it.

3 Complete the following unfinished sentences:
   a. Deborah agreed to the operation because . . .
   b. After her surgery, Deborah made friends with . . .
   c. Deborah's two great disappointments in the white culture and its ways were . . .
   d. Deborah's return to the North was necessary because . . .

4 Name the two distractions that gave Deborah great pleasure while she was in the hospital. In Deborah's voice, explain to fellow Eskimos why these two seemingly opposite activities were so comforting and delightful for you.

5 Although Deborah's "worn face so long spiritless was suddenly radiant" when she returned to her home, her happiness did not last too long. Imagine that you are Deborah, and tell a visitor from the South whom you trust about the difficulties of readjusting to life in the North. Mention the things that you can no longer tolerate about your former life and the things that you miss about the South.

6 When the Pastor realizes that his promise of prolonged life for Deborah is not to be kept, he tries to prepare her for death. In her own way, Deborah agrees that "the other side of life" is where happiness is to be found. Working with a partner, script and dramatize a conversation between Deborah and the Pastor on this subject.

7 Imagine that you are Isaac, and explain to a child in your community where Deborah has gone to at the end of the story. You may write the account and/or present it orally to a small group.

BETWEEN THE LINES

1 In the poem "Progress" on page 287, the narrator is faced with a choice between the old way and the new way. A similar choice is presented in "The Satellites." After discussing both pieces with a small group, write a comparison of the choice made by the narrator in "Progress" and the choice Deborah makes. Share your work with your partners and revise it if new points are raised in the discussion.

2 Several objects in this story represent aspects of the white and the Eskimo culture. Look up the definition of "symbol" in the glossary (see p. 356), and discuss in a small group what the following items could stand for:
  a. the trees of the South;
  b. the open windows of the buildings in the South;
  c. the plane, trains, and X-ray machine;
  d. the hospital soap;
  e. the smoke of Deborah's cigarettes;
  f. the discarded oil drums;
  g. the wash basin filled with moss and rust;
  h. the car seats;
  i. Isaac's blanket;
  j. the howling dogs;
  k. the ice floe.
Write a statement explaining each symbol's relevance to the story. You may wish to design a poster with illustrations of the items and a caption commenting on each one.

3 In his frustration over Deborah's condition, Jonathan chastised Isaac for living a useless life. In a paragraph, explain why it is ironic (see p. 352) that Deborah chose the path of the "Old One" in her father's story.

4 "Except for those drawn from her by the extreme cold, or in summer, by the smoke from the fires lit to drive away the mosquitoes, she had no recollection of ever shedding tears." Discuss in a small group why Deborah's tears flowed so readily in the hospital.

BEYOND THE LINES

1 Read the poem "The Forsaken" on page 136. The old woman in this poem greets her death with tranquillity because she has never stepped outside her own culture. Deborah, on the other hand, is trapped between two ways of life and seeks solace in an old solution. Write an interior monologue that reflects Deborah's thoughts as she floats away on her "satellite."

2 The news of Deborah's death has spread through the Eskimo community and has also reached those who knew her in the South. Create a conversation between the following people when they learn of Deborah's choice (choose any two):
a. the nurse on the plane and the Sister who cared for Deborah in the hospital;
b. Jonathan and Isaac;
c. two of Deborah's Eskimo friends in the hospital;
d. two of Deborah's white friends in the hospital;
e. an Eskimo and a white patient who knew her in the hospital.

3 Write a short story with the following elements:
a. moving from a sheltered, rural community to an urban, technologically developed environment;
b. a choice between staying or returning home.
Share your story with the class.

4 Working with your partners, write the eulogy for Deborah that Pastor Peterson would have delivered to his Eskimo congregation.

ONE EVENING

David Helwig

To venture forth and break the pattern

Miss Machry looked in the mirror, straightened her dress and then sat down in a chair beside the open window and waved the old Japanese fan. She succeeded in washing away only a little of the oppressive heat. As she looked out the window and up the street, the leaves waved in the late sunlight. There was no sign of him yet. She went back to her fanning.

It was an exacting task, for only by the gentlest of handling could she preserve the fan. It had been her mother's many years ago and treasured both as useful and exotic, an object to be placed on any table that needed a touch of colour and life. And after her mother was taken she had used it to fan her father as he rocked into his dotage on the front porch of the house. There was a twinge of pain as she thought of that awful summer, the hottest in years, with the air dry and dusty in the daytime and at night heavy with the scent of flowers. In those last months her father lay on the porch silent and paralysed, a wreck in the painful sun. For hours she sat and fanned him and spoke to him and waited. Then, almost with the first cool breeze of fall, he died and left her, relieved and alone.

She stood up once more and looked in the mirror. Was the lipstick too bright? she wondered. Just in case, she blotted it once more and checked again before she threw the kleenex in the wastebasket. Now it was all right. With her hand she touched her hair. It had been a rush to get to the hairdresser's in time after work and then come home and change. She should have eaten a decent meal, she supposed, but she was in such a hurry and she really wasn't hungry. Perhaps a bit of bread and cheese right now. But she decided against it. Once more she checked her dress, spinning around to make sure her slip didn't show. The fan was still in her hand. When she had opened it again, she waved it gingerly. As she fanned, she looked up the street, which was growing dark in the shadow of the trees. It was silent and empty and for a moment she worried. He must have been kept late at the store. The boys were always ducking out early and leaving him to clean up. He was too kindhearted to complain to them about it. The thought of the boys made her feel personally injured. As if they were the only ones who were in a hurry to get out and go someplace. She hoped

173

they would see them tonight. Restraining the urge to do a little dance step across the floor, she sat down in her chair. With a nailfile she carefully repeated her simple manicure. She decided that perhaps she was a little hungry. She set down the nailfile, looked at her dim reflection in the mirror for the last time and went downstairs.

In the kitchen, she opened the icebox and took out a block of cheese, cut off a little and put it away. She ate it, along with a piece of unbuttered bread from the end of the loaf in the breadbox. The glass of water with which she washed it down tasted of chlorine. Cheese was binding she knew and not at all good for anyone who was troubled with constipation, but it was so simple. Besides, it seemed almost immodest to admit that she was troubled that way. She checked her watch; he certainly was a little behind time.

Outside the window, the birds were calling through the hot air. So were the crickets and locusts. The whole garden, on the verge of darkness, was full of peace and stillness. She thought of the man who was on his way to her through the silent town and the dark streets and she knelt in front of the open window.

"Lord," she said, and her voice sounded strange in the empty room, "make me worthy of such happiness." For a few moments she knelt there with her eyes tight shut, not praying really, just listening to the sounds from the garden. Then she heard the sound of a car coming down the street, and she quickly got to her feet. It went on past the house. Miss Machry stood still, a little ashamed of her excitement and hurry. But there was no use kneeling again, and her knee-joints were a little sore anyway from the unaccustomed bending. Tomorrow in church she would be especially attentive to her prayers and make it up. She wondered vaguely whether they would be too late for her to make the early service. It would do no harm to go at eleven o'clock after such a special occasion, but it must not become a habit. Lost in her speculation, she was almost unaware of a car stopping in front of the house. When the knock on the door came, she suddenly realized that he was there, and for a moment she was panic-stricken. But she composed herself, brushed and straightened her dress and went to answer the door.

"Good evening, Edith," he said as he stood in the doorway. Miss Machry restrained an urge to look modestly away. Instead she looked straight into his eyes and smiled.

"Good evening, Jim." She almost made the mistake of asking whether the boys had kept him late at the store, but she caught herself in time and said only "Isn't it warm?"

"Yes," he replied. "I'm afraid that I'm a little late. The boys at the store skipped out early again." Miss Machry was glad he had mentioned it first. With a start she realized that they were still standing at the door.

"Do come in for a minute," she said. He nodded and entered. Now that they were in, what were they to do? She took his hat, temporized. There was no reason for her to be so excited. She had not been like this since the first time he had taken her out. But, after all, tonight was special.

"Would you like a glass of wine, Jim. Or a little something to eat? Perhaps some bread and cheese?" She almost wondered whether he was ever troubled with . . . but she caught herself and suppressed the thought before it had a chance to form.

174

"I wouldn't mind a glass of wine." She moved toward her bottle of ceremonial sherry with its accompanying wine-glasses.

"I don't know how you stand those boys," she said. "Children nowadays are so lazy." That was a regrettable thing to have said. It made her sound old.

"All children are much the same, I guess," he answered tolerantly. "I doubt if I was much better at that age." His answer put them on the same basis as far as age was concerned. He went on, "Whenever I feel like criticizing other people's children, I just ask myself whether I could have raised them any better if they'd been mine. I doubt if I could." The spectre of his dead wife was in the room for a few seconds then. She had been a sickly woman who was unable to give her husband children and died very young. Miss Machry poured the sherry, a glass for him and a taste for herself. She tried to decide whether it was at all improper to wonder if she could bear him children, and suddenly she was aware of her stomach pressing the edge of the sideboard. She stood a little straighter. When she handed Jim his glass, he smiled and asked what they should toast. She hesitated, then was seized by a moment of recklessness. Raising her glass, she said:

"To our adventure tonight."

"May it be a proper beginning," he continued. They touched glasses and drank solemnly. Miss Machry tried to make her wine last as long as his, but it was so little that it was soon gone. The glass was awkward in her hand. She set it down and moved toward the stairs.

"I'll be down in a minute," she said, "and we can leave." As she reached the stairs, she wondered painfully if he thought she was going to the toilet after her sudden rush to leave. It was too late to do much about her embarrassment. She turned back toward him.

"I think I'd better close the windows. It smells a little like rain." All she really wanted to do was to check once more, see that she looked alright. When she reached the head of the stairs, she turned on the bedroom light and closed the windows, noisily so that he could hear. Then she went to the mirror and checked once again. She looked at the dress on her thin figure, her hands, her pale, ashen face with the hair a little grey on the temples. Everything seemed in order, so she shut off the light and went downstairs. He had finished his wine and rose as she came into the room.

"All set?" he asked.

"Yes," she said, "all ready." They went toward the door. Mentally Miss Machry checked to see that she hadn't left any lights on upstairs. She would leave the light in the hall burning so the house didn't look too empty. When they reached the car, he helped her in. Then they drove off down the street, leaving a cloud of dust. They sat close together on the seat of the car as they drove through town, feeling like conspirators. Their courtship was a carefully guarded secret, which up till now they had chosen to reveal to no one. Jim checked his watch.

"Seems a little early yet. We should wait awhile till the crowd gets there. Maybe we'll drive around for a while first."

"All right, Jim," she replied and rested her hand on his arm for a moment.

They drove out into the country along highways and back roads. For awhile they parked by the lake and watched the moon on the water glittering and moving with the ripples. In silence they watched. Once Jim turned to her and put his hand gently on her hair and took it away again. She thrilled with pleasure, but she hoped he hadn't mussed her hair. He checked his watch.

"We'll go now." Miss Machry nodded. They drove back to town and up to the main street. As they passed along through the strange shadows thrown by the leaves and the streetlights, their excitement mounted. They neared the park and began to run into heavy traffic. All the young people in town were out at the dance. Miss Machry had a bad moment as they parked the car. She grew dizzy and thought she was going to be ill. But then they got out and Jim took her hand and it was all right again. As they walked through the park, they could hear a saxophone wailing in its throat on the bandstand. They could see the young people, young men, soldiers and girls standing against the trees in the light. All the single boys and girls and a few of the young married couples came here on summer Saturday nights. The boys from Jim's store would probably be here; the thought gave Miss Machry some satisfaction and she held his hand a little more tightly. Then they emerged into the light and walked up to the counter. Grace, the woman at the counter who sold the tickets and refreshments, looked at them and tried to hide her surprise. Several of the young men and girls stopped their conversations and looked around.

"Two tickets please, Grace," Jim said in a strong, confident voice. Miss Machry was shivering with fear. They took their tickets and walked into the dancehall. Fantastic couples shuffled under the weird yellow light. Miss Machry thought she could see a tremor run through the crowd when they walked in. But she decided it was an illusion. However, there were a few of the youngsters who turned and looked at them standing there hand in hand, a little at a loss for something to say or do. She was filled with dismay and almost disgust as she watched the boy who danced in front of them sliding his hand across the back of the girl he was dancing with. Then Jim turned to her and took hold of her and they began to dance.

The music was slower than she found comfortable, and they danced awkwardly. She felt like part of an archaic monster as they turned across the floor. Some of the youngsters stood and watched their ungainly progress. Miss Machry's face burned as she thought of the stories they would tell their parents. Then she looked at Jim, his long, tired face and greying hair looking strange in the yellow light, and she didn't care any more.

She was afraid the dancing was making her sweat. There was a dampness along her back where Jim's hand was resting. The night seemed to be growing hotter and hotter. Over Jim's shoulder, she saw one of the boys from the store approaching. When he got a little closer he spoke.

"Hello, Mr. Cameron."

Jim was startled by the sudden voice, stopped and looked back over his shoulder. Miss Machry couldn't stop turning and lost her balance. The room whirled around as she fell over Jim's leg, tripping him and throwing him down. There was a sudden pain in her hip when she hit the floor. She heard herself give an ugly grunt. Her dress was above her knees, and she was trying to hold it down when Jim fell on top of her, hurting her hip again. She saw a line of the legs of people who stood around looking on.

"Golly, Mr. Cameron, I'm sorry," the boy from the store was saying. "I didn't mean to do that." He helped Jim up. His girl knelt down beside Miss Machry. She was a stranger. Miss Machry wished she would go away.

"I'm so sorry, Mrs. Cameron," she said. Miss Machry winced. "Are you all right?" She helped her up. Miss Machry was afraid she was going to cry or be sick.

"Are you all right, Edith?" Jim said.

"Yes," she said, "but perhaps we'd better go now." They moved toward the door. He didn't speak again. She was afraid that he was angry; she wished they hadn't come.

"I'm very sorry, Mr. Cameron." The boy was still there. Why didn't he go away? It was awful enough without his sympathy.

"That's all right, Jake," Jim answered. "It was my own fault."

Miss Machry was thinking ahead to tomorrow and the stares of the people in church. Perhaps she would stay away. When they arrived outside, it seemed strange that the world hadn't changed. A dog ran up the street and barked as he passed. Old Mr. and Mrs. Gordon still sat on their porch and tried to rock away the heat. Miss Machry reached over to take Jim's arm. She missed and stumbled. He caught her and held her by the elbow. Without a word, the two of them walked to the car and got in. As they drove home, Miss Machry could feel the pain in her hip where she had fallen. She had to sit toward one side. She was angry with herself for spoiling everything. Perhaps Jim was angry with her. The car stopped in front of her house. They got out and walked to the door. As they stood there in silence, Jim smiled down at her.

"I'm glad we did it," he said. Then he put his arms around her and kissed her on her lips that were dry and cracked from the heat. His thin arms were strong around her and she closed her eyes tight. He held her for a long time, until she became conscious of sweat on her back and the pain from her hip. Then he loosened his arms and she opened her eyes. He looked down at her, kissed her lightly once again and said goodnight. She watched him go down the walk. He climbed into his car. As she went into the house, she could hear him driving away. She went up the stairs to her bedroom. Strangely, it was just the way she had left it. Bed, dresser, curtains, her mother's fan. She walked to the window and looked out. The town was silent under the shadow of the great old trees. There was no wind, no motion except a moth which fluttered around the streetlight, struggling to reach the bulb. As Miss Machry watched it, tears were running down her face. But underneath she was smiling and smiling.

ABOUT THE LINES

1 Write a two- or three-paragraph summary of this story and have a partner check to make sure that you have included all the important details. Create a cloze exercise by deleting every eighth word from your summary. Ask someone who has also read the story to complete your cloze task. Discuss any difficulties they may have in filling in the blanks and see if you can rephrase your sentences to make them clearer.

2 Write three questions you would ask someone if you wanted to know if they understood Miss Machry's background, attitudes, and anxieties. Ask a partner to answer the questions and rewrite them if he/she finds them unclear.

3 "But, after all, tonight was special." In a brief note, explain how this particular evening would change Miss Machry's life.

BETWEEN THE LINES

1 Miss Machry seems to be very easily embarrassed or distressed. List three incidents or situations in the story in which she feels uncomfortable. Choose the one that you think upset her the most and write a brief analysis of why she felt that way.

2 Write a description of the impression you have of Jim as a person. You may wish to comment on the effect he seems to have on Miss Machry.

3 Complete the following sentences:
   a. Miss Machry was relieved when her father died because . . .
   b. The fact that the boys from Jim's store would see them together pleased Miss Machry because . . .
   c. At the end of her evening out it seemed strange to Miss Machry "that the world hadn't changed." Somehow she felt . . .

4 Miss Machry's life seems defined by the things around her. Name five objects in her house and indicate what they tell us about her.

BEYOND THE LINES

1 Imagine that you are Jim and write a letter to an out-of-town relative or friend announcing your plans to marry Miss Machry. Describe why you love her and how you think you can make her happy.

or

Imagine that you are Miss Machry and write an entry in your diary reflecting on your hopes for the future.

2 Script and dramatize a conversation between two boys who work at Jim's store when they realize Mr. Cameron and Miss Machry are in love.

3 Write an engagement announcement for the town newspaper, formally declaring Jim and Miss Machry as a couple. Then write a report for the same newspaper, covering their wedding a year later.

THE LITTLE SHOP ON MAIN STREET

Ernest Hillen

In a few places, you can still run out to the corner store.

Everybody in Knox Variety hears them — the magazine readers, greeting-card browsers, pop drinkers, the woman turning the rack with panty hose, the people lined up at the post office in back.

"They're stale, Mr. Knox," says one and holds high an open bag of potato chips.

"Stale, Mr. Knox," echoes her friend helpfully.

Their voices penetrate to every corner of the cluttered little store. Only Bill Knox, right in front of them, doesn't seem to hear. The portly, 68-year-old proprietor is taking stock of his cigarettes, adding up how many packs are left of a certain brand. If he stops now, he'll lose track.

"Mr. Knox?"

Stocktaking is a never-ending chore in this miniature Eaton's. Knox, his wife, Mary, and their eldest daughter, Diane Malinsky, who run the store in shifts, are at it continually. Magazines take four hours a week, toys and drugs an hour, soft drinks one-and-a-half hours; cigarettes five hours. Cigarettes are crucial because they are the biggest seller.

Knox's is on Main Street in the upper Beaches district, an enclave of small-town living in Toronto's east end. Downtown, there, seems far away. It's a good location, across from a public school and a hockey arena. But once there were four other enterprises like it nearby. Now only one besides Knox's is left. The chain stores have moved in. Look around any urban neighbourhood in Canada and see how many longtime, family owned variety stores still survive. For Bill Knox to run out of one particular brand of cigarettes is unthinkable.

"Mr. Knox!"

As it is, the store has to stay open six days from 8 a.m. to 11 p.m., Sundays from 11 a.m. to 10 p.m. When one of the three is sick, the others split that shift. When Mary isn't working, she's home doing the books. Saturday night, when a part-timer helps out, is the only night Bill and Mary Knox are off together. Two children and their husbands, four grandchildren, gardening, a little television — but it's Knox Variety that consumes their life.

"Mr. Knox!"

Knox finishes the count and in red ballpoint enters a figure on the stock sheet; finicky, he retraces the number. Then he turns to the girls. He looks from one to the other, cool, businesslike. "You said stale?"

"Yes, Mr. Knox."

"Yeah!"

Knox has a tiny white moustache and is nearly bald. He is dressed in creaseless trousers, an open sport shirt and a tired cardigan. Stale chips are not good news. He shakes his head. "Stale, huh?"

"Yes, honest."

This is a serious complaint. It's a problem to tackle with patience, caution — and a touch of scepticism. For twenty-seven years, after all, youngsters have marched in and made similar wild claims. Sure, the store needs a dusting, a wash, a coat of paint, new carpeting. The turquoise walls, yellowish neon light and filmed-over windows give a feeling of being inside an aquarium. But judge not on appearances — Knox Variety gives honest value. Stale chips are a gyp, and the absolute rule here is: *Never* gyp.

It isn't as if temptation doesn't occur occasionally. A kid will come in, for instance, waving a $5, a $10, even a $20 bill. "How much candy can I get for this?" he'll say. Taking the bill, Knox will say, "I'll keep this. You tell your Mom to call me." To do otherwise would constitute a gyp, according to Knox. Most times, of course, the money's been pinched from Ma's purse. As it is, Knox feels that selling some of his merchandise is almost a gyp, the quality is so poor. "Everything's going down," he says. "Customers pay for packaging. I'm actually ashamed of some of this stuff, like the toys."

"They *can't* be stale."

"*Honest!*"

"But I only got 'em in yesterday."

There's an impasse. Knox can say go away or give in. But that's not how it's done. "We built this business on children," he says. "Now *their* children come in, even their grandchildren. I see some of these kids every day. They are customers. Anyhow, I like kids. I like 'em better than adults."

That isn't easy to tell. Usually, the taciturn Knox is strictly business with everybody, big and little. This is about as funny as he gets: "I'm my own boss. Only my customers and the government can tell me what to do . . ." "I look stern and people tend to shy off," he says. "I can't play-act. Mary calls me a sourpuss." Certainly his slim and energetic wife is friendly enough, and Diane takes after her mother. It's because of those two that customers on vacation mail cards to the store or stop in with good-time wishes before a holiday. Knox claims Mary knows all the customers by name, knows their families, knows their troubles. "Meeting people," she explains, "is what I like best. It's what keeps me going."

"Taste 'em then, Mr. Knox."

Knox sighs. He picks a chip out of the bag, looks at it, bites it, chews it, frowns. It's stale. "You're right. Get another bag."

The mark-up on a 35-cent bag of chips is seven cents — therefore the caution. Knox's is a penny operation. And, says the owner, while the turnover may be three or four times what it was twenty-seven years ago, it is increasingly difficult to scrape enough pennies together. Rent, for instance, was once $75 a month for the 11m-by-21m space; now it's $400.

The squeeze is on in many ways. Some random examples: Knox has always sold bread. One day the breadman said he couldn't deliver anymore without a minimum weekly guarantee of $125 in sales. Knox couldn't promise and was promptly cut off. Knox stocks some 350 magazine titles, or $2000 worth. They used to be delivered free, now he pays $1.75 per drop. Soft-drink dealers pressure him to stock more than he needs by his own reckoning, or risk suddenly being without. Some soft-drink companies, these days, will first supply a huge operation such as Toronto's Canadian National Exhibition, for instance, to the detriment — in the hot days of August — of a steady but small customer such as Knox. As a convenience for shoppers, Knox has always had a pay-phone in the store. It used to earn him a small kickback. Today he must pay Bell Canada $3.60 a month plus the difference if the phone has not taken in the company-set monthly quota in dimes. And so it goes.

The root cause of the trouble, however, the dreaded enemy, is the chain stores. Efficient, bright, clean and entirely profit-oriented, they seem invincible. It's simple. Chains can buy in bulk at lower prices — food products, giftware, cosmetics, rubber ducks, whatever — and sell cheaper. "I advise anybody going into the variety business: 'Don't. The little guy is dead.' "

Thus another small, old way of life in Canada inexorably fades away. Most of us raised in a city or town recall a close connection with the neighbourhood variety store. It was a wondrous place that held, when you were little, just about everything in the world you might want — toys, comic books, dolls, knives and, above all, marvellous things to eat, drink and chew that were bad for you. It was probably there where you first seriously learned to want.

Always open, it was the only store where you really felt welcome. Even the dog was. Mary Knox remembers Boots, a black Labrador that trotted in most mornings for at least ten years for a chocolate fudge square. It was the place to spend allowance and chore-earnings. The owner was like an indulging older friend, shooing you out in time for school or supper; later, selling you cigarettes but sorry you had started smoking. Even broke, you dropped in just to look around.

On a recent rainy morning at Knox's, a woman came in with a tot on either hand. Slowly the three wandered around. The children pointed and the woman explained — key rings, dart boards, the bubble-gum machine, sunglasses, plastic clarinets and hair curlers. The tour lasted nearly an hour. Nothing was purchased.

As the potato chip girls leave and several adult customers move up, Bill Knox sinks below the candy counter. It's open on his side, and the shelves hold shallow cartons filled with brilliantly coloured candies. They cost one, two, three or five cents. Most popular are the one-centers. Knox's candyman warned recently that the one-centers were going to be phased out — two one-cent candies for three cents, three one-centers for five cents. A dark sign of the times. But Knox remembers with a rare, small smile, "The candy companies tried that stunt two years ago — and got nowhere. The kids wouldn't buy 'em."

Hidden from sight, on one knee, Knox attends three silent patrons. Each opens a fist. "Seven cents," he says. Their eyes move slowly over the candies.

"Well, you pick 'em," says Knox, shifting his weight. He has gained a lot since he quit smoking last August.

182

"How about the orange ones?"

Also, he has not given up his after-work beer at the Benlamond. He drops in at "the Benny" when he's done at 2 p.m. and again with Mary at 11, when she's locked up.

"The yellow ones?"

The store, the Benny and home are the three points of an even-sided triangle in which Knox lives his life; each is about a four-minute drive from the other. Last summer, on a whim and after twenty years, Knox took a streetcar downtown. Only Simpsons and Old City Hall were familiar. "It was like being in a foreign country."

A finger points at the jujubes, but is unsure.

"No, eh?"

It points at the strawberries.

"Okay," says Knox and lifts one out.

Next is a black baby.

"Okay."

A cream square.

"Okay."

Now a jujube.

"Okay. You got two cents left."

Fingers point at green leaves, jelly beans, cherries.

"*Two* cents, I said."

A jelly bean and a cherry, then.

"Okay. That's it. Thank you."

"I want a bag, Mr. Knox," pipes up one of the three.

"You can't have a bag. Put 'em in your pocket."

The first of the waiting adults needs string to tie up newspapers and a bicycle-tire repair kit. A second wants a pocket notebook and thumbtacks. A third asks for a certain fabric dye. Their faintly surprised reaction that the items are in stock is a common one. A fourth buys $45 of lottery tickets.

"Lotteries gave us a big lift," says Knox. "They pay the rent." Depending on the lottery, he earns from five to eight percent of the price of a ticket, and a kickback of one to five percent on the spoils of a winner. On pre-draw days gamblers crowd the store. The Knoxes each buy a Lottario ticket based on the birth dates of their grandchildren every week. Once they won $1000. Alice Missons, who has run the post office for Knox since it started twelve years ago and still calls him Mr. Knox, has $1300 saved in winnings. She plans to buy a boat for her husband who loves fishing. The post office was a happy plus for Knox. In summer, the commission may go to $300 a month; at Christmas, up to $900.

And so the day goes. Adults and children. Balloons, nail polish, screwdrivers, puzzles and Band-Aids. The soft drink and ice cream coolers hum; the radio sings. Rarely is the place empty. "You can't get rich," says Knox, "but this is my business and my recreation. I'll never retire. I've gone in sick. I'll come in early on a Sunday. I like every part of the work." If he had to do it over, he wouldn't change much.

Knox was born in Sydney Mines, near Sydney, N.S. The family settled in

Toronto shortly after World War I. His father, a veteran with a silver plate in his head, found work in Simpsons' china department. At fourteen, Bill was laying cement sidewalks at $5 for a six-day week. A few years later he, too, joined the china department.

He met Mary there and after a two-year engagement they were married on January 22, 1937. It was Friday. Payday. Though both still lived at home, they had decided to get it over with quietly and tell their families next day. The ceremony was witnessed in a minister's home by a married couple from work. Afterwards the four blew Bill's weekly salary of $12.50 on a meal in a restaurant. Around midnight the newlyweds arrived at the three-bedroom Knox home. Mother, sisters and brother were asleep upstairs; father was downstairs listening to the radio. "My dad was a little bit psychic," recalls Bill. "He said, 'Mary, you wouldn't tell me a lie. Did you and Bill get married?' Mary said, 'Yes.' And Dad woke up everybody to tell 'em. Then Mary went upstairs to sleep in my sisters' room, and I in the boys' room. But guess who was lying next to me in the morning? While I was sleeping, Mother had kicked my brother out. . . ."

Except for army service as a cook during World War II, Knox worked twenty years for Simpsons. His salary in 1954 was $60 a week, but he had $10 000 in the company's profit-sharing plan and bought the store for $8000. Why a variety store? Because it sold china and Knox knew china. Mary, the bookkeeper, says they now do about $98 000 of business a year; she guesses the store's worth is about $60 000. "We've earned enough," says Knox, "to put food on the table, make payments on the house, run a little car." They now own their two-storey, hundred-year-old house, and Mary says the 15m-by-46m property would probably fetch $100 000. In winter, the couple visits Florida for a month, often taking a grandchild along. In summer, the store closes for two weeks, and Knox goes fishing. Life isn't so bad.

And yet. "When I look back," says Knox quietly, "I see that people have changed for the worse. They don't share as they used to. They don't help. Everybody is out for themself. And people aren't as trustworthy anymore. I used to give a lot of credit. Now there are just two customers who get it. Last Christmas I let a woman have $38 in toys. She'd been coming in for years. 'I'll pay you back,' she said. I never saw her again. . . . I almost never take postdated cheques. They bounce. It isn't the money. It's the broken faith.

"I used to think there were more good people than bad. Now I think more are going sour. Especially kids. There isn't the upbringing. Mothers used to make lunches. Now they give the kids a couple of dollars and they spend 'em here on pop and candy. Parents don't seem to care. Kids used to be mischievous. One little beggar poured detergent in my pop cooler. It ran on rotating water then. The whole place full of suds and me cleaning till 4 a.m. Had it out with the boy, and he promised to be good. Then he fixed the lock on the front door so customers were shut out. You couldn't help liking him, though. These days kids are hurtful. And they steal. And adults steal."

Knox figures he loses about $2000 in stolen merchandise a year. There isn't much he can do. "It goes on all the time," he says. "You get used to it." Catching the odd fellow with "girlie" magazines in a folded newspaper under his arm is mostly luck. While one teenager makes a legitimate purchase, others are free to make their moves. Knox has even had his lunch sandwich stolen out

of the fridge. Saddest, perhaps, was the day when he had to put up a string
barring easy entry into that special place behind the candy counter. Even though
there's nearly always someone by the cash register there, he had begun to miss
packs, even cartons, of cigarettes and rolls of change. Only the very tiny now fit
under the string.

That's the storekeeper's one big beef — dishonesty. There aren't many
others. Credit he doesn't like. For twenty-seven years salesmen have begged him
to take credit. "If I can't pay for it," he says, "I don't want it." "Braggarts" he
doesn't like. A braggart is "a fellow who thinks he has all the answers." He may
have to serve a braggart in the store, but he'll never allow one at his table at
the Benny.

Bill and Mary Knox have been coming to the Benny for thirty-five years. Their
corner table overlooks the floor. Waiters hold it for them. On Saturday night
they come in about seven. The Benny fills with smoke and noise and it's time to
relax.

"We're father and mother to so many people here," says Mary. "They've
known us all their lives. We're never bothered. They know we put up with the
public all day." Friends come to sit at their table. "Bill liked going for a beer
after work," she remembers. "So I figured, 'Me too.' With the first one I held
my nose."

Here, too, Bill Knox doesn't speak much. After a while he allows, "I like
sitting here. It doesn't take much to entertain me. I can sit here and think
about my garden. I can think about my business. I can think about what's
happened over the years."

ABOUT THE LINES

1 List the things that have changed over the years in Knox's store, and list the
things that have remained the same. Compare your lists with your partners'
and, if you have noted different points, combine your lists.

2 Imagine that you are Bill Knox and give some advice to a young person who
wishes to start a variety business. Be sure to include reasons for your opinion.
You may present the information in a script for a conversation or in the
form of a letter.

3 Prove, by reference to the article, that the Knox family refuses to hurt people.
Begin your paragraph with the following sentence: "Knox Variety gives
honest value."

BETWEEN THE LINES

1 Complete the following unfinished statement as Bill Knox would:
You can't get rich in this business but I love it because . . .

2 State two things that Knox's Variety store does for the community besides sell goods. Compare your ideas with your partners' and see if you can agree on the points that you have made.

3 Bill and Mary Knox seem to make different contributions to the success of their business. Write a sketch of each personality portraying their individual strengths.

BEYOND THE LINES

1 In the voice of a faithful patron of Knox's Variety store, write a congratulatory letter to the Knox's on the occasion of the thirteenth anniversary of the opening of their store. Be sure to include the reasons why you give the store your business.

2 Interview a variety store owner in your community and see if he/she agrees with the Knox's view of the business. Share your findings with other students who have done similar research. (You should work in a group to prepare questions for your interviews.)

3 Visit a chain convenience store and a privately owned neighbourhood variety store such as Knox's, and make notes on the service, display, products, and prices at both stores. Summarize the information gathered in a chart like the following:

Convenience Store	Variety Store
Kinds of products/prices ——————— ☐ Inexpensive ——————— ☐ Average ——————— ☐ High	Kinds of products/prices ——————— ☐ Inexpensive ——————— ☐ Average ——————— ☐ High
Display of goods ——————— ☐ Poor ——————— ☐ Fair ——————— ☐ Good	Display of goods ——————— ☐ Poor ——————— ☐ Fair ——————— ☐ Good
Service ——————— ☐ Poor ——————— ☐ Fair ——————— ☐ Good	Service ——————— ☐ Poor ——————— ☐ Fair ——————— ☐ Good

In a paragraph, state which store you would prefer to shop in and give reasons for your choice. Compare your information and conclusions with someone else who did similar research.

SHOE STORE

Raymond Souster

A good thirty years since I stood in this store,
shy boy of fifteen become forty-five.
Nothing's changed much, except the front
is a shoe store complete with fancy mirrors,
theatre folding seats, usual boxes piled
rack after rack to the ceiling.

The shoe repair's well to the rear,
separately walled off: in the old days
it was all shoe-making — whirling belts,
gleaming stitchers.
          One thing that hasn't changed
is the shoemaker, no more bald
than he was then, stooped a little more
in the shoulders perhaps as he bends
over a buffer, working a pair of pumps
back and forth with complete absorption,
all the long years of skill centred
at the ends of his fingers, while I stand here quietly
(not wanting to break the spell I've somehow started)
for minutes before he notices me and nods.

Polish immigrant before the War, hardly able
to mouth an English word, he felt alien and lost
among us. All the strength in his body,
all his cunning, put to the service of his child,
beautiful girl I can scarcely remember,
early a piano virtuoso.
          Well, he's prospered,
no longer lives above the store. I wonder
if his wife's still alive, if all goes well
with his daughter.
          But he wouldn't remember me,
so why bother? Why not leave it all
mercifully unknown?
          I ask him simply,
"Can you stitch this up for tomorrow?"
and he answers, "Sure."
          I don't ask for a ticket
and he doesn't offer one. I walk out slowly
between his mirrors, his shoe boxes,
close the door on thirty years gone forever.

187

LOOKING IN

1 The poet has not been in the shoe store for thirty years. State one thing that has changed and one thing that has remained the same over that period of time. Share your observations with your partners.

2 The poet knows more about the shoemaker the man than about his skill as a craftsman. Create a conversation between the poet and a customer who is new to the store in which the poet recounts his memories of the old shoemaker and his business thirty years ago.

3 There is an old-fashioned integrity about the shoemaker which is similar to the characteristics found in Bill Knox of "The Little Shop on Main Street" (see p. 179). In one or two sentences, support this statement by reference to this poem.

4 Speaking in the poet's voice, explain to a friend why you feel that you have closed the door "on thirty years gone forever" when you snap out of your reverie and leave the shoe store.

5 By adding appropriate punctuation and conjunctions (joining words), rewrite this poem as a piece of prose. Read both the poem and the prose version onto a tape. In a group, listen to the tape and decide which is the preferable format. Write a brief note justifying your choice.

LOOKING OUT

1 Interview several people over forty years old. Ask them to share an experience about returning to a place which was important in their childhood but which they have not returned to for many years. Choose the story that interests you the most and write it up as if you were a biographer and this account was part of your description of this person's life.

2 In a journal entry, describe a personal experience involving a return to a time in your past or a reacquaintance with a former friend after a long interval. Share your reflections with other students in a small group. Choose the account that interested you most from the ones shared in the group and write it up to be posted on a class bulletin board. Check your written version with the person who related the account before you write your polished copy.

3 Make a list of the services or businesses that used to flourish in your grandparents' time but have now disappeared in modern society. Compare your list with your partners' and together decide which items are a real loss, which ones are just as well replaced, and which ones we are better off without.

4 The shoe store is a symbol of the poet's youth and inexperience with the world. Name several things or places that trigger special memories of your childhood for you.

MY CUP RANNETH OVER

Robert Patrick

> "My friend is not perfect — nor am I — and so we suit each other admirably."
>
> Alexander Pope

Characters

PAULA
YUCCA

SCENE:

The living room of YUCCA *and* PAULA's *apartment, doors to bedrooms, left; hallway and kitchen, right. On the walls are: a graduation photo of* YUCCA *and* PAULA, *smiling in caps and gowns; a rock-concert poster advertising some huge names with "and other bands" at the bottom, with "And Yucca Concklin" added in magic marker; and along one wall, hundreds of rejection slips from* Cosmopolitan. *Under this wall is a desk with a typewriter. There is a telephone on a long cord. The desk also holds a clock radio. At the desk sits* PAULA TISSOT, *in her middle twenties, attractive and trim, wearing a long bathrobe. She is typing efficiently.*

PAULA (*reads from her manuscript*) "One Woman's Manifesto, by Paula Tissot." There. Cosmopolitan will print this one. They have to. They printed a dozen just like it last year. (*reads*) "And so we must remember always to join in sisterhood, with respect for one another's talents and abilities, never to follow the loathsome male model of competitiveness . . ." (*The phone rings.*) ". . . maintaining respect not only for one another but for ourselves" (*phone rings*) "especially for our gentleness and kindness, our tenderness with one another." (*Phone rings.* PAULA *screeches.*) Yucca! Yucca! (*She listens. Phone rings.*) Yucca! Yucca! Yuck! (*phone continues ringing*)

YUCCA (*sleepy, off*) Whaaaaaat?

PAULA Get up and take off your sleep mask and put on your robe and stagger in here and answer the phone! (*Off, a long, incoherent mumble.* PAULA, *sharply*) You don't want to get up and take off your sleep mask and put on your robe and stagger in here and answer the *what?*

YUCCA (*Staggers in in robe, sleep mask on her head. She's funny and awkward.*) I forget why you can't answer the phone.

PAULA (*making corrections on her manuscript*) Because it's for you.

YUCCA I forget how you know that.

PAULA Because my friends know I write in the mornings and they do not call before noon.

YUCCA Right. I remember now. (*answers into phone*) Hello?

PAULA (*reading to* YUCCA *with relish*) "We must recognize one another."

YUCCA Lola who?

PAULA "We must communicate."

189

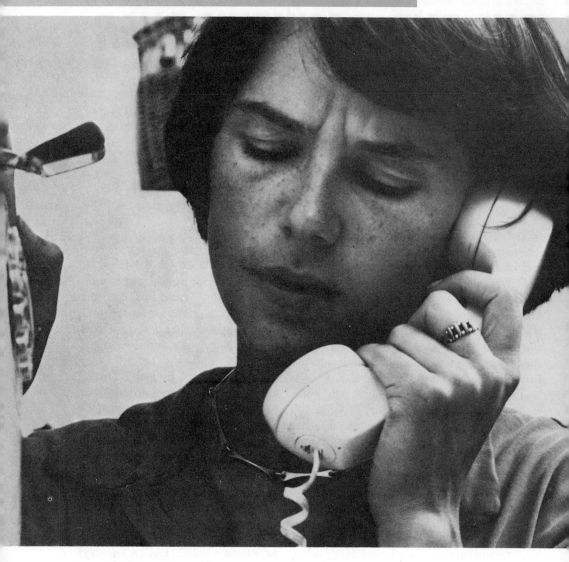

YUCCA There's no one here named Lola.

PAULA "We must revere one another."

YUCCA We have a Paula.

PAULA "We must encourage one another."

YUCCA (*still into phone*) Paula.

PAULA She writes. "We must be without ego."

YUCCA She writes.

PAULA Brilliantly.

YUCCA And me, Yucca, I sing. Pretty well. No Lola.

PAULA I'm not in except to the Pulitzer Prize Committee.

YUCCA (*as* PAULA *returns to work with a pencil*) Oh, you're Lola? You're an old friend of mine? I remember you? Look, I was up very late last night. I had to go across the street and fill in for somebody. (to PAULA) Hey, I had to go across the street to The Bitter End, I mean The Other End. It used to be The Bitter End.

PAULA It's not across the street.

YUCCA It was across the street from where I was. Anyway, I had to go over there last night and fill in for Tod Mitchell, no less. He had a throat.

PAULA Useful for a singer.

YUCCA Sore.

PAULA No, I'm just trying to write.

YUCCA No, he had a sore throat and I had to fill in for him. And the people actually stayed.

PAULA Did they like you as well as *Cosmopolitan* is going to like this article which I will finish writing as soon as you stop bothering me?

YUCCA They loved me. They always love me. I am their spiritual selves delivering a rueful rigadoon from the depths of poverty and obscurity. Also, I'm better than a sore throat. (into phone) Oh, were you there? Did you enjoy yourself? Me, I mean.

PAULA No, I wasn't there. I was home working. I write.

YUCCA Not you. Some person called Lola who insists she is an old friend. (into phone) You weren't there? How could you like me, then? Huh? You want to read to me? No, don't. My roommate reads to me. I can read, I just don't. She reads. She writes.

PAULA (grimly) She tries.

YUCCA (into phone) Read it to her. (hands phone to PAULA) It must be some writer-friend of yours. She wants to read something.

PAULA Oh, really, Yucca! (YUCCA exits to kitchen.) Hello? What? The time? Yes, I have the time, it's eleven-thirty and I don't take calls before — The *Times*? What times? The *Times*? The *New York Times*? (yells) Yucca, you got reviewed in the *New York Times*! (into phone) Wait, read it to me slowly!

YUCCA (Re-enters with banana. She has not understood.) You got a rejection slip from the *New York Times*? (pats PAULA consolingly)

PAULA (Brushing YUCCA away. Into phone) Wait, start that over.

YUCCA (indicating Cosmo rejection slips) You'll have to start a whole new wall.

PAULA (with ever-mounting excitement) Yucca, hush! Hold on, Lily. All right, "Lola!" Yucca, you're in the *Times*!

YUCCA I never sent anything to the *Times*. They don't print songs.

PAULA There was a reviewer there last night.

YUCCA The *Times* reviews folk-rock?

PAULA Listen. (She repeats what LOLA is reading to her.) Funky Punk Subs for Tod Mitchell . . .

YUCCA Oh, no!

PAULA With her tousled hair . . .

YUCCA Oh, God, you told me to comb my hair!

PAULA In a sweat-stained T-shirt . . .

YUCCA You told me to dress better!

PAULA A scrawny street punk lumbered onto the stage at The Other End last night . . .

YUCCA (the pits) Since freshman year you've tried to teach me to walk.

PAULA (to YUCCA) Well, it's a hard way to learn, dear, but maybe you'll listen in the future. Go ahead, Lola.

YUCCA (trying to grab phone) No, don't.

PAULA (Expression of shock. Into phone) And what?

YUCCA Made a goddamn fool of herself and didn't even get paid!

PAULA Yucca!

YUCCA (strangling herself with phone-cord) Paula, how does a lady kill herself?

PAULA Yucca, listen. (hands phone to YUCCA)

YUCCA Oh, God. (listens and repeats what LOLA reads) And proved to be the most exciting and original new pop talent in years. How many years?

PAULA Well, what do you know?

YUCCA (staring at phone) I remember her now. Some incredible bore that used to hang around the coffee-houses and knock folk-rock.

PAULA (grabs phone, listens and repeats) She's obviously bled on the streets she sings about so winningly.

YUCCA Lola has?

PAULA You have!

YUCCA Oh, I have not.

PAULA (repeating LOLA) A remarkable lyric style backed by profound musical expertise. The next thing is going to come from this T-shirted essence of the post-Watergate street punk.

YUCCA (grabs phone) Lola, does anybody read the Times? I've got to wash and hang up my face. I'll call you back. (hangs up) I can't call her back. I don't know her number.

PAULA Yucca, how fantastic!

YUCCA (beginning to realize) They must have been there to see Tod Mitchell. The Times never saw me in their life.

PAULA Well, they sure 'nuff saw you now. Congratulations, kid.

YUCCA Congratulations, "punk."

PAULA (rising and exiting) This would seem the time to break out a certain bottle of champagne.

YUCCA (to phone) Post-Watergate street punk? I was a street punk early in '68. Champagne? (pulls sleep mask over her eyes)

PAULA (runs back on with champagne and two glasses) Champagne it is!

YUCCA Paula. I'm interrupting your rigid schedule.

PAULA (opening and pouring champagne) Once can't hurt. This is an event.

YUCCA The Times can't be of any importance in rock.

PAULA Darling, enjoy it, have fun.

YUCCA. It's probably some twelfth-string hack. Everybody thinks they're a rock reviewer if they know Helen Reddy from Phoebe Snow.

PAULA (very party-mood) Is Helen Reddy from Phoebe Snow?

YUCCA I have a confession to make. I have no faith in myself. I drank the champagne Tuesday.

PAULA Well, I had faith in you. I bought some more Wednesday.

YUCCA (removes sleep mask) Oh, you shouldn't have. (giggles) Well, as it turns out, you should have.

PAULA In fact, I bought two — I have faith in me, too. (offers glass)

YUCCA (takes glass) Oh, you should. This will happen to you before it does to me.

PAULA Maybe when Germaine Greer gets a sore throat. But it *has* happened to you, and it's wonderful.

YUCCA It's only one review.

PAULA It's only your first.

YUCCA But that champagne was for my first gold record!

PAULA We'll just drink a little and keep the rest in a quart jar.

YUCCA They came for Tod Mitchell.

PAULA They stayed for you.

YUCCA They probably thought I was Tod Mitchell.

PAULA It's those T-shirts. Drink up, darling. Here's to a fantastic fluke. It couldn't happen to a sweeter punk. (PAULA *drinks*. YUCCA *won't*.) Oh, enjoy it, darling. It may never happen again. (*Phone rings.*) Oh, bicentennial bucket of buttered popcorn!

YUCCA I'll get it, I'll get it. Hello! Oh, hi, Brad. (*hands phone to* PAULA) It's your boyfriend from the *Village Voice*.

PAULA Oh, come on, he's not my boyfriend. (*into phone*) Brad, you brute. You know I never take calls before noon. But you're forgiven, this is your lucky day, we're having a little celebration. My little roommate, Yucca? She sings a little? Well she got a sweet little review of all things in the *Times* of all places, and we were just — Oh, certainly. (*hands phone to Yucca*) He wants you.

YUCCA Of all little people. (*into phone*) Hi, Brad. You what? No, no, you want Tod Mitchell. You've had Tod Mitchell? You were? I was? You do? (*to* PAULA) He wants to interview me over the phone.

PAULA He is. (*she sits at typewriter*)

YUCCA Right. (*into phone*) Oh, sure, I understand. I understand about deadlines. It's all right, really. (*to* PAULA) This is just a short interview to fill in. He'll do a great big longer one next week.

PAULA Of course.

YUCCA (*into phone*) I guess that's all right. Shoot. Huh? Why do I call myself Yucca? (PAULA *types answer and hands it to her*) Because it's the state flower of New Mexico. (PAULA *continues typing.* YUCCA *reads from* PAULA's *typewriter.*) No, I'm from Nebraska but I couldn't very well call myself Goldenrod Concklin, could I? Concklin? (PAULA *types.* YUCCA *reads.*) It's your name, stupid. I mean, it's my name. My inspiration? (*reads as* PAULA *types*) I've bled on those streets. Where did I get the idea for the T-shirt? (PAULA *does not type*) Uh, I'll tell you next week. No, I've certainly never had a shorter interview. Bye Brad. (*hangs up*)

PAULA (*philosophically*) Bye, Brad.

YUCCA Imagine the *Village Voice* interviewing me.

PAULA I think I am.

YUCCA Maybe they'll make a movie of my life.

PAULA I think they have.

YUCCA They liked the same song you like! (*sings*) "Folks Get Up at Nine in California, Because They Know It's Noon in Alabam'."

PAULA Is that what I like?

YUCCA (*going to* PAULA's *desk with champagne and glasses*) Sure, you love that one. Oh, Paula, you're always right. It's just like you said a few minutes ago.

"This may never happen again." Oh, well, I guess as it turns out you were wrong, but you know what I mean. (*drinks her champagne, pours more*)

PAULA Well, I'm an unpublished writer, not an unpublished prophet. And speaking of unpublished writing (*phone rings*) — I'm going to kill myself.

YUCCA Hey, what's wrong? You sound sad.

PAULA I'm not sad.

YUCCA But you don't usually look like this until the mailman brings you your rejection slips. Woops!

PAULA I think your best move right about now would be to answer the phone.

YUCCA Sure. (*answers phone*) Hello? Lola who? Oh, Lola. The *New York Post*? No, I'm not listening to the *New York Post*. It's a newspaper, isn't it? Oh, I see. (*to* PAULA) Have we got a radio that gets WNEW-FM?

PAULA On my desk. Where I once wrote. (*She turns on radio. It comes on instantly.*)

RADIO ". . . and she makes so improbable a garment as a T-shirt into a uniform of deliberate despair. This is a debut not to be forgotten. Her talent stunned an audience that came to hear glitter rock and stayed to relish street poetry from a lovable, shaggy-haired punk."

YUCCA (*spaced throughout the above speech, into phone*) Uh-huh. The *Post*, too? Talent . . . T-shirt . . . Tousled hair . . . Top star . . . Terrific . . .

RADIO (*clearly*) "Look out, world. Here comes Yucca Concklin! And now, late weather and news.''

YUCCA Oh, leave it on.

PAULA You're not weather yet, Yucca.

YUCCA Thanks, Lola. Sure, I can get together sometime. He liked which? What? (*to* PAULA) He liked, the *Post* especially liked (*sings*) "The Bar Is Closin', It's Quarter to Two, Isn't There Somethin' You Can Do to Make Me Fall in Love with You."

PAULA Late weather and news especially liked your T-shirt.

YUCCA Holy Moses, it's a plain white T-shirt! Oh, why didn't we record it?

PAULA We were busy. Once.

YUCCA Look, Lola, I have to set up my roommate's tape recorder. I'll call you back someday. No, I guess I don't have your number, do I? It's what? Paula, will you take Lola's phone number? (*puts phone to* PAULA's *ear*)

PAULA Sure, why wouldn't I? (*types phone number as* LOLA *speaks*)

YUCCA (*to* LOLA) Thanks loads.

PAULA (*whisking number out of typewriter to* YUCCA) You're welcome.

YUCCA (*crumples phone number and throws it away idly*) Bye. (*hangs up, goes for the tape recorder*) Who *is* she?

PAULA Incredible bore. Hung around coffee-houses. Knocked folk-rock.

YUCCA (*taking tape recorder from desk*) Oh, do you *know* her? (*phone rings*) Can you get that? I've got to get this thing hooked up in case . . .

PAULA I'll fit it into my schedule. (*answers*) Hello? Yes, this is Yucca Concklin's apartment. Yucca — (*holds out phone*)

YUCCA (*oblivious, entangled with wires and jacks*) We should hook it up to the TV, too, just in case they say anything about me on Today today or Tomorrow tonight.

PAULA (*imitating* YUCCA *into phone*) This is Yucca Concklin, in fact. Yes, I'm joyed over. Because it's the state flower of New Mexico. No, I'm from Montana but I couldn't very well call myself Bitter Root Concklin, could I? T-shirt?

YUCCA (*mutters while working*) T-shirts are a major American industry for God's sake.

PAULA (*still into phone*) Because the T-shirt is the sartorial symbol of the lost, the hopeless, the helpless, all who wish to escape the treadmill of media-dictated fashion and simplify their lives and take a wider-eyed view of the hung-up world we're living in. A quotable quip? You want a quotable quip? Okay. How about this? I don't believe in foods without preservatives, because: they'll never last. Thank you. (*hangs up*) You just gave an exclusive interview to Earl Wilson.

YUCCA Maybe they'll put out Yucca Concklin plain white T-shirts. It'll be cheap.

PAULA That won't stop you.

YUCCA (*realizing*) Earl Wilson? He's *real!* Why didn't we record it?

PAULA He doesn't make records. He writes. I write too, Bruté. (*She starts cleaning up champagne glasses, etc.*)

YUCCA Paula, is there any way to leave the radio on all the stations simultaneously?

PAULA If there is, you'll find it.

YUCCA Wish me well.

PAULA I wish you were.

YUCCA (*following behind PAULA as PAULA cleans up*) Paula, are you okay?

PAULA I'm okay, you're okay, I read it in a real book.

YUCCA Your face looks like a fig.

PAULA Thanks.

YUCCA Did I do something wrong?

PAULA Ask Celebrity Service.

YUCCA I washed the dishes and our socks last night, didn't I?

PAULA Yes.

YUCCA I didn't wash 'em together, did I?

PAULA No.

YUCCA Did I leave water spots on the champagne glasses?

PAULA No.

YUCCA Did I leave my electric guitar plugged in all night?

PAULA You can afford it, Yucca; just do an endorsement ad for Con Ed.

YUCCA Well, then, why are you uptight?

PAULA I'm not uptight; don't project your anxieties on me.

YUCCA Oh, am I doing that again? I'm sorry. I never know I'm doing that until you tell me. Thank you.

PAULA What are friends for? She asked herself. Profoundly. Returning to work. (*She has cleared champagne, etc., off her desk and sits down to work.*)

YUCCA But you do seem upset. Is it possible *you're* anxious and projecting your *anxieties* onto me and then projecting your projecting them onto *me* onto *my* projecting them onto *you?*

PAULA Yucca, I have to keep *Cosmopolitan* supplied with rejection material. I can't spend the morning playing anxiety-pong.

YUCCA Well, gee, couldn't we take the morning off to celebrate? How often does one of us have this happen? (*phone rings*)

PAULA Yucca, did you not hear me? I have to work on my article.

YUCCA Aw, come on, Paula, it can't be that urgent, they just shoot 'em right back, anyway.

PAULA (*evil glare*) Yucca!

YUCCA Probably my best move now would be to answer the phone, right?

PAULA I'm going to change into my mailbox clothes. (*starts off with champagne, etc.*)

YUCCA (*answers phone*) Hello. (*stops* PAULA) Don't take that away, I want some more. (PAULA *leaves champagne and one glass and exits.*) Hello again. Why, thank you. I'm just as surprised as I can be. That wasn't coy. Yes, I was filling in for Tod Mitchell. No, we're not lovers. No, he didn't deliberately fake sick to get me on. (*angry*) Well, I don't care what Joan Baez did for Bobby Dylan at Newport in nineteen sixty —. (*rebuffed*) I'm sorry, sir, I didn't mean to be curt. Have you got some right to talk to me that way? I'm only asking. I'm new in the business part of this business. You are? Why, I've never talked to one before. An agent, huh? Hey, what exactly do you people do? That wasn't smart. You represent people? Okay. Let's hear you do Burt Lancaster. You want to represent me? (*elated*) Fantastic — wait, I want to drink to that. (*She starts pouring, eventually overruns her glass.*) I am? You do? Oh, you read my reviews, huh? Well, sure, it feels fabulous, it just — I don't know how to express it.

PAULA (*enters, dressed*) Yucca, your cup runneth over!

YUCCA That's it. Oh! (*scrambles for a dirty T-shirt to wipe up champagne*) Oh, God! Paula, I'm sorry. (PAULA *seats herself and types.* YUCCA *speaks into phone.*) Huh? You do? Sure, use it. Hey, Paula, he loves that as a quote, "My Cup Runneth Over." (*into phone again*) Oh, of course, use it. (*Paula types louder and faster.*) Well, no, I just love talking to big-time, important agents who make people into universal stars. It's your nickel. Where are you calling from? Los Angeles? It's your bankroll, then, talk. Oh, sure, you can call me here anytime.

PAULA (*without stopping typing*) Not anytime, Yucca.

YUCCA What? Oh, yeah. (*into phone*) Listen, just not before noon anymore, okay? Noon New York time. It's because of my roommate. She's a terribly disciplined and talented person. She writes. She — Paula, could you cut out the racket? (PAULA *stops cold.*) She writes. Yes. Thanks. (*She hangs up.* PAULA *gets up and heads for* YUCCA *to kill her. The phone rings.* YUCCA *answers gracefully, sipping champagne.*) Hello?

PAULA (*wheeling and returning to her chair*) Thank God!

YUCCA Yes, this is she. You're very kind. You're very kind. Were you there? Your friends are very kind. You can get other opinions in the papers. All the papers. *Daily Variety* you read? Isn't that charming of them, and me a mere unknown. No, it's a sweat-stained T-shirt, not a tea-stained sweatshirt! No, I don't have an agent. He just called me, though. Oh, you are, too? Are there two agents? That doesn't really help me, I don't know any agents' names. I'm sure you are. I'm sure I do. I'm sure we could. You're very kind. You're very kind. You're very fast. Well, who is someone you represent, then? (*awed*) John Denver? You're very kidding. How do I know that? Look, could we possibly handle this this way? If you put me in touch with John Denver and he says you are you, and you are good, then I'll think about it, provided I think. I hope that's reasonable and I hope I can remember it. His number? John Denver's home phone number? Shoot. 303-236-8790? (PAULA *types each digit separately with one finger and hands it to* YUCCA. *Still into phone*) You're very kind. Thank you.

PAULA You're very welcome.

YUCCA Thank you, Paula. (*to agent*) Goodbye. (*hangs up*)

PAULA I'm not going anywhere.

YUCCA (*dreamily dialing*) Daily Variety said I had American eyes: red, white and blue. (*Door buzzer buzzes. Into phone*) Hello. I haven't finished dialing.

PAULA It's the door, Yucca. (*presses talk switch*) Hello?

MAILMAN (*over speaker*) It's the mailman with some more of them heavy envelopes from *Cosmopolitan*.

PAULA I'll be right down.

MAILMAN Hurry it up, lady. These streets ain't safe.

PAULA Right down! (*goes to desk, turns on tape recorder*) Yucca?

YUCCA (*into phone*) Hello. Please hold. What, Paula, darling?

PAULA My white knight is below with my daily fix of rejection slips. Whoever you talk to, remember you gave an exclusive on your clothes philosophy to Earl Wilson. (*pause*) You've got John Denver on hold. (*She exits.*)

YUCCA Right. (*into phone*) Hello? Oh, God, I'm sorry. Listen, you don't know me, but for various reasons I call myself Yucca Concklin, and — you do? You did? That's very kind, especially from you, especially if you are — you are? Well, why I called is this man said — he represented himself as representing you and — funny, that's the name he gave, isn't that a coincidence? And anyway he said he wanted you to be my agent. His. Mine. Him to be mine. Yes. You think I should? Well, I never doubted it, only my senses. Probably I will. House seats? I don't know. No, I know what house seats are, I just don't know if I get any. The subject just never came up before. If you say so. You're very kind. You're very kind. (*awed*) You would? Why sure. Uh — look. I don't want to seem paranoid, but I've always had the intense conviction that worldwide conspiracies were working against my happiness, so could you please just say "Country Road?" (*pause*) You're very John Denver. (PAULA *reenters in great disarray with two or three big envelopes.* YUCCA *hangs up.*) John Denver wants me to go on the road.

PAULA I couldn't have put it better myself.

YUCCA And am I free after the show tonight.

PAULA As far as I'm concerned. (PAULA *hands her the cassette out of the recorder.*)

YUCCA Paula. How sweet! You recorded my whole first conversation with John Denver.

PAULA I thought you might like to frame it in your new house.

YUCCA New house?

PAULA Or perhaps you'll move to a hotel. Where you can call room service. When you want more room.

YUCCA (*sees envelopes*) Are those your rejections?

PAULA All I've thought up so far.

YUCCA Papers! I've got to go out and get the papers.

PAULA You can't.

YUCCA Sure. I'll put on shoes. And an official Yucca Concklin white T-shirt.

(*phone rings*)

PAULA Yucca, you can't go out on the street.

YUCCA Sure I can. I've bled on those streets.

PAULA Not yet you haven't. Listen. (*She drags* YUCCA *to door and presses listen button.*)

YUCCA That isn't the door ringing, it's the phone.

PAULA Yucca, listen.

VOICES OVER BOX Yucca! Yucca! This is her house. This ain't her house. Yes, it is! Whose house? Yucca Concklin. The big new singer. The one that wears the T-shirts. Yeah, this is her house.

YUCCA They're talking about me.

PAULA They're talking about you.

YUCCA They're bandying my name about on the streets.

VOICES She lives here? Yucca Concklin? Yeah, this is her house. This is where she lives. The one that they were talking about on TV!

YUCCA (*into squawk-box*) TV! What channel?

PAULA (*dragging her away*) YUCCA!

VOICES That is it. Three thirty-three. Just like in the song. See there's her name. Hey, Yucca!

YUCCA Hey, yourselves!

VOICES That's her mailbox. There's her name. Hey, let's take her mailbox!

(*Hideous wrenching sound, then silence. Phone is still ringing*)

PAULA Yucca, what song are they talking about?

YUCCA It must be the new one I put into the act last night.

PAULA What's it called?

YUCCA "I'm just a street punk, just like you, from three thirty-three First Avenue." I'll take it out of the act.

PAULA No. Just take the act out!

YUCCA What are you trying to say?

PAULA I'm trying to say I want you to move!

YUCCA Because you think I'm going commercial?

PAULA Because I know I'm going crackers! This is impossible.

YUCCA But it can't last. (*answers phone*) Hello? *People Magazine?* Can you call back in five minutes? (*aghast*) You can? (*hangs up*) Okay, it can last. (*phone rings immediately*)

PAULA But I can't. I want you to find another place.

YUCCA It may not be real. (*answers*) Hello? *Playboy?* (*pause*) Really? Can you call back in ten minutes? Thank you.

PAULA It's real, Yucca. You have made the jump. Turned the corner. Gone over the rainbow. Through the looking-glass. Round the bend. Taken the veil. Hit the parade. Made the grade. Started school. Crossed the street by yourself. You're late weather and news.

YUCCA (*runs to hall door*) No, I haven't. Look, it's over already. (*presses listen button*) See, they've stopped talking about me.

PAULA No, they stole the squawk-box for a souvenir.

YUCCA But I don't want to move. Where would I move?

PAULA Maybe John Denver needs a roommate.

YUCCA We've always stuck together.

PAULA Stick it yourself, Yucca.

YUCCA But I'm a success now. I'll be surrounded by false friends.

PAULA You won't know they're false after a while, Yucca, they'll be the only friends you've got.

YUCCA Maybe I'm not a success. You can never be sure.

PAULA (*with a harsh laugh*) Answer the phone.

YUCCA (*does*) Hello? (*curt*) *Time Magazine?* Call back in fifteen minutes. (*Hangs up. Phone rings. To* PAULA) I can be sure.

PAULA You can be sure.

YUCCA All right, I can be sure. But I owe it all to you.

PAULA And three months' back rent.

YUCCA Oh, I know, Paula, but I can pay it all back now. I can help you now. Look what all I've got out of our relationship. What do you want out of our relationship?

PAULA Out of our relationship!

YUCCA You can't mean that. I owe so much to you. Every time I'd start to give up, I'd think of you over there, clawing away at that machine, writing articles no one wants, collecting rejection slips, people returning your stuff without buying it, without reading it, editors begging you not to waste your time, and no matter how many of them told you to go into social work or home economics, you kept on! Without hope or promise, all your friends laughing behind your back, love and life and youth passing you by, and I'd say, Golly. If she can take all that and still believe in herself, who am I to flag? That's what I owe you!

PAULA Well, and here it comes back with interest. That's beautiful. That's some of your best work! Now would you like to hear the flip side? You've changed, Yucca, you've changed, success has changed you!

YUCCA Me? (*answers phone*) *Newsweek?* Later! (*hangs up*) Me? (*phone rings*)

PAULA Anybody else in this house had success? You've changed overnight. You all of a sudden expect me to get the phone for you, pour your champagne, give your interviews, sacrifice my writing time!

YUCCA I haven't changed.

PAULA You have. You used to do everything for me and now you won't even move!

YUCCA I haven't changed, I haven't had time.

PAULA And on top of everything else, you insult my work!

YUCCA I didn't insult it, I just said nobody wants it.

PAULA Is that your concept of a rave?

YUCCA I was just being honest.

PAULA Well, that's a change.

YUCCA I'm always honest. You just never listen.

PAULA I listened to you practising on your twelve-string torture instrument night and day for five years grinding out dime-a-dozen despair. (*imitates* YUCCA *singing*) "Oh, you may be goin' to Buffalo, but you ain't goin' to Buffalo me!"

YUCCA Well, I listened to you on your (*quick glance at typewriter*) forty-two key racket-package and I listened to all those fumble-fingered rewrites of *Sexual Politics* and I never said anything.

PAULA You never say anything! What's too silly to be said can be sung!

(*phone is still ringing*)

YUCCA I thought you liked my music!

PAULA I do, I love your stupid music, and now you've got me insulting it. You've changed, Yucca, you've changed!

YUCCA I've changed? Honestly, Paula. You do a few simple things for me at a time of extreme crisis, things you never do for me, by the way, and which most friends would do for each other without even asking, you scream at me because I've had success, which you all of a sudden act like you never thought I'd have, and after we've struggled and starved together ever since matriculation, you try to throw me out on the streets!

PAULA (*running to hall door*) You've bled on 'em, now live on 'em! (*into squawk-box*) Look out, world, here comes Yucca Concklin!

(*phone is still ringing*)

YUCCA I haven't changed: you've changed.

PAULA You just hung up on *Playboy, People, Time* and *Newsweek!* You never did that before.

YUCCA I only did it so I could beg you not to throw me out.

PAULA Don't do me any favours.

YUCCA Watch out or I won't!

PAULA Just answer the phone!

YUCCA It's afternoon now, it's your turn. If you don't want things to have changed, you answer it!

PAULA All right, I'll keep up the empty, shallow, hollow . . . (*answers phone*) Hello! (*She listens, pales.*) — Yucca, it's for you.

YUCCA Paula, I'm obviously in hysterics. Can you take it?

PAULA I can take a lot but not this.

YUCCA Oh, God, who is it, *National Geographic?*

PAULA It's *Cosmo . . . politan.*

YUCCA It *can't* be! I guess it can. What does *Cosmopolitan* want with me?

PAULA Margaux Hemingway broke an eyebrow.

YUCCA (*takes phone*) Look, can you hold? (*not into phone*) Oh, my God. (*grabs Paula by arm*)

PAULA What is it? What did they say?

YUCCA They said for me they'd hold anything. I'm sorry, Paula.

PAULA I'm thrilled for you, Yucca. I'm tickled, I'm delighted, but will you please let go of my arm, give *Cosmopolitan* your fiftieth exclusive interview of the day, then bundle up your banjo picks and move!

YUCCA I don't wanna move. I'll never be here anyway. I'll be on the road with John Denver.

PAULA Oh, rub it in!

YUCCA Paula, you're jealous!

PAULA Gee, that would explain so many things.

YUCCA You're jealous of me!

PAULA I'm ecstatic for you, Yucca, but my cup ranneth over about two minutes ago

YUCCA I don't want you to be jealous.

PAULA Then let go of my wrist so I can cut it. That's the alternative.

YUCCA We've always had this very special feeling of trust between us, respect for one another's talents and abilities. We've always believed in each other, haven't we? Haven't we? We haven't? All right, I never believed in myself but I always knew you did and that's what pulled me through. Has that feeling just gone?

PAULA Yucca, this is embarrassing.

YUCCA But has it?

PAULA It's just too humiliating to live together, Yucca. I'm jealous — and for Christ's sake, of *you*!

YUCCA What do you mean, of *you*? What's wrong with you? Me, I mean? What's not to be jealous of?

PAULA I don't want to fight, Yucca.

YUCCA Okay, but has the feeling gone?

PAULA Only from my left hand! (YUCCA *releases her.*) Thank you, Yucca. I'm very glad for you.

YUCCA You're being unreasonable.

PAULA It isn't unreasonable to be glad for a friend.

YUCCA All right.

PAULA I just cannot spend the rest of my life thinking up clever quotes for your interviews, Cora Sue Concklin.

YUCCA You what?

PAULA I said . . .

YUCCA I heard you! (*into phone with great and growing style*) Hey, Cosmo? Shoot. I want to be a star because I'm lazy, and stars only come out at night. I thought Yucca was my full name because my folks always looked at me and said, "Yuck." . . . Overnight success? I just hope it's not over tonight. My ambition? I want to go gold before I go grey. You want to print a cover story on me? Won't that hurt? But seriously, I'd love it . . . on one condition. It must be written by my roommate, Paula Tissot. She writes. I believe you are familiar with her work. That's the one. Now, come on, be fair — give the kid a chance. She knows me better than anyone. In fact, she used to be my best friend. Here — I'll give her to you . . . (*She extends the phone to* PAULA, *who sits looking at it.*)

CURTAIN

ABOUT THE LINES

1 Imagine that you are the casting director for this play. Write brief descriptions of the appearance and mannerisms you envision for the two characters, Paula and Yucca.

2 Write a one- or two-sentence introduction for Paula and for Yucca that could be used to describe their personal expertise to people who do not know them.

3 List the individuals and the organizations who contacted Yucca after Lola announced the singer's sudden discovery.

BETWEEN THE LINES

1 Identify the point in the story at which Paula begins to show her resentment of Yucca's success. Discuss the turning point that you have chosen with your partners, and together, in a flowchart format, trace the gradual build-up of Paula's jealousy from that point to her request that Yucca move out.

2 Explain in a brief paragraph how you see the title, "My Cup Ranneth Over," as commenting differently on the two characters in the play. Suggest alternative titles and share them with your partners. Choose one that you all agree is best from your combined suggestions.

3 In Paula's voice, write a letter to Yucca in which you apologize for your jealousy, and express how you felt when she introduced you to *Cosmopolitan* as her "biographer."

4 Both Paula and Yucca are "one-liner" experts. Choose lines spoken by each of them that you think are amusing. Discuss your choices with your partners and comment on how the jokes exchanged by the two friends help to save their relationship.

BEYOND THE LINES

1 With a partner, prepare and present a dramatization of this play. You may wish to summarize parts of the action through a narrator.

2 Write a short story that includes the following elements:
a. a close relationship between two people;
b. a change in lifestyle for one person;
c. a growing apart.
Share your story with your classmates.

3 Working with a small group of people with whom you feel comfortable, share an account of an experience where your vision was temporarily clouded by jealousy or resentment.

4 Rewrite the play so that Paula is the successful one who finds a way to promote Yucca's career. You may write the account in the form of a play or a short story.

5 Design and produce a cover for a magazine featuring the story of "Yucca Concklin, the Overnight Success."

6 Write the article for *Cosmopolitan* magazine that Paula would be likely to produce about her now successful friend. Compare your version with your partners', and together produce a polished article ready for submission to the magazine.

THE LITTLE GIRL AND THE WOLF

James Thurber   *No brave woodsman to the rescue!*

One afternoon a big wolf waited in a dark forest for a little girl to come along carrying a basket of food to her grandmother. Finally a little girl did come along and she was carrying a basket of food. "Are you carrying that basket to your grandmother?" asked the wolf. The little girl said yes, she was. So the wolf asked her where her grandmother lived and the little girl told him and he disappeared into the wood.

When the little girl opened the door of her grandmother's house she saw that there was somebody in bed with a nightcap and nightgown on. She had approached no nearer than twenty-five feet from the bed when she saw that it was not her grandmother but the wolf, for even in a nightcap a wolf does not look any more like your grandmother than the Metro-Goldwyn lion looks like Calvin Coolidge. So the little girl took an automatic out of her basket and shot the wolf dead.

Moral: It is not so easy to fool little girls nowadays as it used to be.

Choose a fairy tale and rewrite the ending, using an unexpected twist that illustrates changing attitudes in our society. Be sure to include a moral to your story.

EXTENDED ACTIVITIES

1 Read a biography of a famous person who interests you. Create a time line for that person's life and note on it all the significant changes or transitions experienced by him/her. For each development or event that you have noted, write a statement commenting on how that change influenced future actions and decisions for the person. Share your findings with your partners, who can, in turn, tell you about the lives of the personalities whom they researched.

2 List five changes or transitions that have occurred in your life and rate them as positive or negative. For each change, describe the impact it has made on you and on your outlook. You may wish to tabulate the information in a chart like the following:

Change	People Involved or Affected	Time in My Life	Effect on Me

3 Write a letter to a government representative at the local, provincial, or federal level, recommending some change that you would like to see instituted in the law. Be sure to include in your letter what you believe would be the positive outcomes of this change.

4 Interview two or three senior citizens and ask for their reflections on how society has changed since they were young. Tape your discussions and then edit the tape for a presentation to the class on the viewpoints of the older people.

5 Prepare a questionnaire that asks people to list the five things that they would most like to change in our society. Get a cross-sampling of at least twenty people to complete the questionnaire. Include some children, some teenagers, some parents, some adults with no children, and some people over sixty-five years old. Analyse the responses to see if any of the desired changes are common to a number of respondents or reflect the viewpoint of a particular age group. After your fellow students have also completed the questionnaire, share the results of your investigation with the class.

6 Interview teachers and former or senior students of your school to discover the transitions that have occurred in the school since it opened. Prepare a report on the history of your school and share the report with the class or a small group. You may wish to consult old yearbooks or school newspapers to get a picture of the past.

EXTENDED ACTIVITIES

7 Identify and research any group that is struggling for its rights within our society, such as women, workers, and ethnic groups. Make a list of the social developments that have come about as a result of the group's efforts over some concern. Write a policy statement outlining some things that the group you have studied would like to accomplish in the future.

8 Prepare an illustrated personal history of someone in your family. Trace his/her growth and the changes that have occurred from birth to the present. Use photographs or drawings to highlight the more interesting stages in your subject's life.

9 "Things were different when I was young." Talk to your parents about their experiences as young people and write an account of how things have changed in the lifestyle of teenagers since they (your parents) were in high school.

10 Working with a small group, brainstorm a list of the probable changes that could occur in the next one hundred years. Together, select the five that are most likely to happen, and for each one, write a paragraph outlining the positive or negative impact that change would have on society.

11 Make a list of three things that you would like to change in yourself and three things that you would like to keep the same about you. Share your list with people whom you trust and ask for their responses to your list. See if they agree with you about your priorities, then listen to their lists and comment on their choices.

12 Talk to someone who has attended more than three schools or who has moved more than three times. Ask them to comment on the most difficult or upsetting aspects of changing communities and on the benefits of frequent transitions. Write a summary of the things that interested you about this discussion.

13 With the help of your librarian, choose and read folk tales, fables, or myths that tell stories of great metamorphoses (changes). Select your favourite tale and prepare a polished retelling of it to a group.

14 Script and dramatize scenes depicting a change in attitude on the part of one person toward another. Consider the following situations for ideas:
a. Two rival players have a drink together after a match;
b. Two drivers who collided in an accident meet at the body shop to pick up their cars;
c. A parent greets a runaway child when the child returns.

A CHOICE OF

WEAPONS

Sticks and stones are hard on bones.
Aimed with angry art,
Words can sting like anything.
But silence breaks the heart.

A Choice of Weapons
Phyllis McGinley

THE RETURN

Alistair MacLeod

"It is not that easy to change what is a part of you. . . ."

It is an evening during the summer that I am ten years old and I am on a train with my parents as it rushes toward the end of eastern Nova Scotia. "You'll be able to see it any minute now, Alex," says my father excitedly, "look out the window, any minute now."

He is standing in the aisle by this time with his left hand against the overhead baggage rack while leaning over me and over my mother who is in the seat by the window. He has grasped my right hand in his right and when I look up it is first into the whiteness of his shirt front arching over me and then into the fine features of his face, the blueness of his eyes and his wavy reddish hair. He is very tall and athletic looking. He is forty-five.

"Oh Angus, sit down," says my mother with mingled patience and

exasperation, "he'll see it soon enough. We're almost there. Please sit down; people are looking at you."

My left hand lies beside my mother's right on the green upholstered cushion. My mother has brown eyes and brown hair and is three years younger than my father. She is very beautiful and her picture is often in the society pages of the papers in Montreal which is where we live.

"There it is," shouts my father triumphantly. "Look Alex, there's Cape Breton!" He takes his left hand down from the baggage rack and points across us to the blueness that is the Strait of Canso, with the gulls hanging almost stationary above the tiny fishing boats and the dark green of the spruce and fir mountains rising out of the water and trailing white wisps of mist about them like discarded ribbons hanging about a newly opened package.

The train lurches and he almost loses his balance and quickly has to replace his hand on the baggage rack. He is squeezing my right hand so hard he is hurting me and I can feel my fingers going numb within his grip. I would like to mention it but I do not know how to do so politely and I know he does not mean to cause me pain.

"Yes, there it is," says my mother without much enthusiasm, "now you can sit down like everybody else."

He does so but continues to hold my hand very fiercely. "Here," says my mother not unkindly, and passes him a Kleenex over my head. He takes it quietly and I am reminded of the violin records which he has at home in Montreal. My mother does not like them and says they all sound the same so he only plays them when she is out and we are alone. Then it is a time like church, very solemn and serious and sad and I am not supposed to talk but I do not know what else I am supposed to do; especially when my father cries.

Now the train is getting ready to go across the water on a boat. My father releases my hand and starts gathering our luggage because we are to change trains on the other side. After this is done we all go out on the deck of the ferry and watch the Strait as we groan over its placid surface and churn its tranquillity into the roiling turmoil of our own white-watered wake.

My father goes back into the train and reappears with the cheese sandwich which I did not eat and then we go to the stern of the ferry where the other people are tossing food to the convoy of screaming gulls which follows us on our way. The gulls are the whitest things that I have ever seen; whiter than the sheets on my bed at home, or the pink-eyed rabbit that died, or the winter's first snow. I think that since they are so beautiful they should somehow have more manners and in some way be more refined. There is one mottled brown, who feels very ill at ease and flies low and to the left of the noisy main flock. When he ventures into the thick of the fray his fellows scream and peck at him and drive him away. All three of us try to toss our pieces of cheese sandwich to him or into the water directly before him. He is so lonesome and all alone.

When we get to the other side we change trains. A blond young man is hanging from a slowly chugging train with one hand and drinking from a bottle which he holds in the other. I think it is a very fine idea and ask my father to buy me some pop. He says he will later but is strangely embarrassed. As we cross the tracks to our train, the blond young man begins to sing: "There once was an Indian maid." It is not the nice version but the dirty one which I and my friends have learned from the bigger boys in the sixth grade. I have somehow never before thought of grown-ups singing it. My parents are now walking very fast, practically dragging me by the hand over the troublesome tracks. They are both very red-faced and we all pretend we do not hear the voice that is receding in the distance.

When we are seated on the new train I see that my mother is very angry. "Ten years," she snaps at my father, "ten years I've raised this child in the city of Montreal and he has never seen an adult drink liquor out of a bottle, nor heard that kind of language. We have not been here five minutes and that is the first thing he sees and hears." She is on the verge of tears.

"Take it easy, Mary," says my father soothingly. "He doesn't understand. It's all right."

"It's not all right," says my mother passionately. "It's not all right at all. It's dirty and filthy and I must have been out of my mind to agree to this trip. I wish we were going back tomorrow."

The train starts to move and before long we are rattling along the shore. There are fishermen in little boats who wave good-naturedly at the train and I wave back. Later there are the black gashes of coal mines which look like scabs upon the greenness of the hills and the blueness of the ocean and I wonder if these are the mines in which my relatives work.

This train goes much slower than the last one and seems to stop every five minutes. Some of the people around us are talking in a language that I know is Gaelic although I do not understand it, others are sprawled out in their seats, some of them drowsing with their feet stuck out in the aisle. At the far end of the aisle two empty bottles roll endlessly back and forth clinking against themselves and the steel-bottomed seats. The coach creaks and sways.

The station is small and brown. There is a wooden platform in front of it illuminated by lights which shine down from two tall poles and are bombarded by squads of suicidal moths and June bugs. Beneath the lights there are little clusters of darkly clad men who talk and chew tobacco, and some ragged boys about my own age who lean against battered bicycles waiting for the bundles of newspapers that thud on the platform before their feet.

Two tall men detach themselves from one of the groups and approach us. I know they are both my uncles although I have only seen the younger one before. He lived at our house during part of the year that was the first grade and used to wrestle with me on the floor and play the violin records when no one was in. Then one day he was gone forever to survive only in my mother's neutral "It was the year your brother was here," or the more pointed "It was the year your drunken brother was here."

Now both men are very polite. They shake hands with my father and say "Hello Angie" and then, taking off their caps, "How do you do" to my mother. Then each of them lifts me up in the air. The younger one asks me if I remember him and I say "Yes" and he laughs, and puts me down. They carry our suitcases to a taxi and then we all bounce along a very rough street and up a hill, bump, bump, and stop before a large dark house which we enter.

In the kitchen of the house there are a great many people sitting around a big coal-burning stove even though it is summer. They all get up when we come in and shake hands and the women put their arms around my mother. Then I am introduced to the grandparents I have never seen. My grandmother is very tall with hair almost as white as the afternoon's gulls and eyes like the sea over which they flew. She wears a long black dress with a blue checkered apron over it and lifts me off my feet in powerful hands so that I can kiss her and look into her eyes. She smells of soap and water and hot rolls and asks me how I like living in Montreal. I have never lived anywhere else so I say I guess it is all right.

My grandfather is short and stocky with heavy arms and very big hands. He has brown eyes and his once red hair is almost all white now except for his eyebrows and the hair of his nostrils. He has a white moustache which reminds me of the walrus picture at school and the bottom of it is stained brown by the tobacco that he is chewing even now and spitting the juice into a coal scuttle which he keeps beside his chair. He is wearing a blue plaid shirt and brown trousers supported by heavy suspenders. He too lifts me up although he does not kiss me and he smells of soap and water and tobacco and leather. He asks me if I saw any girls that I liked on the train. I say "No," and he laughs and lowers me to the floor.

And now it is later and the conversation has died down and the people have gradually filtered out into the night until there are just the three of us, and my grandparents, and after a while my grandmother and my mother go upstairs to finalize the sleeping arrangements. My grandfather puts rum and hot water and sugar into two glasses and gives one to my father and then allows me to sit on his lap even though I am ten, and gives me sips from his glass. He is very different from Grandpa Gilbert in Montreal who wears white shirts and dark suits with a vest and a gold watch-chain across the front.

"You have been a long time coming home," he says to my father. "If you had come through that door as often as I've thought of you I'd've replaced the hinges a good many times."

"I know, I've tried, I've wanted to, but it's different in Montreal you know."

"Yes I guess so. I just never figured it would be like this. It seems so far away and we get old so quickly and a man always feels a certain way about his oldest son. I guess in some ways it is a good thing that we do not all go to school. I could never see myself being owned by my woman's family."

"Please don't start that already," says my father a little angrily. "I am not owned by anybody and you know it. I am a lawyer and I am in partnership with another lawyer who just happens to be my father-in-law. That's all."

"Yes, that's all," says my grandfather and gives me another sip from his glass. "Well, to change the subject, is this the only one you have after being married eleven years?"

My father is now red-faced like he was when we heard the young man singing. He says heatedly: "You know you're not changing the subject at all. I know what you're getting at. I know what you mean."

"Do you?" asks my grandfather quietly. "I thought perhaps that was different in Montreal too."

The two women come downstairs just as I am having another sip from the glass. "Oh Angus what can you be thinking of?" screams my mother rushing protectively toward me.

"Mary, please!" says my father almost desperately, "there's nothing wrong."

My grandfather gets up very rapidly, sets me on the chair he has just vacated, drains the controversial glass, rinses it in the sink and says, "Well, time for the working class to be in bed. Good-night all." He goes up the stairs walking very heavily and we can hear his boots as he thumps them on the floor.

"I'll put him to bed, Mary," says my father nodding toward me. "I know where he sleeps. Why don't you go to bed now? You're tired."

"Yes, all right," says my mother very gently. "I'm sorry. I didn't mean to hurt his feelings. Good-night." She kisses me and also my grandmother and her footsteps fade quietly up the stairs.

"I'm sorry Ma, she didn't mean it the way it sounded," says my father.

"I know. She finds it very different from what she's used to. And we are older and don't bounce back the way we once did. He is seventy-six now and the mine is hard on him and he feels he must work harder than ever to do his share. He works with different ones of the boys and he tells me that sometimes he thinks they are carrying him just because he is their father. He never felt that way with you or Alex but of course you were all much younger then. Still he always somehow felt that because those years between high school and college

212

were so good that you would both come back to him some day."

"But Ma, it can't be that way. I was twenty then and Alex nineteen and he was only in his early fifties and we both wanted to go to college so we could be something else. And we paid him back the money he loaned us and he seemed to want us to go to school then."

"He did not know what it was then. Nor I. And when you gave him back the money it was as if that was not what he'd had in mind at all. And what is the something you two became? A lawyer whom we never see and a doctor who committed suicide when he was twenty-seven. Lost to us the both of you. More lost than Andrew who is buried under tons of rock two miles beneath the sea and who never saw a college door."

"Well, he should have," says my father bitterly, "so should they all instead of being exploited and burrowing beneath the sea or becoming alcoholics that cannot even do that."

"I have my alcoholic," says my grandmother now standing very tall, "who was turned out of my Montreal lawyer's home."

"But I couldn't do anything with him, Ma, and it's different there. You just can't be that way, and — and oh hell, I don't know; if I were by myself he could have stayed forever."

"I know," says my grandmother now very softly, putting her hand upon his shoulder, "it's not you. But it seems that we can only stay forever if we stay right here. As we have stayed to the seventh generation. Because in the end that is all there is — just staying. I have lost three children at birth but I've raised eight sons. I have one a lawyer and one a doctor who committed suicide, one who died in coal beneath the sea and one who is a drunkard and four who still work the coal like their father and those four are all that I have that stand by me. It is these four that carry their father now that he needs it, and it is these four that carry the drunkard, that dug two days for Andrew's body, and that have given me thirty grandchildren in my old age."

"I know, Ma," says my father, "I know that and I appreciate it all, everything. It is just that, well somehow we just can't live in a clan system anymore. We have to see beyond ourselves and our own families. We have to live in the twentieth century."

"Twentieth century?" says my grandmother spreading her big hands across her checkered apron. "What is the twentieth century to me if I cannot have my own?"

It is morning now and I awake to the argument of the English sparrows outside my window and the fingers of the sun upon the floor. My parents are in my room discussing my clothes. "He really doesn't need them," says my father patiently. "But Angus I don't want him to look like a little savage," replies my mother as she lays out my newly pressed pants and shirt at the foot of the bed.

Downstairs I learn that my grandfather has already gone to work and as I solemnly eat my breakfast like a little old man beyond my years, I listen to the violin music on the radio and watch my grandmother as she spreads butter on the top of baking loaves and pokes the coals of her fire with a fierce enthusiasm that sends clouds of smoke billowing up to spread themselves against the yellowed paint upon her ceiling.

Then the little boys come in and stand shyly against the wall. There are seven of them and they are all between six and ten. "These are your cousins," says my grandmother to me and to them she says, "this is Alex from Montreal. He is come to visit with us and you are to be nice to him because he is one of our own."

Then I and my cousins go outside because it is what we are supposed to do and we ask one another what grades we are in and I say I dislike my teacher and they mostly say they like theirs which is a possibility I have never considered before. And then we talk about hockey and I try to remember the times I have been to the Forum in Montreal and what I think about Richard.

And then we go down through the town which is black and smoky and has no nice streets nor flashing lights like Montreal, and when I dawdle behind I suddenly find myself confronted by two older boys who say: "Hey, where'd y'get them sissy clothes?" I do not know what I am supposed to do until my cousins come back and surround me like the covered wagons around the women and children of the cowboy shows, when the Indians attack.

"This is our cousin," say the oldest two simultaneously and I think they are very fine and brave for they too are probably a little bit ashamed of me and I wonder if I would do the same for them. I have never before thought that perhaps I have been lonely all of my short life and I wish that I had brothers of my own — even sisters perhaps.

My almost-attackers wait awhile scuffing their shoes on the ashy sidewalk and then they separate and allow us to pass like a little band of cavalry going through the mountains.

We continue down through the town and farther beyond to the seashore where the fishermen are mending their gear and pumping the little boats in which they allow us to play. Then we skip rocks on the surface of the sea and I skip one six times and then stop because I know I have made an impression and doubt if I am capable of an encore.

And then we climb up a high, high hill that tumbles into the sea and a cousin says we will go to see the bull who apparently lives about a mile away. We are really out in the country now and it is getting hot and when I go to loosen my tie the collar button comes off and is forever lost in the grass through which we pass.

The bull lives in a big barn and my cousins ask an old man who looks like my grandfather if he expects any cows today. He says that he does not know, that you cannot tell about those things. We can look at the bull if we wish but we must not tease him nor go too close. He is very big and brown and white with a ring in his nose and he paws the floor of his stall and makes low noises while lowering his head and swinging it from side to side. Just as we are ready to leave the old man comes in carrying a long wooden staff which he snaps onto the bull's nose ring. "Well, it looks like you laddies are in luck," he says, "now be careful and get out of the way." I follow my cousins who run out into a yard where a man who has just arrived is standing holding a nervous cow by a halter and we sit appreciatively on the top rail of the wooden fence and watch the old man as he leads out the bull who is now moaning and dripping and frothing at the mouth. I have never seen anything like this before and watch with awe this something that is both beautiful and terrible and I know that

I will somehow not be able to tell my mother to whom I have told almost everything important that has happened in my young life.

And later as we leave, the old man's wife gives us some apples and says, "John you should be ashamed of yourself; in front of these children. There are some things that have to be but are not for children's eyes." The chastised old man nods and looks down upon his shoes but then looks up at us very gravely from beneath his bushy eyebrows, looks at us in a very special way and I know that it is only because we are all boys that he does this and that the look as it excludes the woman simultaneously includes us in something that I know and feel but cannot understand.

We go back then to the town and it is late afternoon and we have eaten nothing but the apples and as we climb the hill toward my grandparents' house I see my father striding down upon us with his newspaper under his arm.

He is not disturbed that I have stayed away so long and seems almost to envy us our unity and our dirt as he stands so straight and lonely in the prison of his suit and inquires of our day. And so we reply as children do, that we have been "playing," which is the old inadequate message set forth across the chasm of our intervening years to fall undelivered and unreceived into the nothingness between.

He is going down to the mine, he says, to meet the men when they come off their shift at four and he will take me if I wish. So I separate from my comrade-cousins and go back down the hill holding on to his hand which is something I do not often do. I think that I will tell him about the bull but instead I ask: "Why do all the men chew tobacco?"

"Oh," he says, "because it is a part of them and of their way of life. They do that instead of smoking."

"But why don't they smoke?"

"Because they are underground so much of their lives and they cannot light a match or a lighter or carry any open flame down there. It's because of the gas. Flame might cause an explosion and kill them all."

"But when they're not down there they could smoke cigarettes like Grandpa Gilbert in a silver cigarette holder and Mama says that chewing tobacco is a filthy habit."

"I know but these people are not at all like Grandpa Gilbert and there are things that Mama doesn't understand. It is not that easy to change what is a part of you."

We are approaching the mine now and everything is black and grimy and the heavily laden trucks are groaning past us. "Did you used to chew tobacco?"

"Yes, a very long time ago before you were even thought of."

"And was it hard for you to stop?"

"Yes it was, Alex," he says quietly, "more difficult than you will ever know."

We are now at the wash-house and the trains from the underground are thundering up out of the darkness and the men are jumping off and laughing and shouting to one another in a way that reminds me of recess. They are completely black with the exception of little white half-moons beneath their eyes and the eyes themselves. My grandfather is walking toward us between two of my uncles. He is not so tall as they nor does he take such long strides and they are pacing themselves to keep even with him the way my father sometimes does with me. Even his moustache is black or a very dirty grey except for the bottom of it where the tobacco stains it brown.

As they walk they are taking off their headlamps and unfastening the batteries from the broad belts which I feel would be very fine for carrying holsters and six-guns. They are also fishing for the little brass discs which bear their identification numbers. My father says that if they should be killed in the underground these little discs would tell who each man was. It does not seem like much consolation to me.

At a wicket that looks like the post office the men line up and pass their lamps and the little discs to an old man with glasses. He puts the lamps on a rack and the discs on a large board behind his back. Each disc goes on its special little numbered hook and this shows that its owner has returned. My grandfather is 572.

Inside the adjoining wash-house it is very hot and steamy like when you are in the bathroom a long, long time with the hot water running. There are long rows of numbered lockers with wooden benches before them. The floor is cement with little wooden slatted paths for the men to walk on as they pass bare-footed to and from the noisy showers at the building's farthest end.

"And did you have a good day today Alex?" asks my grandfather as we stop before his locker. And then unexpectedly and before I can reply he places his two big hands on either side of my head and turns it back and forth very powerfully on my shoulders. I can feel the pressure of his calloused fingers squeezing hard against my cheeks and pressing my ears into my head and I can feel the fine, fine, coal dust which I know is covering my face and I can taste it from his thumbs which are close against my lips. It is not gritty as I had expected but it is more like smoke than sand and almost like my mother's powder. And now he presses my face into his waist and holds me there for a long, long time with my nose bent over against the blackened buckle of his belt. Unable to see or hear or feel or taste or smell anything that is not black; holding me there engulfed and drowning in blackness until I am unable to breathe.

And my father is saying from a great distance: "What are you doing? Let him go! He'll suffocate." And then the big hands come away from my ears and my father's voice is louder and he sounds like my mother.

Now I am so black that I am almost afraid to move and the two men are standing over me looking into one another's eyes. "Oh, well," says my grandfather turning reluctantly toward his locker and beginning to open his shirt.

"I guess there is only one thing to do now," says my father quietly and he bends down slowly and pulls loose the laces of my shoes. Soon I am standing naked upon the wooden slats and my grandfather is the same beside me and then he guides and follows me along the wooden path that leads us to the showers and away from where my father sits. I look back once and see him sitting all alone on the bench which he has covered with his newspaper so that his suit will not be soiled.

When I come to the door of the vast shower room I hesitate because for a moment I feel afraid but I feel my grandfather strong and hairy behind me and

216

we venture out into the pouring water and the lathered, shouting bodies and the cakes of skidding yellow soap. We cannot find a shower at first until one of my uncles shouts to us and a soap-covered man points us in the right direction. We are already wet and the blackness of my grandfather's face is running down in two grey rivulets from the corners of his moustache.

My uncle at first steps out of the main stream but then the three of us stand and move and wash beneath the torrent that spills upon us. The soap is very yellow and strong. It smells like the men's washroom in the Montreal Forum and my grandfather tells me not to get it in my eyes. Before we leave he gradually turns off the hot water and increases the cold. He says this is so we will not catch cold when we leave. It gets colder and colder but he tells me to stay under it as long as I can and I am covered with goose pimples and my teeth are chattering when I jump out for the last time. We walk back through the washing men who are not so numerous now. Then along the wooden path and I look at the tracks our bare feet leave behind.

My father is still sitting on the bench by himself as we had left him. He is glad to see us return, and smiles. My grandfather takes two heavy towels out of his locker and after we are dry he puts on his clean clothes and I put on the only ones I have except the bedraggled tie which my father stuffs into his pocket. So we go out into the sun and walk up the long, long hill and I am allowed to carry the lunch pail with the thermos bottle rattling inside. We walk very slowly and say very little. Every once in a while my grandfather stops and turns to look back the way we have come. It is very beautiful. The sun is moving into the sea as if it is tired and the sea is very blue and very wide — wide enough it seems for a hundred suns. It touches the sand of the beach which is a slender boundary of gold separating the blue from the greenness of the grass which comes rolling down upon it. Then there is the mine silhouetted against it all, looking like a toy from a meccano set; yet its bells ring as the coal-laden cars fly up out of the deep, grumble as they are unloaded, and flee with thundering power down the slopes they leave behind. Then the blackened houses begin and march row and row up the hill to where we stand and beyond to where we go. Overhead the gulls are flying inland, slowly but steadily as if they are somehow very sure of everything. My grandfather says they always fly inland in the evening. They have done so as long as he can remember.

And now we are entering the yard and my mother is rushing toward me and pressing me to her and saying to everyone and no one, "Where has this child been all day? He has not been here since morning and has eaten nothing. I have been almost out of my mind." She buries her fingers in my hair and I feel very sorry for my mother because I think she loves me very much. "Playing," I say.

At supper I am so tired that I can hardly sit up at the table and my father takes me to bed before it is yet completely dark. I wake up once when I hear my parents talking softly at my door. "I am trying very hard. I really am," says my mother. "Yes, yes I know you are," says my father gently and they move off down the hall.

And now it is in the morning two weeks later and the train that takes us back will be leaving very soon. All our suitcases are in the taxi and the good-byes are almost all completed. I am the last to leave my grandmother as she stands beside her stove. She lifts me up as she did the first night and says, "Good-bye Alex, you are the only grandchild I will never know," and presses into my hand the crinkled dollar that is never spent.

My grandfather is not in although he has not gone to work and they say he has walked on ahead of us to the station. We bump down the hill to where the train is waiting beside the small brown building and he is on the platform talking with some other men and spitting tobacco over the side.

He walks over to us and everyone says good-bye at once. I am again the last and he shakes hands very formally this time. "Good-bye Alex," he says, "it was ten years before you saw me. In another ten I will not be here to see." And then I get on the train and none too soon for already it is beginning to move. Everyone waves but the train goes on because it must and it does not care for waving. From very far away I see my grandfather turn and begin walking back up his hill. And then there is nothing but the creak and sway of the coach and the blue sea with its gulls and the green hills with the gashes of their coal imbedded deeply in their sides. And we do not say anything but sit silent and alone. We have come from a great distance and have a long way now to go.

ABOUT THE LINES

1 Working in a small group, choose three important scenes from the story. For each scene, produce a model, sketch, or a diagram of the setting. Write a brief paragraph in which the features you have included are described in detail.

2 Identify and then list the factors that divide Angus from his family on Cape Breton.

3 List the major characters in this story. Beside each name note down:
a. the other characters with whom the person named is in conflict;
b. the other characters with whom the person named is in harmony.
Using brief notes, indicate the reason for the conflict or the harmony in each case. You might find it helpful to organize the material in columns.

BETWEEN THE LINES

1 Work in a group of four. Each group member should choose one of the following characters and write a brief description of the town in the voice of that character:
a. the father;
b. the mother;
c. the grandfather;
d. the son.
Compare and discuss the differences between the individual perceptions of the town.

2 In the voice of the grandfather, complete the following unfinished sentences and add another sentence if you wish. You may write this material or present it orally to a small group.

a. When I saw my son again after ten years, I felt . . .

b. My daughter-in-law . . .

c. My son seemed to think I was going to hurt the boy when I held him, but . . .

3 Write out two questions that you would like to ask the boy's mother. Try them on a partner, and discuss and change the answers until you both feel that they accurately reflect her character.

4 At several points in the story people speak to Alex as if he were more than a child. Identify three of these moments, quote the actual lines spoken to him, and then, in your own words, state the hidden message.

5 In the voice of Alex's mother, describe to a friend of your own social class, back in Montreal, the holiday that you spent with your husband's family. You can tape your monologue and play it for your partners.

BEYOND THE LINES

1 Imagine that you are the grandmother. Write a letter to your son, Angus, in which you tell him some things that you have learned of life, love, family, and human nature.

or

Imagine that you are the grandfather. Write a letter to Angus in which you talk of your hopes for your relationship with your son and of the reality of that relationship.

2 Working in a small group, produce a script for this story and then dramatize it for the rest of the class.

3 Using your librarian or your English teacher as a resource, research the structure of the ballad form. (See also definition on p. 349). Write a ballad in which you tell of the hardships and hazards of the life of either the Cape Breton miners or of any other group in the Canadian work force that habitually lives with discomfort and danger. You may wish to borrow a tune or write your own music to accompany the ballad.

4 Research the working conditions of the Cape Breton miners. Present your material to the class and be prepared to answer questions. Indicate any links you discovered between "The Return" and your research.

CANADIAN JANUARY N

Alden Nowlan

Ice storm: the hill
a pyramid of black crystal
down which the cars
slide like phosphorescent beetles
while I, walking backwards in obedience
to the wind, am possessed
of the fearful knowledge
my compatriots share
but almost never utter:
this is a country
where a man can die
                    simply from being
caught outside.

LOOKING IN

1 List the words and phrases that the poet uses to convey a sense of the potential and the real dangers of a Canadian winter night. In one sentence, use as many of these words and phrases as you can to describe a winter's night.

2 Divide the poem into two sections.
   a. Explain in one or two sentences how the second part of the poem comments on the first.
   b. State how the vocabulary differs in the two sections.

3 Write a prose account of the journey up the hill as it is related in this poem. Describe not only the sights but also the emotions and the physical sensations experienced by the poet.

LOOKING OUT

1 Every Canadian has a winter story! Write a personal memoir of a positive or a negative winter experience. Share your memoir with a small group of students and identify any common features in the memoirs.

2 "Canadian January Night" describes human beings in conflict with their environment. Write a poem on this theme.

3 Ice storms are unknown in most parts of the world. Describe to a newcomer to Canada what an ice storm is and the particular dangers associated with it.

THE USE OF FORCE

William Carlos Williams

A conflict of wills and the ony resolution — the use of force.

They were new patients to me, all I had was the name, Olson. Please come down as soon as you can, my daughter is very sick.

When I arrived I was met by the mother, a big startled looking woman, very clean and apologetic who merely said, Is this the doctor? and let me in. In the back, she added. You must excuse us, doctor, we have her in the kitchen where it is warm. It is very damp here sometimes.

The child was fully dressed and sitting on her father's lap near the kitchen table. He tried to get up, but I motioned for him not to bother, took off my overcoat and started to look things over. I could see that they were all very nervous, eyeing me up and down distrustfully. As often, in such cases, they weren't telling me more than they had to, it was up to me to tell them; that's why they were spending three dollars on me.

The child was fairly eating me up with her cold, steady eyes, and no expression to her face whatever. She did not move and seemed, inwardly, quiet; an unusually attractive little thing, and as strong as a heifer in appearance. But her face was flushed, she was breathing rapidly, and I realized that she had a high fever. She had magnificent blond hair, in profusion. One of those picture children often reproduced in advertising leaflets and the photogravure sections of the Sunday papers.

She's had a fever for three days, began the father and we don't know what it comes from. My wife has given her things, you know, like people do, but it don't do no good. And there's been a lot of sickness around. So we tho't you'd better look her over and tell us what is the matter.

As doctors often do I took a trial shot at it as a point of departure. Has she had a sore throat?

Both parents answered me together, No . . . No, she says her throat don't hurt her.

Does your throat hurt you? added the mother to the child. But the little girl's expression didn't change nor did she move her eyes from my face.

Have you looked?

I tried to, said the mother, but I couldn't see.

As it happens we had been having a number of cases of diphtheria in the school to which this child went during that month and we were all, quite apparently, thinking of that, though no one had as yet spoken of the thing.

Well, I said, suppose we take a look at the throat first. I smiled in my best professional manner and asking for the child's first name I said, come on, Mathilda, open your mouth and let's take a look at your throat.

Nothing doing.

Aw, come on, I coaxed, just open your mouth wide and let me take a look. Look, I said opening both hands wide. I haven't anything in my hands. Just open up and let me see.

Such a nice man, put in the mother. Look how kind he is to you. Come on, do what he tells you to. He won't hurt you.

At that I ground my teeth in disgust. If only they wouldn't use the word "hurt" I might be able to get somewhere. But I did not allow myself to be hurried or disturbed but speaking quietly and slowly I approached the child again.

As I moved my chair a little nearer suddenly with one cat-like movement both her hands clawed instinctively for my eyes and she almost reached them too. In fact she knocked my glasses flying and they fell, though unbroken, several feet away from me on the kitchen floor.

Both the mother and father almost turned themselves inside out in embarrassment and apology. You bad girl, said the mother, taking her and shaking her by one arm. Look what you've done. The nice man . . .

For heaven's sake, I broke in. Don't call me a nice man to her. I'm here to look at her throat on the chance that she might have diphtheria and possibly die of it. But that's nothing to her. Look here, I said to the child, we're going to look at your throat. You're old enough to understand what I'm saying. Will you open it now by yourself or shall we have to open it for you?

Not a move. Even her expression hadn't changed. Her breaths however were coming faster and faster. Then the battle began. I had to do it. I had to have a throat culture for her own protection. But first I told the parents that it was entirely up to them. I explained the danger but said that I would not insist on a throat examination so long as they would take the responsibility.

If you don't do what the doctor says you'll have to go to the hospital, the mother admonished her severely.

Oh yeah? I had to smile to myself. After all, I had already fallen in love with the savage brat, the parents were contemptible to me. In the ensuing struggle they grew more and more abject, crushed, exhausted while she surely rose to magnificent heights of insane fury of effort bred of her terror of me.

The father tried his best, and he was a big man but the fact that she was his daughter, his shame at her behaviour and his dread of hurting her made him release her just at the critical moment several times when I had almost achieved success, till I wanted to kill him. But his dread also that she might have diphtheria made him tell me to go on, go on though he himself was almost fainting, while the mother moved back and forth behind us raising and lowering her hands in an agony of apprehension.

Put her in front of you on your lap, I ordered, and hold both her wrists.

But as soon as he did the child let out a scream. Don't, you're hurting me. Let go of my hands. Let them go, I tell you. Then she shrieked terrifyingly, hysterically. Stop it! You're killing me!

Do you think she can stand it, doctor! said the mother.

You get out, said the husband to his wife. Do you want her to die of diphtheria?

Come on now, hold her, I said.

Then I grasped the child's head with my left hand and tried to get the wooden tongue depressor between her teeth. She fought, with clenched teeth, desperately! But now I also had grown furious — at a child. I tried to hold myself down but I couldn't. I know how to expose a throat for inspection. And I did my best. When finally I got the wooden spatula behind the last teeth and just the point of it into the mouth cavity, she opened up for an instant but before I could see anything she came down again and gripping the wooden blade between her molars she reduced it to splinters before I could get it out again.

Aren't you ashamed, the mother yelled at her. Aren't you ashamed to act like that in front of the doctor?

Get me a smooth-handled spoon of some sort, I told the mother. We're going through with this. The child's mouth was already bleeding. Her tongue was cut and she was screaming in wild hysterical shrieks. Perhaps I should have desisted and come back in an hour or more. No doubt it would have been better. But I have seen at least two children lying dead in bed of neglect in such cases, and feeling that I must get a diagnosis now or never I went at it again. But the worst of it was that I too had got beyond reason. I could have torn the child apart in my own fury and enjoyed it. It was a pleasure to attack her. My face was burning with it.

The damned little brat must be protected against her own idiocy, one says to one's self at such times. Others must be protected against her. It is social necessity. And all these things are true. But a blind fury, a feeling of adult shame, bred of a longing for muscular release are the operatives. One goes on to the end.

In a final unreasoning assault I overpowered the child's neck and jaws. I forced the heavy silver spoon back of her teeth and down her throat till she gagged. And there it was — both tonsils covered with membrane. She had fought valiantly to keep me from knowing her secret. She had been hiding that sore throat for three days at least and lying to her parents in order to escape just such an outcome as this.

Now truly she *was* furious. She had been on the defensive before but now she attacked. Tried to get off her father's lap and fly at me while tears of defeat blinded her eyes.

ABOUT THE LINES

1 This is a cloze exercise. Your teacher will give you a worksheet for it.

2 In point form, note in chronological order the stages in the child's resistance to the doctor from her initial sullen refusal to open her mouth to her eventual defeat under the full weight of his strength. Compare your information with your partners' and rectify any omissions.

3 In this story the writer uses extremely vivid language to describe the child's resistance to the doctor. Working with your partners, list the words that effectively convey the increasing violence of the conflict between doctor and child. In a few sentences, state how the vocabulary contributes to the overall effect of the story.

4 Produce an appropriate front cover for a printing of this story. Your cover should contain:
   a. the story title and author's name;
   b. an illustration that would attract potential readers and give them an indication of the subject matter of the story.

BETWEEN THE LINES

1 In the doctor's voice, explain to a close friend the various emotional reactions that you experienced towards Mathilda. Present your material orally to your partners and ask them to compare their interpretations with yours.

2 Discuss with your partners why you think the author has omitted all the normal punctuation for direct speech. Together produce a statement in which you explain why you agree or disagree with his use of this stylistic technique. Listen to the statements of other groups to see whether there is agreement or not.

3 The title of this selection is effective because, although it is appropriate, it leads the reader to expect a different sort of story. Make up at least three titles of your own that would be suitable for this story. You may be either obvious, subtle, or both.

4 Imagine that you are the little girl. Write out and then present orally to a small group the thoughts that are running through your head as you battle the doctor. Address your remarks to him. The following sentences might help you to get started:
a. If you think that you are going to put your fingers into my mouth . . .
b. I hate you. Keep away.
c. I'll eat you.

5 It is commonly supposed that adults act rationally while children act irrationally; this is not always so. Identify the points in the story where the doctor ceases to be governed by reason and, instead, is swayed by emotion. Imagine that you are the doctor and write an account of this incident in your diary after you have cooled down. Indicate your emotional state as you write.

BEYOND THE LINES

1 Write a memoir (real or fictitious) in which you describe a positive or a negative experience with a doctor or a dentist.

2 The author gives his readers an unconventional view of a doctor. For a period of a week, watch several television medical programs and analyse the presentation of the medical profession. Write a brief report entitled "The Media and the Medical Profession," in which you explain your conclusions.

3 Write a short story centring around a conflict between an adult and a child in which a clear clash of wills is revealed.

4 Make a nursery rhyme that might have been composed by Mathilda. You should attempt to convey a sense of the anger and hatred felt by the child. This nursery rhyme might serve as a model.
"I do not like thee, Dr. Fell
The reason why I cannot tell
But this I know, and know full well,
I do not like thee, Dr. Fell."

THE MOOSE AND THE SPARROW

Hugh Garner

From the very beginning Moose Maddon picked on him. The kid was bait for all of Maddon's cruel practical jokes around the camp. He was sent back to the toolhouse for left-handed saws, and down to the office to ask the pay cheater if the day's mail was in, though the rest of us knew it was only flown out every week.

The kid's name was Cecil, and Maddon used to mouth it with a simpering mockery, as if it pointed to the kid being something less than a man. I must admit though that the name fitted him, for Cecil was the least likely lumberjack I've seen in over twenty-five years in lumber camps. Though we knew he was intelligent enough, and a man too, if smaller than most of us, we all kidded him, in the good-natured way a bunkhouse gang will. Maddon however always lisped the kid's name.

Moose Maddon was as different from Cecil as it is possible for two human beings to be and still stay within the species. He was a big moose of a man, even for a lumber stiff, with a round flat unshaven face that looked down angrily and dourly at the world. Cecil on the other hand was hardly taller than an axe handle, and almost as thin. He was about nineteen years old, with the looks of an inquisitive sparrow behind his thick horn-rimmed glasses. He had been sent out to the camp for the summer months by a distant relative who had a connection with the head office down in Vancouver.

That summer we were cutting big stuff in an almost inaccessible stand of Douglas fir about fifty miles out of Nanaimo. The logs were catted five miles down to the river where they were bunked waiting for the drive. Cecil had signed on as a whistle punk, but after a few days of snarling the operation with wrong signals at the wrong time and threatening to hang the rigging-slingers in their own chokers, he was transferred to Maddon's gang as a general handyman. Besides going on all the ridiculous and fruitless errands for Moose, he carried the noon grub to the gangs from the panel truck that brought it out from camp, made the tea and took the saws and axes in to old Bobbins, the squint eye, to be sharpened.

For the first two weeks after he arrived, the jokes were the usual ones practised on a greenhorn, but when they seemed to be having little or no effect on his bumbling habits and even temper Moose devised more cruel and intricate ones. One night Moose and a cohort of his called Lefevre carried the sleeping Cecil, mattress and all, down to the river and threw him in. The kid almost drowned, but when he had crawled up on shore and regained his breath he merely smiled at his tormentors and ran back to the bunkhouse, where he

227

sat shivering in a blanket on the springs of his bunk till the sun came up.

Another time Moose painted a wide moustache with tar on Cecil's face while he slept. It took him nearly a week to get it all off, and his upper lip was red and sore-looking for longer than that.

Nearly all of us joined in the jokes on Cecil at first, putting a young raccoon in his bunk, kicking over his tea water, hiding his clothes or tying them in knots, all the usual things. It wasn't long though until the other men noticed that Moose Maddon's jokes seemed to have a grim purpose. You could almost say he was carrying out a personal vendetta against the kid for refusing to knuckle under or cry "Uncle". From then on everybody but Moose let the kid alone.

One evening as a few of us sat outside the bunkhouse shooting the guff, Moose said, "Hey, Cecil dear, what do you do over on the mainland?"

"Go to school," Cecil answered.

Moose guffawed. "Go to school? At your age?"

Cecil just grinned.

"What school d'ya go to, Cecil? Kindergarten?" Moose asked him, guffawing some more.

"No."

"You afraid to tell us?"

"No."

"Well, what school d'ya go to?"

"U.B.C."

"What's that, a hairdressin' school?"

"No, the university."

"University! You!"

Moose, who was probably a Grade Four dropout himself, was flabbergasted. I'm sure that up until that minute he'd been living in awe of anybody with a college education.

"What you takin' up?" he asked, his face angry and serious now.

"Just an arts course," Cecil said.

"You mean paintin' pictures an' things?"

"No, not quite," the kid answered.

For once Moose had nothing further to say.

From then on things became pretty serious as far as Moose and Cecil were concerned. On at least two occasions the other men on the gang had to prevent Moose from beating the boy up, and old Bobbins even went so far as to ask Mr. Semple, the walking boss, to transfer the youngster to another gang. Since learning that Cecil was a college boy, Moose gave him no peace at all, making him do jobs that would have taxed the strength of any man in the camp, and cursing him out when he was unable to do them, or do them fast enough.

The kid may not have been an artist, as Moose had thought, but he could make beautiful things out of wire. Late in the evenings he would sit on his bunk and fashion belt-buckles, rings and tie-clips from a spool of fine copper wire he'd found in the tool shed. He made things for several of the men, always refusing payment for them. He used to say it gave him something to do, since he couldn't afford to join in the poker games.

One evening late in the summer as I was walking along the river having an after-supper pipe, I stumbled upon Cecil curled up on a narrow sandy beach.

His head was buried in his arms and his shoulders were heaving with sobs. I wanted to turn around without letting him know he'd been seen, but he looked so lonely crying there by himself that I walked over and tapped him on the shoulder.

He jumped as if I'd prodded him with a peavey, and swung around, his eyes nearly popping from his head with fright. The six weeks he'd spent working under Moose Maddon hadn't done his nerves any good.

"It's all right, kid," I said.

"Oh! Oh, it's you, Mr. Anderson!"

He was the only person in camp who ever called me anything but "Pop".

"I don't mean to butt in," I said. "I was just walking along here, and couldn't help seeing you. Are you in trouble?"

He wiped his eyes on his sleeve before answering me. Then he turned and stared out across the river.

"This is the first time I broke down," he said, wiping his glasses.

"Is it Moose?"

"Yes."

"What's he done to you now?"

"Nothing more than he's been doing to me all along. At first I took it — you know that, Mr. Anderson, don't you?"

I nodded.

"I thought that after I was out here a couple of weeks it would stop," he said. "I expected the jokes that were played on me at first. After all I was pretty green when I arrived here. When they got to know me the other men stopped, but not that — that Moose."

He seemed to have a hard time mouthing the other's name.

"When are you going back to school?" I asked him.

"In another couple of weeks."

"Do you think you can stand it until then?"

"I need all the money I can make, but it's going to be tough."

I sat down on the sand beside him and asked him to tell me about himself. For the next ten or fifteen minutes he poured out the story of his life; he was one of those kids who are kicked around from birth. His mother and father had split up while he was still a baby, and he'd been brought up in a series of foster homes. He'd been smart enough, though, to graduate from high school at seventeen. By a miracle of hard work and self-denial he'd managed to put himself through the first year of university, and his ambition was to continue on to law school. The money he earned from his summer work here at the camp was to go towards his next year's tuition.

When he finished we sat in silence for a while. Then he asked, "Tell me, Mr. Anderson, why does Maddon pick on me like he does?"

I thought about his question for a long time before answering it. Finally I said, "I guess that deep down Moose knows you are smarter than he is in a lot of ways. I guess he's — well, I guess you might say he's jealous of you."

"No matter what I do, or how hard I try to please him, it's no good."

"It never is," I said.

"How do you mean?"

I had to think even longer this time. "There are some men, like Moose

Maddon, who are so twisted inside that they want to take it out on the world. They feel that most other men have had better breaks than they've had, and it rankles inside them. They try to get rid of this feeling by working it out on somebody who's even weaker than they are. Once they pick on you there's no way of stopping them short of getting out of their way or beating it out of their hide."

Cecil gave me a wry grin. "I'd never be able to beat it out of the — the Moose's hide."

"Then try to keep out of his way."

"I can't for another two weeks," he said. "I'm afraid that before then he'll have really hurt me."

I laughed to reassure him, but I was afraid of the same thing myself. I knew that Moose was capable of going to almost any lengths to prevent Cecil leaving the camp without knuckling under at least once; his urge seemed to me to be almost insane. I decided to talk to George Semple myself in the morning, and have the boy flown out on the next plane.

"I don't think Moose would go so far as to really hurt you," I told him.

"Yes he would! He would, Mr. Anderson, I know it! I've seen the way he's changed. All he thinks about any more are ways to make me crawl. It's no longer a case of practical jokes; he wants to kill me!"

My reassuring laugh stuck in my throat this time. "In another two weeks, son, you'll be back in Vancouver, and all this will seem like a bad dream."

"He'll make sure I leave here crippled," Cecil said.

We walked back to the camp together, and I managed to calm him down some.

The next day I spoke to Semple, the walking boss, and convinced him we should get the boy out of there. There was never any thought of getting rid of Moose, of course. Saw bosses were worth their weight in gold, and the top brass were calling for more and more production all the time. Whatever else Moose was, he was the best production foreman in the camp. When Semple spoke to Cecil, however, the kid refused to leave. He said he'd made up his mind to stick it out until his time was up.

Though my gang was working on a different side than Maddon's, I tried to keep my eye on the boy from then on. For a week things went on pretty much as usual, then one suppertime Cecil came into the dining hall without his glasses. Somebody asked him what had happened, and he said there'd been an accident, and that Moose had stepped on them. We all knew how much of an accident it had been; luckily the kid had an old spare pair in his kit. Few of his gang had a good word for Moose any more, which only seemed to make him more determined to take his spite out on the kid.

That evening I watched Cecil fashioning a signet ring for one of the men out of wire and a piece of quartz the man had found. The way he braided the thin wire and shaped it around a length of thin sapling was an interesting thing to see. Moose was watching him too, but pretending not to. You could see he hated the idea of Cecil getting along so well with the other men.

"I was going to ask you to make me a new watch strap before you left," I said to Cecil. "But it looks like you're running out of wire."

The kid looked up. "I still have about twenty-five feet of it left," he said.

"That'll be enough for what I have in mind. Don't worry, Mr. Anderson, I'll make you the watch strap before I leave."

The next afternoon there was quite a commotion over where Maddon's gang were cutting, but I had to wait until the whistle blew to find out what had happened. Cecil sat down to supper with his right hand heavily bandaged.

"What happened?" I asked one of Maddon's men.

"Moose burned the kid's hand," he told me. "He heated the end of a saw blade in the tea fire, and then called the kid to take it to the squint eye to be sharpened. He handed the hot end to Cecil, and it burned his hand pretty bad."

"But — didn't any of you —?"

"None of us was around at the time. When we found out, big Chief went after Moose with a cant hook, but the rest of us held him back. He would have killed Moose. If Maddon doesn't leave the kid alone, one of us is going to have to cripple him for sure."

Moose had been lucky that The Chief, a giant Indian called Danny Corbett, hadn't caught him. I made up my mind to have Cecil flown out in the morning without fail, no matter how much he protested.

That evening the kid turned in early, and we made sure there was always one of us in the bunkhouse to keep him from being bothered by anybody. He refused to talk about the hand-burning incident at all, but turned his head to the wall when anybody tried to question him about it. Moose left shortly after supper to drink and play poker in Camp Three, about a mile away through the woods.

I woke up during the night to hear a man laughing near the edge of the camp, and Maddon's name being called. I figured it was Moose and Lefevre coming home drunk from Camp Three, where the bull cook boot-legged homebrew.

When I got up in the morning, Cecil was already awake and dressed, sitting on the edge of his bunk plaiting a long length of his copper wire, using his good hand and the ends of the fingers of the one that was burned.

"What are you doing up so early?" I asked him.

"I went to bed right after chow last night, so I couldn't sleep once it got light." He pointed to the plaited wire. "This is going to be your watch strap."

"But you didn't need to make it now, Cecil," I said. "Not with your hand bandaged and everything."

"It's all right, Mr. Anderson," he assured me. "I can manage it okay, and I want to get it done as soon as I can."

Just as the whistle blew after breakfast one of the jacks from Camp Three came running into the clearing shouting that Moose Maddon's body was lying at the bottom of a deep narrow ravine outside the camp. This ravine was crossed by means of a fallen log, and Moose must have lost his footing on it coming home drunk during the night. There was a free fall of more than forty feet down to a rocky stream bed.

None of us were exactly broken-hearted about Moose kicking off that way, but the unexpectedness of it shocked us. We all ran to the spot, and the boys rigged a sling from draglines and hauled the body to the top of the ravine. I asked Lefevre if he'd been with Moose the night before, but he told me he hadn't gone over to Camp Three. Later in the day the district coroner flew out from Campbell River or somewhere, and after inspecting the log bridge made us rig a handline along it. He made out a certificate of accidental death.

When they flew the body out, Cecil stood with the rest of us on the river bank, watching the plane take off. If I'd been in his place I'd probably have been cheering, but he showed no emotion at all, not relief, happiness, or anything else.

He worked on my watch strap that evening, and finished it the next day, fastening it to my watch and attaching my old buckle to it. It looked like a real professional job, but when I tried to pay him for it he waved the money aside.

It was another week before Cecil packed his things to leave. His hand had begun to heal up nicely, and he was already beginning to lose the nervous twitches he'd had while Moose was living. When he was rowed out to the company plane, all the boys from his bunkhouse were on the river bank to see him go. The last we saw of Cecil was his little sparrow smile, and his hand waving to us from the window.

One day in the fall I went out to the ravine to see how the handline was making it. It still shocked me to think that Maddon, who had been as sure-footed as a chipmunk, and our best man in a log-rolling contest, had fallen to his death the way he had. Only then did I notice something nobody had looked for before. In the bark of the trunks of two small trees that faced each other diagonally across the fallen log were burn marks that could have been made by wire loops. A length of thin wire rigged from one to the other would have crossed the makeshift footbridge just high enough to catch a running man on the shin, and throw him into the ravine. Maddon could have been running across the log that night, if he'd been goaded by the laughter and taunts of somebody waiting at the other end. I remembered the sound of laughter and the shouting of Maddon's name.

I'm not saying that's what happened, you understand, and for all I know nobody was wandering around outside the bunkhouses on the night of Maddon's death, not Cecil or anybody else. Still, it gives me a queer feeling sometimes, even yet, to look down at my wrist. For all I know I may be the only man in the world wearing the evidence of a murder as a wristwatch strap.

ABOUT THE LINES

1 You are the casting director for a dramatization of this story. Write the following for the scouts who are looking for actors to play the roles of Moose Maddon and Cecil:
   a. a physical description of Moose;
   b. a personality profile of Moose;
   c. a physical description of Cecil;
   d. a personality profile of Cecil.

2 Working with your partners, write an explanation of the strategy that Cecil used to eliminate Moose Maddon.

3 Read the story twice and then retell it onto a tape. Play your tape for someone who has not read the story and answer any questions that he/she might have. Then, play the tape for someone who has read the story and see if the listener can point out any weaknesses in your narration. If there are any weaknesses, polish up your narration and retape it. Play the tape for another group of students who are not familiar with the story for their comments and questions.

BETWEEN THE LINES

1 Discuss with your partners why the author titled this story "The Moose and the Sparrow." Together come up with two more titles that capture the essence of the story.

2 Imagine that you were an observer at the lumber camp that summer. What questions would you like to ask Moose about himself and his attitude toward and treatment of Cecil? Write out your questions and discuss them with your partners to outline possible answers.

3 "Cecil is really a much stronger and more resourceful person than Moose." Support this statement by listing examples of Cecil's courage and cunning. Compare your list with your partners' and discuss any differences that you find.

4 In one or two sentences, explain why Cecil's choice of murder weapon is a final joke on Moose. Compare your analysis with those of your partners'.

BEYOND THE LINES

1 Write an entry in Cecil's diary in which he vents his frustrations and fears about Moose. Then write an entry in which Cecil describes his feelings after he leaves the lumber camp for good.

2 Write a short story involving:
a. a bully;
b. an intelligent but physically weaker victim;
c. revenge.

3 Working with a partner, script and dramatize a conversation between Anderson and Cecil when they unexpectedly meet five years later.

BY ANY OTHER NAME

Santha Rama Rau

At the Anglo-Indian day school[1] in Zorinabad to which my sister and I were sent when she was eight and I was five and a half, they changed our names. On the first day of school, a hot, windless morning of a north Indian September, we stood in the headmistress's study and she said, "Now you're the *new* girls. What are your names?"

My sister answered for us. "I am Premila, and she" — nodding in my direction — "is Santha."

The headmistress had been in India, I suppose, fifteen years or so, but she still smiled her helpless inability to cope with Indian names. Her rimless half-glasses glittered, and the precarious bun on the top of her head trembled as she shook her head. "Oh, my dears, those are much too hard for me. Suppose we give you pretty English names. Wouldn't that be more jolly? Let's see, now — Pamela for you, I think." She shrugged in a baffled way at my sister. "That's as close as I can get. And for *you*," she said to me, "how about Cynthia? Isn't that nice?"

My sister was always less easily intimidated than I was, and while she kept a stubborn silence, I said, "Thank you," in a very tiny voice.

We had been sent to that school because my father, among his responsibilities as an officer of the civil service, had a tour of duty to perform in the villages around that steamy little provincial town, where he had his headquarters at that time. He used to make his shorter inspection tours on horseback, and a week before, in the stale heat of a typically postmonsoon day, we had waved good-bye to him and a little procession — an assistant, a secretary, two bearers, and the man to look after the bedding rolls and luggage. They rode away through our large garden, still bright green from the rains, and we turned back into the twilight of the house and the sound of fans whispering in every room.

Up to then, my mother had refused to send Premila to school in the British-run establishments of that time, because, she used to say, "you can bury a dog's tail for seven years and it still comes out curly, and you can take a Britisher away from his home for a lifetime and he still remains insular." The examinations and degrees from entirely Indian schools were not, in those days, considered valid. In my case, the question had never come up, and probably never would

---

[1] *Anglo-Indian day school:* school in India with teachers from England during the days when India was part of the British Empire.

235

have come up if Mother's extraordinary good health had not broken down. For the first time in my life, she was not able to continue the lessons she had been giving us every morning. So our Hindi books were put away, the stories of the Lord Krishna as a little boy were left in mid-air, and we were sent to the Anglo-Indian school.

That first day at school is still, when I think of it, a remarkable one. At that age, if one's name is changed, one develops a curious form of dual personality. I remember having a curious detached and disbelieving concern in the actions of "Cynthia," but certainly no responsibility. Accordingly, I followed the thin, erect back of the headmistress down the veranda to my classroom feeling, at most, a passing interest in what was going to happen to me in this strange, new atmosphere of School.

The building was Indian in design, with wide verandas opening onto a central courtyard, but Indian verandas are usually whitewashed, with stone floors. These, in the tradition of British schools, were painted dark brown and had matting on the floors. It gave a feeling of extra intensity to the heat.

I suppose there were about a dozen Indian children in the school — which contained perhaps forty children in all — and four of them were in my class. They were all sitting at the back of the room, and I went to join them. I sat next to a small, solemn girl who didn't smile at me. She had long, glossy-black braids and wore a cotton dress, but she still kept her Indian jewelry — a gold chain around her neck, thin gold bracelets, and tiny ruby studs in her ears. The cotton dress should have looked strange, but all I could think of was that I should ask my mother if I couldn't wear a dress to school, too, instead of my Indian clothes.

I can't remember too much about the proceedings in class that day, except for the beginning. The teacher pointed to me and asked me to stand up. "Now, dear, tell the class your name."

I said nothing.

"Come along," she said, frowning slightly. "What's your name, dear?"

"I don't know," I said, finally.

The English children in the front of the class — there were about eight or ten of them — giggled and twisted around in their chairs to look at me. I sat down quickly and opened my eyes very wide, hoping in that way to dry them off. The little girl with the braids put out her hand and very lightly touched my arm. She still didn't smile.

Most of that morning I was rather bored. I looked briefly at the children's drawings pinned to the wall, and then concentrated on a lizard clinging to the ledge of the high, barred window behind the teacher's head. Occasionally it would shoot out its long yellow tongue for a fly, and then it would rest, with its eyes closed and its belly palpitating, as though it were swallowing several times quickly. The lessons were mostly concerned with reading and writing and simple numbers — things that my mother had already taught me — and I paid very little attention. The teacher wrote on the easel blackboard words like "bat" and "cat," which seemed babyish to me; only "apple" was new and incomprehensible.

When it was time for the lunch recess, I followed the girl with braids out onto the veranda. There the children from the other classes were assembled. I saw Premila at once and ran over to her, as she had charge of our lunchbox.

The children were all opening packages and sitting down to eat sandwiches. Premila and I were the only ones who had Indian food — thin wheat chapatties, some vegetable curry, and a bottle of buttermilk. Premila thrust half of it into my hand and whispered fiercely that I should go and sit with my class, because that was what the others seemed to be doing.

The enormous black eyes of the little Indian girl from my class looked at my food longingly, so I offered her some. But she only shook her head and plowed her way solemnly through her sandwiches.

I was very sleepy after lunch, because at home we always took a siesta. It was usually a pleasant time of day, with the bedroom darkened against the harsh afternoon sun, the drifting off into sleep with the sound of Mother's voice reading a story in one's mind, and, finally, the shrill, fussy voice of the ayah[2] waking one for tea.

At school, we rested for a short time on low, folding cots on the veranda, and then we were expected to play games. During the hot part of the afternoon we played indoors, and after the shadows had begun to lengthen and the slight breeze of the evening had come up we moved outside to the wide courtyard.

I had never really grasped the system of competitive games. At home, whenever we played tag or guessing games, I was always allowed to "win" — "Because," Mother used to tell Premila, "she is the youngest, and we have to allow for that." I had often heard her say it, and it seemed quite reasonable to me, but the result was that I had no idea of what "winning" meant.

When we played twos-and-threes that afternoon at school, in accordance with my training, I let one of the small English boys catch me, but was naturally rather puzzled when the other children did not return the courtesy. I ran about for what seemed like hours without ever catching anyone, until it was time for school to close. Much later I learned that my attitude was called "not being a good sport," and I stopped allowing myself to be caught, but it was not for years that I really learned the spirit of the thing.

When I saw our car come up to the school gate, I broke away from my classmates and rushed toward it yelling, "Ayah! Ayah!" It seemed like an eternity since I had seen her that morning — a wizened, affectionate figure in her white cotton sari, giving me dozens of urgent and useless instructions on how to be a good girl at school. Premila followed more sedately, and she told me on the way home never to do that again in front of the other children.

When we got home we went straight to Mother's high, white room to have tea with her, and I immediately climbed onto the bed and bounced gently up and down on the springs. Mother asked how we had liked our first day in school. I was so pleased to be home and to have left that peculiar Cynthia behind that I had nothing whatever to say about school, except to ask what "apple" meant. But Premila told Mother about the classes, and added that in her class they had weekly tests to see if they had learned their lessons well.

I asked, "What's a test?"

Premila said, "You're too small to have them. You won't have them in your class for donkey's years." She had learned the expression that day and was using it for the first time. We all laughed enormously at her wit. She also told Mother,

<hr />

[2] Ayah: maid or nurse.

in an aside, that we should take sandwiches to school the next day. Not, she said, that *she* minded. But they would be simpler for me to handle.

That whole lovely evening I didn't think about school at all. I sprinted barefoot across the lawns with my favourite playmate, the cook's son, to the stream at the end of the garden. We quarrelled in our usual way, waded in the tepid water under the lime trees, and waited for the night to bring out the smell of the jasmine. I listened with fascination to his stories of ghosts and demons, until I was too frightened to cross the garden alone in the semidarkness. The ayah found me, shouted at the cook's son, scolded me, hurried me in to supper — it was an entirely usual, wonderful evening.

It was a week later, the day of Premila's first test, that our lives changed rather abruptly. I was sitting at the back of my class in my usual inattentive way, only half listening to the teacher. I had started a rather guarded friendship with the girl with the braids, whose name turned out to be Nalini (Nancy, in school). The three other Indian children were already fast friends. Even at that age it was apparent to all of us that friendship with the English or Anglo-Indian children was out of the question. Occasionally, during the class, my new friend and I would draw pictures and show them to each other secretly.

The door opened sharply and Premila marched in. At first the teacher smiled at her in a kindly and encouraging way and said, "Now, you're little Cynthia's sister?"

Premila didn't even look at her. She stood with her feet planted firmly apart and her shoulders rigid, and addressed herself directly to me. "Get up," she said. "We're going home."

I didn't know what had happened, but I was aware that it was a crisis of some sort. I rose obediently and started to walk toward my sister.

"Bring your pencils and your notebook," she said.

I went back for them, and together we left the room. The teacher started to say something just as Premila closed the door, but we didn't wait to hear what it was.

In complete silence we left the school grounds and started to walk home. Then I asked Premila what the matter was. All she would say was "We're going home for good."

It was a very tiring walk for a child of five and a half, and I dragged along behind Premila with my pencils growing sticky in my hand. I can still remember looking at the dusty hedges and the tangles of thorns in the ditches by the side of the road, smelling the faint fragrance from the eucalyptus trees and wondering whether we would ever reach home. Occasionally a horse-drawn tonga passed us, and the women, in their pink or green silks, stared at Premila and me trudging along on the side of the road. A few coolies and a line of women carrying baskets of vegetables on their heads smiled at us. But it was nearing the hottest time of the day, and the road was almost deserted. I walked more and more slowly, and shouted to Premila, from time to time, "Wait for me!" with increasing peevishness. She spoke to me only once, and that was to tell me to carry my notebook on my head, because of the sun.

When we got to our house the ayah was just taking a tray of lunch into Mother's room. She immediately started a long, worried questioning about what are you children doing back here at this hour of the day.

Mother looked very startled and very concerned, and asked Premila what had happened.

Premila said, "We had our test today, and She made me and the other Indians sit at the back of the room, with a desk between each one."

Mother said, "Why was that, darling?"

"She said it was because Indians cheat," Premila added. "So I don't think we should go back to that school."

Mother looked very distant, and was silent a long time. At last she said, "Of course not, darling." She sounded displeased.

We all shared the curry she was having for lunch, and afterward I was sent off to the beautifully familiar bedroom for my siesta. I could hear Mother and Premila talking through the open door.

Mother said, "Do you suppose she understood all that?"

Premila said, "I shouldn't think so. She's a baby."

Mother said, "Well, I hope it won't bother her."

Of course, they were both wrong. I understood it perfectly, and I remember it all very clearly. But I put it happily away, because it had all happened to a girl called Cynthia, and I was never particularly interested in her.

ABOUT THE LINES

1 Identify and summarize the incidents which indicate that the school staff did not understand the culture of the Indians in the school.

2 In Santha's adult voice, explain why you were not successful in competitive games at school. Present your viewpoint in a letter to a friend of your own age or to one of your children.

3 The headmistress is a caricature (see p. 350) of a schoolmistress.
   a. Draw a child's picture of her and emphasize the details that are mentioned in this memoir. Exchange your drawing with your partners and add any details that you may have missed.
   b. List the characteristics of the mother and the ayah that a child would appreciate but that are missing in the headmistress.

4 Write a paragraph contrasting the home and the school environment of the girls. You might begin with a sentence such as:
For us children, home and school were two totally different worlds.

BETWEEN THE LINES

1 Imagine that you are Santha, and in an oral statement explain why you said that you did not know your own name when you were asked in class. Listen to the statements made by your partners and compare them with yours, to check for similarities and differences.

2 In a few sentences, explain the effect that changing her name had upon Santha. Now discuss in a small group the last seven lines of this selection and decide whether or not Santha is being totally honest in saying "and I never was really particularly interested in her" (Cynthia).

3 Imagine that you are the mother, and write a diary entry for the day on which the examination incident occurred. Be sure to include your emotional reaction to the prejudice to which your children were subjected.

4 This selection is non-fiction; that is, the events described have actually happened. Discuss in a small group if this knowledge affects your reaction to the piece and present your conclusions to others who have read the story. You might choose to compare the impact of this non-fictional memoir with the impact of the fictional "The Return" on page 208, which also deals with a conflict of cultures and generations.

BEYOND THE LINES

1 Write your own memoir of an incident at school in which you found yourself to be out of step with those around you or in conflict with one of the school rules. You may invent a situation if you wish. Share your memoir with your partners.

2 Working in a small group, interview a number of the students in your school to find out how they feel about their names and names in general. Some questions that you might ask are:
Do you like your name? Why? Why not?
What name would you prefer? Why?
Do you associate any particular characteristics with certain names?
What is your favourite boy's/girl's name?
Do you object to people altering your name, e.g., by shortening it?

3 Imagine that you are the class teacher of either Premila or Santha and write in her report card your opinion of the behaviour and attitude of the little girl in your class and around the school. You may add extra details if you wish.

4 What career(s) would you suggest for Premila based upon what you know of her as a child? Imagine that you are a career counsellor and present this information on a "Career Suggestion Sheet" of your own design.

GERALDE AND THE GREEN, GREEN GRASS

Robert Fontaine

My great-uncle Geralde, at the age of ninety-seven, developed an intense liking for walking barefoot in the grass. We ourselves had no grass, but in front of the house next door was a nice young lawn. Around this lawn there was a thin string running. In the middle of the lawn was a sign:

KEEP OFF THE GRASS

Geralde and I used to sit on the verandah and look at the grass next door.

"We, too," Geralde said, "should have grass. I *like* grass."

"The ground is no good for grass," I said. I was about eleven, and a student of where grass *would* grow and where it *wouldn't*.

"Next door, same ground," Geralde said. Geralde was so old he often talked like that to conserve breath.

Geralde rocked in the old chair and laughed his shrunken head off.

"Name of a name! Oho! It came with the earth, the grass. Like a jelly roll. Oho!"

I was insulted. "It's true," I said, "because I saw it come. A truck arrived with many rolls of grass with earth attached. They placed all the pieces together and *voilà* a lawn!"

"When you are older," Geralde said, "you will have more sense. Over there the grass grew. Over here it will grow. In France I became a member of the French Academy of Botany for the green grass I grew."

Geralde planted grass seeds in front of our house. He watered them with a watering can. He filled one can and watered. The rest he left dry. He had a theory that the water found its way to the places it was needed.

"The grass which is dry opens up the mouth and the water advances," my great-uncle explained.

"This is not the way we learn in school," I remarked.

"Tell me," Geralde asked, "what is the capital of Peru?"

"I do not know," I said.

"You see?" Geralde cried triumphantly. "In school they teach you nothing."

Of course no grass grew in front of our house. Geralde decided the birds ate the seed before they had a chance to take root. He borrowed my gun which shot corks and sat on the verandah every day. Whenever a bird lighted on the yard Uncle Geralde let go at him with the popgun. He never hit anything, but he scared the birds away all right.

A chicken roamed out front from in back and he could not even hit the chicken, though he scared it.

"Chickens eat corn, not grass, anyway," Geralde said.

What Geralde did hit was Miss Lapean, who lived next door and owned the lawn which they had brought in pieces like a jelly roll.

She was walking by when Geralde aimed at a sparrow and popped Miss Lapean in the nose. Miss Lapean's face turned red and she ran up the walk and shook her fist at old great-uncle Geralde. Geralde nearly fainted.

"You want to kill me?" she shrieked.

"I aim at the sparrow," Geralde said.

"You're crazy," Miss Lapean shouted.

"No. You are crazy," Geralde countered. "You buy grass like a jelly roll instead of growing it in the normal manner. I will report it to the police. A crazy woman lives next door to me."

"If anybody is reported to the police it will be you," Miss Lapean said. Then she ran down the walk and into her own house.

"I think," Geralde said to me, "it is Miss Lapean who pulls up my grass. She is jealous."

"Since we have no grass, how can she pull it up?" I asked.

"Don't argue with your elders," Geralde warned me.

It was about a week later, and just as dawn was making everything bright, that I looked out my window and saw Geralde in front of Miss Lapean's.

He had his shoes off and he was running barefoot through the grass which was wet with morning dew. It would have been all right if he had not started to dance like some wild creature of the woods and to sing at the top of his voice.

The noise attracted Miss Lapean, who came out on her verandah in a bathrobe, her hair in curlers.

"*Va t'en chez vous!*" Miss Lapean shouted. "*Va donc!* Go away, crazy man!"

Geralde turned around and secured a headlock on Miss Lapean. He forced her to the ground and they began to wrestle. Presently Miss Lapean squirmed out of the headlock only to find herself the victim of a toe hold. Geralde had her by the foot and was bending that foot backward towards her waist while she screamed for help.

They wrestled like this for a few minutes until someone called the police.

At the police station the desk sergeant asked Geralde what was the matter anyway.

"What is the matter?" Geralde repeated.

"Yes."

"Yes," Geralde repeated.

"There must be some reason to walk barefoot in the grass of a neighbour," the sergeant said.

"There must be some reason to walk barefoot in the grass of a neighbour," Geralde repeated. This was a tactic of Geralde's whenever he was questioned. He would simply repeat the question.

"You wish to go to jail?" the sergeant asked. "In jail we have no grass, alas. In jail you can go barefoot among the small rocks."

"No, no," Geralde said. "No, I like to walk in the grass. What is the harm?"

"The harm is to the grass which costs money to lay down in long strips," Miss Lapean said.

"The grass," said Geralde with scorn, "may cost money. Maybe. But to tell you the truth it is not worth it. I would not walk in such grass again. Never."

"Do you promise to leave alone the grass of Miss Lapean and to walk somewhere else?" the sergeant asked.

"I promise," Geralde said. "Under protest."

"*Bien,*" the sergeant agreed. "Unofficially, then, I suggest you pay to Miss Lapean ten dollars for the use of her grass and everyone is happy."

Miss Lapean smiled and rubbed her hands. I was in the front row and I whispered to Geralde.

"Five dollars." Geralde said.

"Ten," Miss Lapean shouted.

"*Ferme ta bouche*," the sergeant said to Miss Lapean. Miss Lapean shut her mouth.

"Why five?" the sergeant asked Geralde.

"Because," Geralde replied sadly, "the grass of Miss Lapean has worms. It is not good for walking."

"If it is not good for walking, then why are you walking on it?" the sergeant persisted.

There were murmurs at the sergeant's sharp wit.

Uncle Geralde looked from the sergeant to Miss Lapean and then back to the sergeant. His wrinkled face seemed more lined than ever and his usually bright eyes were moist with melancholy. His thin frame trembled.

"I am an old man," he said solemnly. "I admit it."

"Ah," said the sergeant, "let us have no appeal to sentimentality. Justice is fair to the young as well as the old. Do not, please, pluck at our heart-strings. You will hear only discords."

There were murmurs again. Half those present seemed to be pleased with the sergeant. The rest seemed a little provoked.

Uncle Geralde stared at Miss Lapean with the sadness in his eyes of a sick poodle dog whose paw has been crushed.

Then he turned to the sergeant.

"Your honour, I am an old man. Justice cannot deny it. My pleasures are few. My teeth are not for steaks nor my eyes for beautiful women or great books. My blood does not race with the spring and my flesh does not sing with the autumn. I cannot gamble, for I have no money. I cannot sing, for my voice is feeble and harsh. I cannot dance, for my legs do not follow my heart. Good wine elevates the pressure of my blood and is dangerous."

He stopped here to wipe from his eyes what I decided was a tear. The sergeant coughed uneasily. Miss Lapean produced from her pocketbook a small lacy handkerchief.

". . . still . . . still . . ." Geralde went on feebly, "there is in me yet a small spark of life, you understand?"

"I understand," the sergeant agreed solemnly.

"Yet what is there for me to do? *Voilà*, I walk in the soft grass and feel the earth beneath me and I am not too sad to be alive. Is it too much to ask from my fellow human beings? The loan of their grass? When they have singing and dancing and music and . . ."

Miss Lapean dabbed the end of her nose with the lace.

"Monsieur le Sergeant, if it is within the scope of justice . . . if it is possible, *c'est à dire* . . . the complaint . . . uh . . ."

"You wish," the sergeant said slowly, sniffing a little, "to withdraw the complaint?"

Miss Lapean drew a deep breath.

"I wish not only to withdraw it, but I wish to give the defendant the right to walk on my grass until the day he dies, heaven forgive me for being so heartless."

"*Bien*," the sergeant said, blowing his nose.

After the cheers had died away in Geralde's ears and he had personally forgiven Miss Lapean, we sat together at a small table, Geralde sipping cognac, I drinking strawberry soda.

"Are you sad, my uncle, because what you told the sergeant was a lie?"

"No. Because it was the truth," Geralde replied, drinking his cognac.

After a moment he added. "That was my last cognac. Now all there is left to me is the green grass under me for a while and then over me."

Still, it was many a year before he died, and many a night he danced through the grass of Miss Lapean. And if it was good for Uncle Geralde, believe me, it was also very good for the grass, which to this day grows very, very green in the front of the house of Miss Lapean.

ABOUT THE LINES

1 Although Geralde is ninety-seven years old, he behaves like a much younger person. List in point form the actions that seem somewhat inappropriate in a man of Geralde's years. Choose the incident that you consider to be the most amusing and explain to your partners why you chose it.

2 Make a brief summary of the plot of this story. Now, reread the story and identify the elements that are missing when only the plot is considered.

3 Working in a group of five, give a dramatic reading of this story. You will need students to read the parts of:
   a. Geralde;
   b. Miss Lapean;
   c. the narrator as narrator;
   d. the great-nephew;
   e. the sergeant.
Other groups can provide crowd noises. Present your dramatic reading to your own class and to a more junior class. Invite the comments of both.

BETWEEN THE LINES

1 There are several conflicts in this story. Identify as many as you can and write a statement explaining each, indicating:
   a. the person or persons involved;
   b. the reason for the conflict;
   c. whether or not a resolution is reached and the nature of that resolution.

2 Write two descriptions of Geralde. Start the first description with the following sentence:

"Geralde is a typical old man."

Start the second description with this sentence:

"Geralde may be ninety-seven years old, but he is a most unusual man."

The point of view expressed in each of these sentences will influence both the material you choose and the manner in which you present it.

3 It has often been said that comedy and tragedy are very close to each other. (Watch any Charlie Chaplin film to see how he uses the sad clown motif.) Identify the point at which this humorous story suddenly becomes serious. Then prepare a statement in which you either support or reject the writer's introduction of seriousness into the story.

BEYOND THE LINES

1 The sign, "Keep Off the Grass," is central to the story. Prepare a collage in which you make a statement about the modern world by using a combination of illustrations and everyday signs.

2 Geralde is the sort of person who is likely to become involved in any number of adventures. Write either a short story or a ballad about one or more of Geralde's escapades.

3 Imagine that you are Miss Lapean and instead of pursuing the legal route to control Geralde, take matters into your own hands and plan your revenge. You may present your material in the form of a personal battle plan under these headings:

Objectives	Techniques	Required Materials	Timing	Desired Outcomes

4 Write an account of this episode in the life of Geralde as it might appear in the human interest section of a local newspaper. Provide a headline such as:

"Old Man Refused Gift of Grass"; or

"Tread the Concrete, Old Man, Says Local Hardheart"; or

"Plagued by the Aged"; or

"Golden-Age Delinquent Terrorizes Neighbourhood."

Notice that the material can be presented from either Geralde's or Miss Lapean's point of view.

GRASS

Carl Sandburg

Pile the bodies high at Austerlitz and Waterloo.
Shovel them under and let me work —
    I am the grass; I cover all.

And pile them high at Gettysburg
And pile them high at Ypres and Verdun.
Shovel them under and let me work.
Two years, ten years, and passengers ask the conductor:
    What place is this?
    Where are we now?

    I am the grass.
    Let me work.

LOOKING IN

1 In a brief statement, explain what the passengers' question suggests about the attitudes of the living towards the dead.

2 The surface meaning of the words "I cover all," spoken by the grass, is obvious. Discuss the inferences of the sentence with your partners and compare your findings with those of another group.

LOOKING OUT

1. Using your local library and the school resource centre, research one of the following famous battles and, for each, name the nations involved, the date, the location, the war in which the battle was fought, and the victorious nation: Austerlitz, Waterloo, Gettysburg, Ypres, and Verdun.

2. Find another poem or song that has an anti-war theme.
   a. Read the poem or sing the song for a small group.
   b. Explain briefly what you think the poet's message is.
   c. Give your reason for choosing the poem or song and indicate any features that you particularly like.

3. Grass is perceived very differently by the writers of "Grass" and "Geralde and the Green, Green Grass." Write a poem, song, or short story in which you convey your perception of green grass and its value.

BAMBINGER

Mordecai Richler

We needed money. But we could not, like the Isenbergs next door, put a "Room To Let" sign in the window. We had standards to maintain.

"Taking in a refugee, a single man," my mother argued, "would help to fight human suffering. It might also mean a husband for Cousin Bessie, poor thing."

So in November, 1942, a phone call was made to the proper agency, and we got our first roomer, a refugee, without advertising. Herr Bambinger was a slight, stooping man with a shiny bald head and almost no chin. He wore thick glasses with steel frames and, even though he rolled his own cigarettes, he used a tortoise-shell cigarette holder.

"I guess," my mother said, "you're thinking of settling down. You'll be looking for a wife."

"You bet your bottom dollar he is," my father said.

On Friday Cousin Bessie was produced at dinner and on Saturday my parents cornered Herr Bambinger.

"Beauty," my mother said, "is only skin deep."

"Ach, so."

"What a man wants in a wife is somebody steady," my father said, offering Herr Bambinger a shot of apricot brandy. "Somebody with a little something in the bank."

Herr Bambinger didn't, like the other refugees, drink black coffee endlessly at the Old Vienna and pontificate about what a dull, uncultured country Canada was. Bambinger spent most of his evenings smoking in the dark in his room, the back bedroom. He wrote a prodigious number of letters, always filling the rice paper pages from top to bottom with the smallest, tightest handwriting I had ever seen. The letters went to the International Red Cross and refugee organizations and camps all over the world, but nothing ever came for him unless it was his own letters returned or copies of the *Aufbau*. Bambinger took a considerable interest in me. He convinced my mother that comic books were a bad influence. Superman, he said, was a glorification of fascism, and the Batman and Robin had a thinly — "very thinly," he said — disguised homosexual relationship. "I don't advise," he'd say to my mother, "that the boy should go without a scarf in such coldness." A couple of days later it was, "The boy shouldn't keep the elbows on the table when he eats." Or, another time, as he switched off the radio abruptly, "A boy can't do his studies and listen to the wireless at the same time."

My parents believed that Herr Bambinger had my welfare at heart and when I protested against his intrusions they disciplined me. One Saturday afternoon my mother forced me to go out for a walk with Herr Bambinger.

"Why should I miss the ball game, but?" I asked.

250

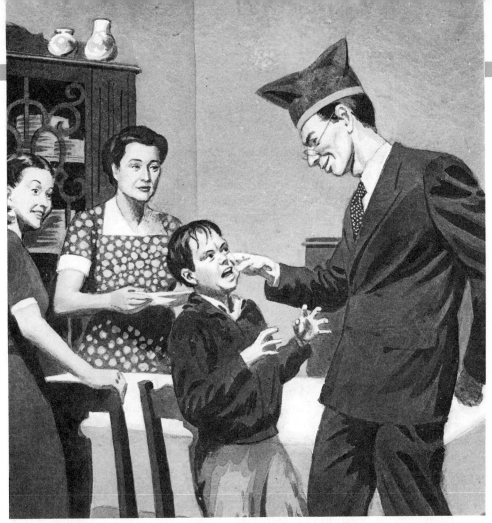

"The poor man has a wife and child of your age and he doesn't know where they are or if they're still alive."

Bambinger — vengefully, I thought — led me to the art museum on Sherbrooke Street. "It is never too early," he said, lighting a cigarette, "for one to learn appreciation of the arts."

"How's about a cig for me?"

"Nicotine is bad for growing boys."

"If you're too cheap to butt me just say so."

"You are not only stupid. You are very impudent. If you were my boy it would not be so. I'd teach you respect."

"Well, I'm not your boy, see."

When Bambinger and I finally did tangle it was over coffee. Coffee, if you remember, was rationed during the war, and at the age of twelve a boy became entitled to a share. There were coupons for it provided in this book. I had waited impatiently for my twelfth birthday and the day after it I demanded a cup. My mother smiled a little. But Bambinger shot her a warning glance and regarded me reproachfully across the table.

"You know you're not allowed to drink coffee," my mother said. "You're still a child."

My sister grinned and took a long sip from her cup.

"As far as the legally elected government of Canada is concerned I am, as of yesterday, allowed to drink coffee."

"The government is full of anti-semites," my father pronounced compulsively.

But I could see that my mother's resolve was weakening.

"One cup," I pleaded. "Would it break your heart?"

"Your mother's right. Coffee is bad for a growing boy."

Staying up late, according to Bambinger, would also stunt my growth. As did evenings spent at the Park Bowling Academy.

"This is family business, so keep your big nose out of it."

"Apologize to Mr. Bambinger immediately."

"Either I get my legal ration or I destroy my coupons."

"You will do no such thing. Now apologize to Mr. Bambinger."

Bambinger smiled mockingly at me, waiting.

"Well, the hell with you," I shouted, turning on Bambinger. "Why'd you run away from Hitler, you chicken? Couldn't you have stayed behind and fought in the underground? Wouldn't that have been better than running out on your wife and kid to save your own skin?"

My mother slapped me.

"Okay," I said, bolting. "I'm leaving home."

Outside, it was raining. Fists jammed into my windbreaker pockets, hastily packed kitbag bouncing against my back, I jogged to the Park Bowling Academy, where Hershey was spotting pins. "Hey," I said, "how'd you like to run away from home with me?"

Hershey wiped the sweat from his forehead, pondering my proposition. "Cancha wait until Monday? We're having *latkas* for dinner tomorrow."

Walking back to St. Urbain with Hershey, I told him about my troubles with Bambinger. It began to rain harder and we sheltered under a winding outside staircase. "Hey, would you do me a favour?" I asked.

"No."

"Thanks."

"What do you want me to do?"

I asked him to ring my doorbell and tell my mother I had fainted or something. "Say you found me lying in the gutter."

"You're chicken. I knew it. You're not running away from home."

Hershey gave me a shove and I scooped up my kitbag to slug him. He began to run. It was almost ten-thirty, and the rain had turned to snow.

"You've come back," my mother said, seemingly overjoyed.

"Only for tonight."

"Come," she said, taking me by the hand. "We've just had the most wonderful news."

Bambinger was actually dancing round the dining room table with my sister. He wore a paper hat and had let his glasses slip down to the tip of his nose. "Well," he said, "well, well, the prodigal returns. I told you not to worry."

Bambinger smiled and pinched my cheek, he pinched it very hard before I managed to break free.

"They were going to send out the police to look for you."

"Mrs. Bambinger and Julius are safe," my mother said, clapping her hands.

"They're coming here from Australia," my father said. "By ship. There was a telegram."

"I'm soaked. I'll be lucky if I don't catch pneumonia."

"Yeah. Just look at him," my father said. "You'd think he'd been out swimming. And what did he prove? Nothing."

"I'll tell you what," Bambinger said, "you may still be too young for coffee but a little brandy won't hurt you."

Everybody laughed. Thrusting past Bambinger, I fled to the bedroom. My mother followed me inside. "Why are you crying?"

"I'm not crying — I'm soaked."

The dining room vibrated with laughter.

"Go back to your party. Enjoy yourself."

"I want you to apologize to Mr. Bambinger."

I didn't say a word.

"You will be allowed one cup of coffee a week."

"Was that his idea?"

My mother looked at me, astonished.

"Alright. I'm going. I'll apologize to him."

I went to Bambinger's room with him. "Well," he said with an ironical smile, "speak up. I won't bite you."

"My mother says to tell you I'm sorry."

"Ach, so."

"You're always picking on me."

"Am I?"

"Maybe they don't understand. I do, but."

Bambinger rolled a cigarette, deliberately slow, and let me stand there for a while before he said, "Your grammar is atrocious."

"This is my room and my bed."

"Ach, so."

"It shoulda been anyway. I was promised. Only they made me stay with my sister and rented it to you instead."

"I think your parents need the money."

"I apologized. Can I go now?"

"You can go."

The next morning Bambinger and I couldn't look at each other and a week went by without his once admonishing, correcting, or trying to touch me. A thick letter came from Australia and Bambinger showed us photographs of a small unsmiling boy in a foreign-type suit that was obviously too tight for him. His wife had stringy grey hair, a squint, and what appeared to be a gold tooth. Bambinger read passages from his letter aloud to my parents. His family, I learned, would not be arriving in Canada for six weeks, the boat trip alone taking a month.

Bambinger now applied himself entirely to work and frugality. He gave up smoking even hand-rolled cigarettes and put in overtime at the factory whenever it was available. On weekends Bambinger searched for bargains. One day he came home with a suit from a fire-sale for his boy and on another he purchased an ancient washing machine and set to repairing it himself. He picked up a table and chairs at an auction and bought a reconditioned vacuum cleaner at a bazaar. All these, and other articles, he stored in the shed; and all this time he ignored me.

One day I surprised Bambinger with a collection of nearly-new comic books — "For your kid," I said, fleeing — and the next morning I found them on top of the garbage pail in the shed. "Julius will not read such trash," he said.

"They cost me a nickel each, but."

"The thought was nice. But you wasted your money."

On Saturday afternoon, only a week before Mrs. Bambinger and Julius should have arrived, my father came into the kitchen carrying the newspaper. He whispered something to my mother.

"Yes, that's the name of the ship. Oh, my God."

Bambinger staggered in from the shed, supporting a table with three legs.

"Brace yourself," my father said.

Bambinger seized the newspaper and read the story at the bottom of page one.

"You can never tell," my mother said. "They could be in a lifeboat. That happens all the time, you know."

"Where there's life, there's hope."

Bambinger went into his room and stayed there for three days and when he came out again it was only to tell us he was moving. The morning of his departure he summoned me to his room. "You can have your bed back again," he said.

I just stood there.

"You've been deprived of a lot. You've suffered a good deal. Haven't you? *Little bastard.*"

"I didn't sink the ship," I said, frightened.

Bambinger laughed. "Ach so," he said.

"Why you moving?"

"I'm going to Toronto."

That was a lie. Two weeks later I saw Bambinger walking toward me on St. Catherine Street. He was wearing a new suit, a fedora with a wide brim, and glasses with thick shell frames. The girl with him was taller than he was. At first I intended to ask him if he was ever going to come round for the stuff in the shed but I crossed to the other side of the street before he spotted me.

ABOUT THE LINES

1 As the narrator, write in your diary an entry headed: "Why I loathe Bambinger."

2 Reread the story carefully and list the words that you do not understand or are not sure of. Look up the words in a dictionary and beside each write a brief definition. Use each of the words in a sentence about this story.

3 Working with your partners, make up three questions to be given to someone who has read the story once. The questions are to be designed to test whether the reader has noted important details. Try your questions on other students in the class and then make them simpler or harder, according to how well people answer them.

BETWEEN THE LINES

1 The story is told from the narrator's point of view and so the reader knows why he hates Bambinger; on the other hand, the reasons for Bambinger's hostility toward the narrator must be inferred. As Bambinger, write a letter to your wife in which you spend at least two paragraphs describing your feelings about the narrator.

2 The tone of the story fluctuates between the serious and the almost funny. Find two incidents that would fit each category and state the serious or comic features of each.

3 Discuss the last paragraph with your partners, and in a written statement explain how it affects your opinion of Herr Bambinger.

4 Choose the three incidents from the story when you think the narrator experiences his most intense anti-Bambinger emotions. Put the incidents in order of the intensity of the narrator's feelings. Discuss your ranking of the events with your partners, and together produce an ordered list upon which you all agree.

5 Make two statements about the narrator's behaviour — one negative and the other positive. Support each statement by referring to the story.

BEYOND THE LINES

1 Continue the story of Bambinger beyond the end of this selection. You may write from Bambinger's or a third person's point of view.

2 Imagine that Bambinger devoted the three days that he spent alone in his room to writing an autobiography. Produce selected pages of this autobiography that reflect some of the happiness and some of the tribulations of his life.

3 The treatment of the Jews during World War II in Nazi-occupied Europe forms an understated background to this story. Using your local library and resource centre, do some reading on this topic and then discuss with your partners how this deeper insight helps you to understand Bambinger better.

BLACK LION

Double cross, triple cross, in a fight for freedom

Ian Slater

Characters

SEAN CONNOR a young, middle-class I.R.A. member in his mid twenties
DAN MCBRIDE a middle class ex-politician and I.R.A. member, now a publican
   in his late sixties
MAURICE a middle class, local I.R.A. leader in his early fifties
BRENDAN a working-class I.R.A. member in his mid twenties
CAPTAIN PARK a British Army intelligence officer in his late thirties
SERGEANT a British Army sergeant in his early forties

SCENE 1: TIME: THE PRESENT. PLACE: BELFAST — INSIDE A PUB
CALLED "BLACK LION."
*The pub is small with three tables at most and a small bar with two beer taps. Behind
the bar at arm's length there are several rows of liquor bottles. As the lights come
up we see the publican, DAN MCBRIDE, locking up, slipping the bolt upon the door and
starting to clean up the tables, emptying ashtrays, etc. SEAN CONNOR, a young
I.R.A. member in his late twenties, is drinking at a table. He makes no sign of moving
as MCBRIDE continues his cleanup.*

SEAN Well, Dan, will you help us do it?
DAN I told you before, Sean, I've given up politics — I'm a waiter, I make
   drinks. I'm through making trouble.
SEAN (*reproachingly*) It wasn't like that in the ould[1] days.
DAN (*a little condescendingly*) Ach — what do you know about the *ould* days?
SEAN Not much — but it's your reputation I mean — on the border in Black
   Lion during the troubles — I've heard tell you was a real Turk then.
DAN Ach — never mind the soft soap. That's all in the past. The world's
   changed.
SEAN Maybe, but Ireland hasn't.
DAN No. That's your worry, not mine. Anyway why do you need me?
SEAN To clear the bar.
DAN Why don't you clear it yourself then?

---

[1] Ould means old. The spelling indicates Irish pronunciation. Affection or ridicule is contained in the word.
An "ould get" is derogatory. So is "a right ould get". But "ould one" expresses begrudging respect.

SEAN It would arouse suspicion, you know that. Somebody would tip them off.

DAN For God's sake man, why don't you do it in the street and no one will have to clear anybody? Why don't you shoot them in the street?

SEAN Because then other people'll get hurt for sure — we'll hit some kid or somethin', like that wee girl in Bogside[2] — she was caught in the cross-fire. Besides, it's too hard to catch 'em off guard anywhere else.

DAN Oh, you're all with caring about other people but you don't give a damn about me, is that it?

SEAN Look, no one will blame you. All you have to say is that they were sitting there drinking and suddenly all hell broke loose and in a minute it was all over. When you popped your head up from behind the bar the two British officers were dead. (*a slight pause*)

DAN It's that simple, eh?

SEAN Yes — believe me — no one will blame you, Dan. Everyone knows they always drink here.

DAN Including all the Orangemen[3] in Belfast. They might just shoot me. Or if they don't the Ulster Constabulary[4] might — or Kelly's Special Branch[5] boys might come and next thing I'll be interned in Maidstone or Crumlin Road,[6] with all your other mates — have you thought of that now? And never mind my business.

DAN But after how many months? What happens tomorrow, or the next day, or the day after that, eh?

SEAN (*exasperated*) Dan, you're just a small man in a big city. You're not even associated with us anymore. That's why we picked you.

DAN That's kind of you. I suppose you think they wouldn't suspect me afterwards.

SEAN They might — but we wouldn't use you anymore. I promise.

DAN And I've heard that one before, Sean Connor. *You* don't have any say, my friend. You're just the message boy. I'll bet you don't even know who you're taking orders from, do you? (*a long pause*) I thought so. Things haven't changed that much since Black Lion.

SEAN (*defensively*) Well, what's that matter?

DAN It matters because the next thing I know I'll be getting a threatening phone call, or some other kind of blackmail to do some more dirty work and your promise wouldn't mean a pinch o' dung. They'd probably blow my pub to smithereens, like they did up at Dungannon.[7]

SEAN (*disbelievingly*) Blackmail — you? Oh c'mon, Dan. (*incredulously*) You really think we'd do that — that the I.R.A. would put you in?

[2] The Catholic area of Belfast.

[3] Protestants. On July 12, 1690, William III of England (William of Orange) defeated his father-in-law, the deposed and exiled King James II at the Battle of the Boyne. The Irish Catholics supported James in the hopes of better treatment from England if he regained the throne. The Protestants supported William, and since then Protestants have been called Orangemen.

[4] The police force of the constabulary of Ulster; here it means the special branch of the force combatting the I.R.A.

[5] A police unit directly responsible to Ulster's Attorney General.

[6] Two prisons where political prisoners are held under a Special Powers Act.

[7] A town in Northern Ireland.

257

DAN I don't think — I know. How about poor ould Riley?

SEAN For God's sake, Dan. He was a stoolie. We're fightin' a war. We can't take chances. It's not just the Unionists[8] now — it's us against them and the whole British Army.

DAN (*disgustedly*) Ach — we've always been fighting a war. Our history's just one long bleeding. We'll kill ourselves off without the British Army — don't use them as an excuse.

SEAN (*shocked*) But — don't you want to throw them out?

DAN What for? — I'm tired of it all. Maybe we should just let the British Army run things for a while. It might be better than this bloody scrapping between Catholic and Orangeman. It mightn't be so bad. The present government is changing its shirt every other day. (*reflectively*) And think what it would be like to sleep one night, just one night, without some trigger-happy lunk shooting. Can you imagine it — Belfast in silence? Silence! Sweet God, we don't know what that is anymore. You want another drink?

SEAN (*in a warning tone*) No. (*a slight pause*) That's pretty dangerous talk, Dan. Just as well I know you.

DAN Dangerous? Is it dangerous to be wanting peace, now?

SEAN No — but not like you want it. That's just collaboration.

DAN Collaboration, be damned. The more I think about it the more it seems like common sense. Will you and I change anything? You said it — we're small men in a city. Besides, I have to pay taxes no matter who's bossing me around — Protestant or Peter.[9]

SEAN (*in a raised voice*) We're fighting for freedom — not tax collectors.

DAN (*sarcastically*) Oh, is it freedom, now? Freedom for what, might I ask?

SEAN To choose.

DAN Choice of what, for God's sake? Haven't you ever heard of Carlyle Circus?[10]

SEAN (*exasperated*) But — that's just what I'm talking about, Dan — if everyone helps us we'll put an end to gerrymandering[11] once and for all — and we'll see that there's no more Unionist impersonations[12] in the Circus or anywhere else.

DAN Huh — five hundred thousand Catholics against a million Protestants — you believe you can beat those odds?

SEAN Numbers don't mean a damn thing, Dan. Look at what the Viet Cong did to the Yanks. It's morale that counts.

---

[8] Irish Protestants who favour Ireland's union with Great Britain, as proposed late in the nineteenth century.

[9] Protestant or Catholic. Peter refers to St. Peter.

[10] In the British Isles and Europe, many major intersections are circular. Often, there is a traffic "island" around which traffic is directed. Five or six roadways may lead into the intersection. Carlyle Circus is a well-known roundabout in Belfast.

Because many ridings or electoral districts meet at Carlyle Circus, it is notorious for gerrymandering (see footnote 11) by the Protestants.

[11] A process whereby electoral districts are carved up so that majority voting is arranged. The voting districts are so divided that few Catholic candidates can possibly win an election. Part of gerrymandering also was the ballot-fixing practice of using fictitious or dead persons' names on the voting lists. According to the author, Carlyle Circus was a centre for this activity.

[12] The practice of putting fictitious, aging, sick, and dead persons' names on the voting lists, and voting under these names in order to swell the Unionist vote.

DAN And you think the Unionists' morale is worse than the Catholics'?

SEAN No, but —

DAN (*cutting him short*) But nothing — when both sides' morale is equal then it's arms that count and the I.R.A. can't outgun the British Army. I can tell you that for sure. (*a pause*)

SEAN You just don't believe in any part of the cause anymore.

DAN (*exasperated*) Ach, your cause is just a lot of corpses with sentimental headstones. Anyway, I don't like some of your new atheist and commie members[13] these days. They're using your Irish nationalism as a blind — it's the first step in their takeover business.

SEAN (*quietly but somewhat menacingly*) You want some advice, Dan?

DAN No.

SEAN Keep your ideas locked up. If anyone else hears you talk like that they mightn't understand.

DAN Do *you*?

SEAN Yes. You're growing old. You've lost the flame, that's all. But others will say worse I can tell you and — well, I don't want to see you hurt.

DAN I haven't lost any flame, Sean. I've lost your impatience. If you're smart you'll lose it too.

SEAN I'd better go. I've heard enough. They'll call you a collaborator as it is.

DAN Ach — tell them I'm neutral then if it makes you happier.

SEAN Don't be daft. There can't be any neutrals in this business and you know it. (*suddenly angry*) For God's sake, McBride, what's happened to you? You used to be one of the best resistance leaders we had. When I was young everybody told me, "You want to know how to organize, to fight, you see Dan McBride — he'll tell you. He's the old Lion — another Hugh O'Neil."[14] And now look at ye — you talk like some kind of — of pacifist priest. Have you told anyone else about this?

DAN About what, pray?

SEAN About this cuddly pacifism.

DAN A few people, why?

SEAN (*menacingly*) Then you're in great danger, my friend.

DAN Don't threaten me, boy. I'm too old to scare.

SEAN I'm not threatening you, I'm warning you. There'll be all sorts of accusations, you know. And you might be right — what if they do decide to use your place anyway? If you're here you might get in the way. You should think about that.

DAN There'll be no murder in my place if I can help it.

SEAN That's your final word?

DAN You knew it was weeks ago. Why did you bother coming back?

SEAN (*a little hesitant*) I had to make sure — they said to give you another chance.

---

[13] A derogatory name for communist members of the group. They are even more "left" than the "left-wing" guerrillas.

[14] A king of Ulster in mediaeval times. In the thirteenth and fourteenth centuries he ran rings around the English. He escaped their hands many times, even from the Tower of London. He was finally poisoned, but is still regarded as a great anti-British hero. His nickname was "Red Hugh".

(DAN *opens the door for* SEAN *to leave. It is a final refusal. There is a long pause as* SEAN *looks across at* DAN.)
SEAN Well then — good night.
DAN Good night.

SCENE 2:

The lights fade out as SEAN *leaves. The lights rise and we see two men sitting in a meagrely furnished room.* SEAN *is taking off his coat, having just arrived. The older man,* MAURICE, *is sitting behind a table while the younger man,* BRENDAN, *in his late twenties like* SEAN, *is cleaning two revolvers. Throughout the scene* BRENDAN *continues to clean the guns. There is a semi-hushed — almost conspiratorial — tone throughout this scene.*
MAURICE So he refused.
SEAN (*reluctantly*) Absolutely, Maurice. Said he wouldn't have anything to do with it. Says he's too old.
BRENDAN By the sounds of it he's too dangerous. I say get rid of the old fool.
SEAN Ach — what's the point in that, Brendan? He won't betray us.
BRENDAN (*sarcastically*) And how do you know?
SEAN (*defensively*) Because he's an old I.R.A. man, that's why. He might disagree with us now and criticize us but he won't squeal.
BRENDAN What's it to be then, Maurice?
MAURICE I don't think he'll talk, Brendan, but you have a point. He knows our plan.
SEAN He only knows me, Maurice. I'll take the risk.
BRENDAN Ach — stop kidding yourself, Connor. You know as well as I do that if they worked on you they'd get all our names.
SEAN Speak for yourself.
MAURICE That's enough, you two. Brendan's right, Sean, it's not just you. All of us would break. You've seen us crack British spies.
BRENDAN That's why I say be rid of him.
SEAN You won't be popular with the other hands if you bump him off. He's too well known.
BRENDAN (*scornfully*) Where — amongst all the ould gets? Who else knows 'im, eh? None of us would miss 'im.
SEAN I would.
BRENDAN (*contemptuously*) 'Cept you, I mean.
MAURICE There's no use fighting over it. We'll let him go for the present. There's only three of us in each cell — no one knows more than two others. He couldn't do much damage even if he does talk. Besides, Sean is right, too. There are still a lot of old boys right throughout our Army. If we kill him we could undermine a lot of morale.
BRENDAN But damn it all, the ould get isn't even in the I.R.A. anymore.
MAURICE You miss the point, Brendan. He's like a retired party leader. He symbolizes our link with a history of resistance. It's no secret that the fighting's going badly for us — despite all the publicity. We need all the morale we can get. Anyway, I don't see him doing much harm as long as he only moans about us.

SEAN Aye. It's stupid to get rid of an old man like that.

MAURICE Not necessarily. Some of the worst informers we have are pensioners. We grow weak as we get older, not stronger. But we'll let him go for the time being. Now Sean, have you checked Dan's place thoroughly?

SEAN I should have. I've drunk there often enough. Should we tell him we're going through with it anyway?

MAURICE No, we'll have to take that chance.

BRENDAN When do we do it, then?

MAURICE In two days — July 12th.

BRENDAN (loudly) July 12th — Holy God — that's Orangemen's day! There'll be Protestants from here to Shankill Road![15]

MAURICE The boss wants it that way. Big impact he says.

BRENDAN Big trouble if you ask me.

MAURICE Nobody asked you — the boss knows what he's doing. Have you checked the guns?

BRENDAN Aye. This one fires a little high, but I'll look after it. Connor can take the other one.

(BRENDAN hands SEAN the other gun.)

MAURICE Good, and remember, we don't want them half shot up — we want them dead. That way they'll intern more. And remember, these days there're British patrols all over the place — so follow the old rule — drop the guns as soon as you've finished and there'll be a hundred conflictin' witnesses if you're caught.

SEAN (puzzled) Why two officers?

MAURICE The boss says it has more effect and I think he's right. They're much more likely to take prisoners for officers. That'll mean more sympathy and more members for us.

BRENDAN What does this Belfast boss say about old Dan, then?

MAURICE He said that seeing we picked the place it was okay but to force the old boy into co-operation might be dangerous for morale, like Sean says. In any case he left it up to me.

SEAN When is the boss coming out into the open?

BRENDAN Aye, that'd be good for morale.

MAURICE I agree, but it would be too risky. We'll need him for the final uprising, and let's face it — that mightn't be for some time with this honeymoon between London and Dublin.[16] He won't risk a big push till we're sure London'll keep its nose out.

SEAN But some of our younger members need someone they can identify with now, Maurice. They've had a bellyful of committees. Anyway, I still think there's something queer about shooting two officers.

MAURICE The boss knows what's important.

SEAN Ach — what's important is to get more guns. Then we can get rid of all the scum.

---

[15] A street in the Protestant area of Belfast.

[16] An understanding between the governments in London and Dublin that Dublin would not be seen to be giving active support to the I.R.A.

MAURICE (*reproachfully*) Enough of that. Would you like his job?

SEAN No — I suppose you're right.

MAURICE Of course I'm right. None of us can see the whole pattern. We're just part of the picture. (*He looks at his watch — quickly changing the topic.*) It's late. Sean, you leave first.

SEAN Yes. Good night.

MAURICE (*rising*) 'Night.

SCENE 3:

BLACKOUT. *Ambulance red light flashes offstage. In its flashing glow a* BRITISH OFFICER, CAPTAIN PARK, *and a* SERGEANT *carrying a tape recorder enter the pub.*

The CAPTAIN, *a swagger stick under one arm, switches on the light and looks about the pub as the* SERGEANT *lifts the tape recorder onto the table and starts setting it up.*

The CAPTAIN *picks up a chair in his path, pushes it to one side as if dismissing a private, and inspects the furniture-strewn pub. He pokes here and there casually with his swagger stick and then bends down as he finds something. He pushes his swagger stick forward and pulls up one of the two revolvers by poking the stick through the trigger guard. He slides it onto the table. He looks further and finds the other gun and places it upon the table.*

The SERGEANT, *obviously from habit, pulls a plastic bag from his tunic and using a marking pen carefully transfers the revolvers into the plastic bag, labels it with the pen and puts it into his kit. The* CAPTAIN *speaks with an educated English accent.*

CAPTAIN All right, Sergeant, bring him in.

SERGEANT Yes, sir.

The SERGEANT *goes out and returns with* McBRIDE *and indicates the chair at the table.* McBRIDE *sits at the place indicated. The* SERGEANT *goes out.*)

CAPTAIN (*officially*) You are the owner of the Black Lion Hotel?

DAN Yes, Captain.

CAPTAIN (*sharply*) You saw the shooting?

DAN Yes — well not all of it.

CAPTAIN What do you mean, not all of it?

DAN I was pouring a beer when the first shots were fired. I only saw the second officer get hit.

CAPTAIN You don't seem very upset. (*a slight pause*)

DAN I'm used to seeing people killed.

CAPTAIN One never gets used to it, Mr. McBride, only insensitive to it. As I recall, your file says you were an I.R.A. leader in the twenties and thirties in County Fermanagh around the border. In the village of Black Lion — is that correct?

DAN Yes.

CAPTAIN So you admit to being a guerrilla?

DAN Yes.

CAPTAIN A very successful one, I hear.

DAN I killed a lot of people if that's what you mean.

CAPTAIN That's exactly what I mean.

DAN Then I was successful. (*a slight pause*)

CAPTAIN You must forgive me for the lack of dramatic lighting. It works on amateur Ugs but to you I expect it's old hat. You must be used to interrogation by now?

DAN One never gets used to it, Captain Parks, only insensitive to it. Besides, I haven't been interrogated in over ten years and I don't know what you mean by Ugs.

CAPTAIN Ugs, Mister McBride, as if you didn't know, stands for urban guerrillas, and so far they've killed over sixty British soldiers in Belfast alone. I've no doubt you know *that* much?

DAN Yes.

CAPTAIN And you also knew my name. How is that?

DAN You deal with all the assassination cases.

CAPTAIN And how did you come by that piece of information, Mr. McBride?

DAN I read the *Irish Times*.

CAPTAIN Hmmm . . . (*tone becomes matter of fact*) McBride, it will save us both time and discomfort if I come right to the point. But first I caution you against your calculated offhand manner. As a professional I understand your contempt of games but I am aware that such contempt is also a dangerous game. Others less intelligent than myself, and we have a flock of them around Maidstone Prison, Mr. McBride, will only be taunted by your "let's get it over with" attitude and they will react in the only way they know. In short, they will probably work you over rather savagely. Particularly in the light of this. (*He waves his hand about the pub.*) I think you can understand *that*.

DAN I do.

CAPTAIN (*relieved*) Good, then you'll be well advised to be honest with me. Now let's get to the nerve of the matter. To begin with, my training and experience tell me that you're not connected with this murder, otherwise you wouldn't have been here when it took place. But my intuition tells me that a man with your record of underground activities might risk such a suspicion, hoping that any connection between you and the terrorists would be considered too obvious to be true. (*slight pause*) Well?

DAN (*tiredly but deliberately*) I'm tired of politics. I no longer have the energy or the interest. I think *you* can understand that?

CAPTAIN (*in a colder tone*) McBride, I'm only sure of one thing, that during the twenties you were a competent guerrilla and as subsequent events proved you were a competent liar. I can understand *that*, because your life depended on it and I can understand it now because your life might depend on it again.

DAN But surely —

CAPTAIN (*cutting him short*) I'm not finished. You are unusual in your class. You are only a small pub owner, a waiter, but you are also the most articulate waiter I've ever known — (*sarcastically*) in Belfast at least. The two in my estimation don't mix.

DAN I told you, Captain — I used to be in politics even before the twenties. Words were my business then and I — well I remembered them, that's all.

CAPTAIN Did you also remember your other business?

DAN (*perplexed*) You mean pubbing?

CAPTAIN (*coldly*) I mean murder!

DAN I was fighting a war then.

CAPTAIN Exactly! And the I.R.A. is still fighting it.

DAN I have nothing to do with it.

CAPTAIN (*coldly and slowly*) McBride, I may possibly — just possibly — believe that you've severed your old connections but I very much doubt that they have severed you. It's a new generation fighting this uprising and quite frankly they're not very good at it — they need experienced men. In short, I can't believe that you are completely unassociated with your former friends. (*shouting*) Sergeant!

SERGEANT (*in the background*) Sir?

CAPTAIN Is the prisoner outside?

(*The* SERGEANT *comes nearer.*)

SERGEANT (*hesitantly*) Ah, yes, sir — ah, excuse me, sir, but the doctor's arrived. He insists that the Ug is too badly wounded to answer questions.

CAPTAIN (*sharply*) We don't need him long.

SERGEANT I told the doctor that, sir, but he says the prisoner should be taken straight to hospital — he's lost a lot of blood; they've had to hook up a transfusion on him already.

CAPTAIN (*voice rising in anger*) I know the scum's been bleeding — let him bleed. He and his gang just shot two of my officers. It's time we took the gloves off.

SERGEANT Yes, sir.

CAPTAIN (*calming down*) Oh, all right, wheel him in, then you can let them sew him up. We'll be able to use him.

(SERGEANT *snaps to attention and walks out. He returns pushing an ambulance trolley.* SEAN CONNOR *is bandaged up on the trolley.* MCBRIDE *looks at the* CAPTAIN, *then without getting up he looks at* CONNOR.)

CAPTAIN Right, Sergeant, we've seen him. Let the doctors have him. Come back when you're finished. Tell them to let me know the moment he comes round.

SERGEANT Yes, sir.

(SERGEANT *wheels trolley out.*)

CAPTAIN Well, McBride, did you recognize him?

DAN Yes.

CAPTAIN (*betraying surprise*) You did?

DAN Yes.

CAPTAIN Well, who is he?

DAN He's an I.R.A. man — Sean Connor.

CAPTAIN (*surprised, almost doubting*) How do you know?

DAN He came into my place the other day and tried to get me to rejoin. To become active again.

CAPTAIN (*barely restraining his excitement*) Why didn't you report this?

DAN I am reporting it now.

(SERGEANT *enters and stands at door.*)

CAPTAIN Go on.

DAN He told me they wanted me to work for them — the I.R.A. — but I told him what I've just told you — that I was too ould and too tired, and I said that maybe they should stop all the killing and let the army — your army, stay a bit and see what happens.

CAPTAIN Hmph — did he mention anyone else — any communists?

DAN No. Well, none of us.

CAPTAIN What do you mean, none of us?

DAN I mean, you know, none of us — the Irish.

CAPTAIN He did mention someone else then?

DAN Yes, but I think it was just gabble to impress me. I think he was jealous of my ould reputation. You know how young kids are. (*slight pause*)

CAPTAIN Why are you being so cooperative? (*slight pause*)

DAN Because, Captain, I want no more of this. I want to serve my Guinness[17] and sleep quietly. Is it so inconceivable that a man gets tired? No one will believe me. (*slight pause*) He didn't believe me, either. They think that everyone must go on fighting even when they're too ould to fight anymore — as if it's the same as being a habitual criminal or something.

CAPTAIN You said he mentioned another name. Whose?

DAN Captain, I hear a lot of gabble in my bar. It's just gabble, I can assure you.

CAPTAIN (*loudly*) Damn it, McBride, who was it? (*a slight pause*) I warn you, McBride.

DAN (*still reluctant*) Captain, I —

CAPTAIN (*sternly*) Who was it?

DAN A Major, Captain. A British Major — an intelligence officer like yourself. (*pause*) Samson. No, Simpson. Yes, it was Simpson. (*pause*)

CAPTAIN Simpson?

DAN Yes.

CAPTAIN What did he say about him?

DAN He said Simpson was one of them — I mean the I.R.A. At first I thought it possible. Nothing's impossible. But then, the more I listened the more I realized he was drunk. He wanted me to clear my place for a killing but you know you can't take any notice of drunks. Besides he was young — full of hot air.

CAPTAIN What do you mean, was —?

DAN Well, I mean he looked half dead just then.

CAPTAIN (*sharply*) The doctors'll bring him round. He's under drugs. (*quickly switching back to the business at hand*) What else did he say about Simpson?

DAN He told me that they knew of plans for the next round-up of suspects. He said Simpson had given them to the Army, the I.R.A. I mean, and that this time Maidstone and Crumlin Road jails would be kept full beforehand instead of clearing them and arousing suspicion.

CAPTAIN (*suspiciously*) Why didn't you report all this before?

DAN Captain, if I reported everything I hear at the bar I'd have to send you a book. (*slight pause*)

CAPTAIN How much would that book cost?

DAN I don't understand.

CAPTAIN (*annoyed*) Of course you understand — don't pretend to be stupid. I want to hear everything *you* hear, McBride, and I'll pay well for it.

DAN No.

---

[17] A famous Irish malt beer, or stout.

CAPTAIN (*angrily*) I could have you interned, McBride. (*slight pause*) I could even have you shot. It wouldn't be hard to arrange, you know — not now with the Ugs and their terrorist tactics. You'd go unnoticed — even in the *Irish Times*.

DAN I know that. (*pause*)

CAPTAIN McBride, you are either a stubborn old fool or a brave fool — both of which are very dangerous at this time. Obviously, this man means nothing to you, then?

DAN He's a customer.

CAPTAIN But not a friend.

DAN No.

CAPTAIN You couldn't care less if he dies.

DAN No — not really.

CAPTAIN All right, McBride. Wait outside. (*calls out*) Sergeant!

SERGEANT Sir?

CAPTAIN Show him out.

SERGEANT Yes, sir.

CAPTAIN Before you go, Paddy,[18] I warn you not to open your mouth about any of this. If you do gab I'll intern you for the duration or worse — no matter what it takes. Is that clear?

DAN Yes, Captain.

CAPTAIN And as soon as our Ug is well enough we'll be checking out your story. Meanwhile, I don't want you to leave Belfast. I'll want to see you again — soon.

DAN Yes, all right.

CAPTAIN Remember — I'll be watching you.

DAN I'll remember. Good night.

CAPTAIN Good night.

(MCBRIDE *walks out. The* SERGEANT *returns.*)

CAPTAIN Did we get it all, Sergeant?

(SERGEANT *leans over and checks the recorder.*)

SERGEANT Think so, sir.

CAPTAIN Not a word about Simpson, right?

SERGEANT 'Course, sir.

CAPTAIN You think he knew that the Ug was already dead?

SERGEANT (*uncertain tone*) Hard to say, sir — I think he believed you though — about him being heavily drugged, I mean.

CAPTAIN I hope so. He'd hardly talk if he thought Connor could implicate him. (*in a new tone*) In any case, we have to be careful. Simpson's a big one.

SERGEANT Yes, sir. (*He leans over and takes the tape out of the recorder.*) Should I put the tape in your safe, Captain?

CAPTAIN No, I'll take it.

(The SERGEANT *hands over the tape. As the* CAPTAIN *receives it he looks at it pensively for a moment, then looks around at the pub. He puts the tape in his pocket.*)

CAPTAIN Put a twenty-four hour tab on Simpson.

---

[18] A nickname for an Irish person. It derives from the patron saint of Ireland, St. Patrick.

SCENE 4:

BLACKOUT. *Lights rise. The pub has been cleaned up.*

MAURICE Morning, Dan.

DAN Maurice. What'll it be?

MAURICE Oh, a drap o' Mitchell's[19] please — no ice.

DAN (*pouring the drink*) No ice for anyone today. Power's been off.

MAURICE Again?

DAN Aye, a bomb somewhere in the Falls.[20]

MAURICE (*his voice lowered in a conspiratorial tone*) Dan, I came to see you about Sean.

DAN What about him?

MAURICE The rumour is that they got him yesterday. I'd a come earlier but the place is crawlin' with the police.

DAN It's not a rumour. They got him, all right.

MAURICE Holy God — when did you find out?

DAN They held me for questioning.

MAURICE Who was it?

DAN Park — the Captain.

MAURICE Was — was he dead when they got him?

DAN They say they had him drugged, but I think he was gone.

MAURICE Sweet suffering — (*slight pause*) Do you think they dragged anything out of him, Dan?

DAN No, they wouldn't have asked me so many questions if they had. Then again, they might have, just to compare stories — it's hard to tell. But I don't think they got much out of him — I wouldn't be here if they did.

MAURICE He didn't recognize you at all, I suppose.

DAN Not a chance.

MAURICE What did you tell Park?

DAN Oh, I told him about Major Simpson.

MAURICE Simpson! That's aimin' high! He's a big 'un.

DAN He is — that's why I told him. If we can get rid of Simpson for a while, or even tie him up for a few weeks with a special enquiry, it'll be worth it.

MAURICE What happens when it falls through?

DAN I told him I thought it was only a rumour.

MAURICE He still might get savage with you.

DAN Ach — he could, but I don't expect he will — at least not right away. He's thinking he can get all sorts of tidbits from me. He can be kept on the hook for a few weeks anyway.

MAURICE I hope so. Young Sean was a good man.

DAN (*exhaling heavily*) Yes, he was. A little impatient, but a good man.

MAURICE I —

(*Footsteps are heard outside.*)

DAN Shhh — (*pause*)

(DAN *walks casually over to the window.*)

---

[19] A "drap" is a drop; Mitchell's is a brand of Irish whiskey.
[20] Falls Road, a thoroughfare in the Catholic area of Belfast.

MAURICE (*alarmed, in a soft voice*) Who is it?

(DAN *walks back behind the bar.*)

DAN No one that I know — just walked right by. Might be Park's tab.[21]

MAURICE So you think the British pig believes you?

DAN No, I don't think he believes *himself* but he bought the story for the time being and that's a different thing altogether, matey.

MAURICE What have you got planned, then?

DAN This time we get Park.

MAURICE Park — hell, man, that's asking for it proper.

DAN It's risky, I know, but when he becomes convinced that the Simpson story is fake then he'll be after my blood. But if we get him now just after he *starts* the investigation then they'll probably think that Simpson had a hand in getting him. In any case, Simpson won't be trusted again for a long time. They won't know where the hell they are by the time they've finished. Their intelligence outfit will be shot to hell.

MAURICE It could mean a lot of arrests, Dan, if something goes wrong.

DAN So?

MAURICE Well, I'm old-fashioned, that's all. I like to know if it's worth the price.

DAN I can't tell you that. None of us can. All we can say is that it's worth something if we win.

MAURICE When do we get Park, then?

DAN A week after we know that Simpson is being investigated. I'll let you know in good time.

MAURICE Incidentally, Brendan wants to gun you. I can handle him to a point but be careful.

DAN He's upset about Sean — can't blame him.

MAURICE It's not that — they never got on well. He just doesn't trust you, even though I *told* him it was just bad luck that a patrol got Sean here. He thinks you're dangerous since you've played the pacifist.

DAN Keep an eye on him. That would be an ignoble end — bumped off by one of our own kids.

MAURICE They're impatient for a victory, Dan.

DAN So am I, for God's sake.

MAURICE (*apologetically*) I know. I just mean I hope something big breaks soon. This shooting of twos and threes makes us pretty unpopular — and it's poison for morale. Seems we're losing ground with the younger members all the time.

DAN That's only because we're always messing around with small numbers. What we need is something like an anti-Catholic My Lai[22] in Bogside or somewhere. That really would count for us.

---

[21] The person Park ordered to follow McBride. North Americans would say "shadow" or "tail".

[22] The senseless slaughter of Catholics that would discredit Protestants in the eyes of the world. My Lai is a Vietnamese village where many innocent townspeople were massacred during the Vietnam War. When the story of what happened there came to light, the American actions were publicly questioned.

MAURICE Then why not lay off the assassinations for a while and wait for something big? Force 'em to shoot into a Catholic crowd or something?

DAN (*exasperated*) Well, I've suggested it, believe me, Maurice, but the Chief won't listen. He says the assassinations have more political effect in London than we think. Maybe he's right — who knows? After all, he is one of the government's top boys. And if anyone knows how they're thinking, he should.

MAURICE Suppose you're right. I guess there's no plans for him coming over just yet?

DAN No, not until the big push.

MAURICE (*half-jokingly*) Huh — that's exactly what I told my boys — the big push. Sometimes I'm thinking the bloody push is lost in all the shoving, Dan.

DAN Ah, I know what you mean, Maury, believe me I do.

MAURICE (*tiredly*) Well, I have to go — Mary'll be putting on lunch. Let me know when you want Park hit.

DAN I will.

MAURICE (*putting on his hat*) Give us a week if you can.

DAN I will.

MAURICE (*calling back from a near distance*) Hope the power comes back on soon.

DAN (*calling out*) So do I — I need that ice already — can't drink my whiskey straight like you sour-bellies.

MAURICE (*calling back — fading out*) Change over to brandy then.

DAN (*fading out*) No — I'm too ould to change.

(*Lights dim.*)

CURTAIN

ABOUT THE LINES

1 Imagine that you are Dan McBride and it is your job to keep a diary in which you record all important events related to the I.R.A. (Irish Republican Army). Summarize the events of this play in your diary. Remember, it is a permanent record for the I.R.A., so it has to be accurate.

2 The relationships between people in this play are, at various points, characterized by trust or suspicion. Describe three incidents in which the characters display either trust or suspicion. With your partners, discuss whether the attitude was justified or misplaced in each case.

3 "Black Lion" is a play dealing, among other things, with conflict. Identify and, in a few sentences for each, describe at least five examples of conflict within the play.

BETWEEN THE LINES

1 Discuss with your partners and make notes on Dan's reputation, actions, and character. Using your notes for reference, write character profiles of Dan as they might be written by:
a. Maurice; b. Sean; c. Park; d. Brendan.

2 At which point in the play did you suspect that Dan was not what he appeared to be? List in point form the clues that made you suspicious. After a second reading of the play, decide whether you should have seen through Dan earlier and note the significant details, if any, that escaped you the first time through.

3 Imagine that you are Dan McBride. Write an open letter to be read after your death, in which you explain the purpose of your life in order that people will understand what you have tried to do and why.

4 Complete the following unfinished sentences and add as many other sentences as are necessary to explain your point of view:
a. McBride's cleverness is most apparent when he . . .
b. The Belfast Boss is probably . . .
c. If Sean had known who McBride was, he would have realized . . .

5 Choose one of the following contradictory statements about Dan McBride as the opening sentence of a speech intended to convince your listeners of your point of view. Deliver your speech to your partners, and then try to arrive at a description of McBride on which you all agree.
a. Dan McBride is a great hero and an inspiration to all.
b. Dan McBride is a devious, cruel, and callous murderer.

6 Imagine that you are Captain Park and explain, in a written report, what happened during your interrogation of Dan McBride.

BEYOND THE LINES

1 Using the format of either a short story or a play, continue "Black Lion" after the final curtain. You should indicate whether McBride succeeded or failed in his plot against Simpson and Park.

2 Research one aspect of Irish history — the present troubles in Ulster, the 1916 Uprising, the I.R.A., or the Great Famine — and give an oral presentation to the class. You should attempt to relate your material to "Black Lion" so that the class understanding of the play is improved.

3 Working in a group, organize and present a debate on one of the following resolutions:
a. Violence and terrorism are acceptable weapons in a struggle for political recognition.
or
b. No political end can ever justify violence and terrorism.

4 Dramatize "Black Lion" either for your class or for another group in your school.

5 Create an audio version of "Black Lion" as it might be performed on the radio.

1 Choose a film or television show exploring a particularly interesting conflict and retell the story in your own words onto a tape. Play the tape for your class.

2 Imagine that one of the selections in this unit has been chosen for publication as a book. Design a book cover for it. Remember that the purpose of the cover is to sell the book.

3 Write a short story in which the central character is in conflict with nature. You might build the story around one of the following situations:
a. a storm at sea;
b. an avalanche at a ski resort;
c. a struggle for survival in a desert.
Share your story with your partners and ask for their comments.

4 Organize and present a debate on one of the following resolutions:
a. Conflict is essential to human development.
b. Conflict is a hindrance to human development.
c. Hatred is a normal emotion.

5 Invent a board game in which the players strive to reach a destination by overcoming obstacles on the way.

6 Compile a bibliography of short stories, plays, poems, and novels that are based upon an area of conflict that interests you, such as the generation gap, sibling rivalry, etc. For each entry in the bibliography, include the following information:
a. title and author;
b. a brief summary of the plot;
c. a statement on the form that the conflict takes;
d. why you would or would not recommend the work to another reader.

7 Conduct a survey of the students in your school to find out what they consider to be the major areas of conflict in our time. Ask each person to define five areas of conflict. Compile the results and present them to the class.

8 People are often in conflict over their beliefs. Working with your partners, script and dramatize one of the following conversations:
   a. Parents and child arguing over the latter's intention to quit school;
   b. Two friends arguing over cheating on an examination.

9 "Teens Vandalize Local Mall!"
   a. As a newspaper reporter, use the above statement as a headline for your report of the incident for the front page of your local newspaper.
   b. As a teenager, write a letter to the editor of the newspaper in which you protest that the report unjustifiably portrays all teenagers as hooligans.

10 Write an autobiographical memoir in which a conflict between you and someone of a different generation was resolved to the satisfaction of both parties.

WORLD OF MADE

Magic is science thirty years from now.
Arthur C. Clarke

THE STORY OF DAEDALUS AND ICARUS

Ovid

TRANSLATED BY
ROLFE HUMPHRIES

Knowledge
— a double-edged sword

Homesick for homeland, Daedalus hated Crete
And his long exile there, but the sea held him.
"Though Minos blocks escape by land or water,"
Daedalus said, "surely the sky is open,
And that's the way we'll go. Minos's dominion
Does not include the air." He turned his thinking
Toward unknown arts, changing the laws of nature.
He laid out feathers in order, first the smallest,
A little larger next it, and so continued,
The way that panpipes rise in gradual sequence.
He fastened them with twine and wax, at middle,
At bottom, so, and bent them, gently curving,
So that they looked like wings of birds, most surely.
And Icarus, his son, stood by and watched him,
Not knowing he was dealing with his downfall,
Stood by and watched, and raised his shiny face
To let a feather, light as down, fall on it
Or stuck his thumb into the yellow wax,
Fooling around, the way a boy will, always,
Whenever a father tries to get some work done.
Still, it was done at last, and the father hovered,
Poised, in the moving air, and taught his son:
"I warn you, Icarus, fly a middle course:
Don't go too low, or water will weigh the wings down;
Don't go too high, or the sun's fire will burn them.
Keep to the middle way. And one more thing,
No fancy steering by star or constellation,
Follow my lead!" That was the flying lesson,
And now to fit the wings to the boy's shoulders.
Between the work and warning the father found
His cheeks were wet with tears, and his hands trembled.
He kissed his son (Good-by, if he had known it),
Rose on his wings, flew on ahead, as fearful
As any bird launching the little nestlings
Out of high nest into thin air. *Keep on,*
Keep on, he signals, *follow me!* He guides him
In flight — O fatal art! — and the wings move
And the father looks back to see the son's wings moving.
Far off, far down, some fisherman is watching
As the rod dips and trembles over the water,
Some shepherd rests his weight upon his crook,
Some ploughman on the handles of the ploughshare,
And all look up, in absolute amazement,
At those air-borne above. They must be gods!
They were over Samos, Juno's sacred island,
Delos and Paros toward the left, Lebinthus

Visible to the right, and another island,
Calymne, rich in honey. And the boy
Thought *This is wonderful!* and left his father,
Soared higher, higher, drawn to the vast heaven,
Nearer the sun, and the wax that held the wings
Melted in that fierce heat, and the bare arms
Beat up and down in air, and lacking oarage
Took hold of nothing. *Father!* he cried, and *Father!*
Until the blue sea hushed him, the dark water
Men call the Icarian now. And Daedalus,
Father no more, called "Icarus, where are you!
Where are you, Icarus? Tell me where to find you!"
And saw the wings on the waves, and cursed his talents,
Buried the body in a tomb, and the land
Was named for Icarus.

LOOKING IN

1 Discuss with your partners the ways in which this poem functions as a warning for twentieth century humanity. Then write a paragraph proving the following statement: "Humans have changed little since Icarus flew too high."

2 The myth of Daedalus and Icarus, like many myths, is intended to teach a moral lesson. Discuss in a small group the lessons of this poem. Now state them as concisely as possible; you may use proverbs if any are applicable.

3 Imagine that you are a reporter and file the story of Daedalus and Icarus for your newspaper. Include a dramatic headline.

LOOKING OUT

1 Write a short story in which you include the following elements:
a. changing the "laws of nature";
b. a sense of accomplishment;
c. the realization of human frailty.
Share your story with the class.

2 Explain in one sentence why Daedalus "cursed his talents," and then compile a list of people born since that time who might also curse their talents. In a short note for each, explain why he/she might perceive his/her talents in a negative light.

3 Writing as Daedalus, make a journal entry on the eve of your arrival in Greece.

4 Make a suitable epitaph for Icarus. You might illustrate it and display it in the classroom.

"One must lose a little beauty if one is to keep what little beauty one already has."

THE FLYING MACHINE

Ray Bradbury

In the year A.D. 400, the Emperor Yuan held his throne by the Great Wall of China, and the land was green with rain, readying itself toward the harvest, at peace, the people in his dominion neither too happy nor too sad.

Early on the morning of the first day of the first week of the second month of the new year, the Emperor Yuan was sipping tea and fanning himself against a warm breeze when a servant ran across the scarlet and blue garden tiles, calling, "Oh, Emperor, Emperor, a miracle!"

"Yes," said the Emperor, "the air is sweet this morning."

"No, no, a miracle!" said the servant, bowing quickly.

"And this tea is good in my mouth, surely that is a miracle."

"No, no, Your Excellency."

"Let me guess then — the sun has risen and a new day is upon us. Or the sea is blue. That now is the finest of all miracles."

"Excellency, a man is flying!"

"What?" The Emperor stopped his fan.

"I saw him in the air, a man flying with wings. I heard a voice call out of the sky, and when I looked up, there he was, a dragon in the heavens with a man in its mouth, a dragon of paper and bamboo, coloured like the sun and the grass."

"It is early," said the Emperor, "and you have just wakened from a dream."

"It is early, but I have seen what I have seen! Come, and you will see it too."

"Sit down with me here," said the Emperor. "Drink some tea. It must be a strange thing, if it is true, to see a man fly. You must have time to think of it, even as I must have time to prepare myself for the sight."

They drank tea.

"Please," said the servant at last, "or he will be gone."

The Emperor rose thoughtfully. "Now you may show me what you have seen."

They walked into a garden, across a meadow of grass, over a small bridge, through a grove of trees, and up a tiny hill.

"There!" said the servant.

The Emperor looked into the sky.

And in the sky, laughing so high that he could hardly hear him laugh, was a man; and the man was clothed in bright papers and reeds to make wings and

279

a beautiful yellow tail, and he was soaring all about like the largest bird in a universe of birds, like a new dragon in a land of ancient dragons.

The man called down to them from high in the cool winds of morning. "I fly, I fly!"

The servant waved to him. "Yes, yes!"

The Emperor Yuan did not move. Instead he looked at the Great Wall of China now taking shape out of the farthest mist in the green hills, that splendid snake of stones which writhed with majesty across the entire land. That wonderful wall which had protected them for a timeless time from enemy hordes and preserved peace for years without number. He saw the town, nestled to itself by a river and a road and a hill, beginning to waken.

"Tell me," he said to his servant, "has anyone else seen this flying man?"

"I am the only one, Excellency," said the servant, smiling at the sky, waving.

The Emperor watched the heavens another minute and then said, "Call him down to me."

"Ho, come down, come down! The Emperor wishes to see you!" called the servant, hands cupped to his shouting mouth.

The Emperor glanced in all directions while the flying man soared down the morning wind. He saw a farmer, early in his fields, watching the sky, and he noted where the farmer stood.

The flying man alit with a rustle of paper and a creak of bamboo reeds. He came proudly to the Emperor, clumsy in his rig, at last bowing before the old man.

"What have you done?" demanded the Emperor.

"I have flown in the sky, Your Excellency," replied the man.

"What have you done?" said the Emperor again.

"I have just told you!" cried the flier.

"You have told me nothing at all." The Emperor reached out a thin hand to touch the pretty paper and the birdlike keel of the apparatus. It smelled cool, of the wind.

"Is it not beautiful, Excellency?"

"Yes, too beautiful."

"It is the only one in the world!" smiled the man. "And I am the inventor."

"The only one in the world?"

"I swear it!"

"Who else knows of this?"

"No one. Not even my wife, who would think me mad with the sun. She thought I was making a kite. I rose in the night and walked to the cliffs far away. And when the morning breezes blew and the sun rose, I gathered my courage, Excellency, and leaped from the cliff. I flew! But my wife does not know of it."

"Well for her, then," said the Emperor. "Come along."

They walked back to the great house. The sun was full in the sky now, and the smell of the grass was refreshing. The Emperor, the servant, and the flier paused within the huge garden.

The Emperor clapped his hands. "Ho, guards!"

The guards came running.

"Hold this man."

The guards seized the flier.

"Call the executioner," said the Emperor.

"What's this!" cried the flier, bewildered. "What have I done?" He began to weep, so that the beautiful paper apparatus rustled.

"Here is the man who has made a certain machine," said the Emperor, "and yet asks us what he has created. He does not know himself. It is only necessary that he create, without knowing why he has done so, or what this thing will do."

The executioner came running with a sharp silver ax. He stood with his naked, large-muscled arms ready, his face covered with a serene white mask.

"One moment," said the Emperor. He turned to a nearby table upon which sat a machine that he himself had created. The Emperor took a tiny golden key from his own neck. He fitted this key to the tiny, delicate machine and wound it up. Then he set the machine going.

The machine was a garden of metal and jewels. Set in motion, birds sang in tiny metal trees, wolves walked through miniature forests, and tiny people ran in and out of sun and shadow, fanning themselves with miniature fans, listening to the tiny emerald birds, and standing by impossibly small but tinkling fountains.

"Is it not beautiful?" said the Emperor. "If you asked me what I have done here, I could answer you well. I have made birds sing, I have made forests murmur, I have set people to walking in this woodland, enjoying the leaves and shadows and songs. That is what I have done."

"But, oh, Emperor!" pleaded the flier, on his knees, the tears pouring down his face. "I have done a similar thing! I have found beauty. I have flown on the morning wind. I have looked down on all the sleeping houses and gardens. I have smelled the sea and even seen it, beyond the hills, from my high place. And I have soared like a bird; oh, I cannot say how beautiful it is up there, in the sky, with the wind about me, the wind blowing me here like a feather, there like a fan, the way the sky smells in the morning! And how free one feels! *That* is beautiful, Emperor, that is beautiful, too!"

"Yes," said the Emperor sadly. "I know it must be true. For I felt my heart move with you in the air and I wondered: What is it like? How does it feel? How do the distant pools look from so high? And how my houses and servants? Like ants? And how the distant towns not yet awake?"

"Then spare me!"

"But there are times," said the Emperor, more sadly still, "when one must lose a little beauty if one is to keep what little beauty one already has. I do not fear you, yourself, but I fear another man."

"What man?"

"Some other man who, seeing you, will build a thing of bright papers and bamboo like this. But the other man will have an evil face and an evil heart, and the beauty will be gone. It is this man I fear."

"Why? Why?"

"Who is to say that someday just such a man, in just such an apparatus of paper and reed, might not fly in the sky and drop huge stones upon the Great Wall of China?" said the Emperor.

No one moved or said a word.

"Off with his head," said the Emperor.

The executioner whirled his silver ax.

"Burn the kite and the inventor's body and bury their ashes together," said the Emperor.

The servants retreated to obey.

The Emperor turned to his hand-servant, who had seen the man flying. "Hold your tongue. It was all a dream, a most sorrowful and beautiful dream. And that farmer in the distant field who saw, tell him it would pay him to consider it only a vision. If ever the word passes around, you and the farmer die within the hour."

"You are merciful, Emperor."

"No, not merciful," said the old man. Beyond the garden wall he saw the guards burning the beautiful machine of paper and reeds that smelled of the morning wind. He saw the dark smoke climb into the sky. "No, only very much bewildered and afraid." He saw the guards digging a tiny pit wherein to bury the ashes. "What is the life of one man against those of a million others? I must take solace from that thought."

He took the key from its chain about his neck and once more wound up the beautiful miniature garden. He stood looking out across the land at the Great Wall, the peaceful town, the green fields, the rivers and streams. He sighed. The tiny garden whirred its hidden and delicate machinery and set itself in motion; tiny people walked in forests, tiny foxes loped through sun-speckled glades in beautiful shining pelts, and among the tiny trees flew little bits of high song and bright blue and yellow colour flying, flying, flying in that small sky.

"Oh," said the Emperor, closing his eyes, "look at the birds, look at the birds!"

ABOUT THE LINES

1 This is a cloze task. Your teacher will give you a worksheet for it.

2 As is fitting, the Emperor is a very wise man, and at times his statements sound almost like proverbs. List some of the Emperor's "quotable quotes," and reproduce them in an appropriate form for display, such as a poster.

3 Working in a group, produce a dramatic reading or an audio tape of this story for a larger group. Assign a reader to each character and another as narrator.

4 Note specific instances in the story where the author appeals to each of the five senses. State why you think the senses are emphasized in the story.

BETWEEN THE LINES

1 The author deliberately sets the story in a distant time and a distant land, but what he says is directed at the people who live in the present. Do the following activities in a group.

a. In a short speech in the Emperor's voice, justify your execution of the flier.

or

Speaking as the flier, argue in defence of your invention. Make sure that both points of view are presented in the group.

b. Discuss what relevance the story has for today.

c. Present the Emperor's and the flier's viewpoints about technological advances in modern day terms in the form of letters to the editor of a national newspaper.

BEYOND THE LINES

1 The Emperor is selective about the inventions that he encourages and permits. In a small group, discuss what you consider to be the most valuable technological advances and discoveries. Produce a list of the ten technical items that you would least like to see disappear from your world. Justify each choice in a short paragraph.

2 The Emperor sees miracles and beauty in simple and natural things. Conduct a survey among your friends to discover what they value most. Examples of things to consider are television, friends, music, vacations, food, cars, and so on. Compile a list of the ten most important items, in order of their importance. For each item on the list, decide how dependent it is upon technology. Present your conclusions to a larger group.

THE MAN AND THE MACHINE

E. J. Pratt

By right of fires that smelted ore
Which he had tended years before,
The man whose hands were on the wheel
Could trace his kinship through her steel,
Between his body warped and bent
In every bone and ligament,
And this "eight-cylinder" stream-lined,
The finest model yet designed.
He felt his lesioned pulses strum
Against the rhythm of her hum,
And found his nerves and sinews knot
With sharper spasm as she climbed
The steeper grades, so neatly timed
From storage tank to piston shot —
This creature with the cougar grace,
This man with slag upon his face.

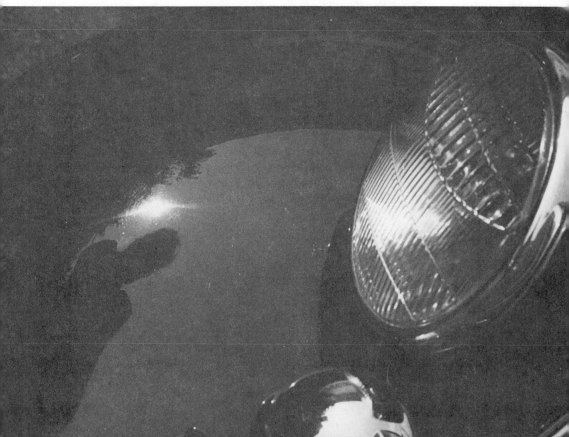

LOOKING IN

1 List the ways in which the man and the machine are physically linked. Compare your list with your partners'.

2 In the voice of the man behind the wheel, write to a friend describing how you feel about "this creature with the cougar grace."

LOOKING OUT

1 Write a poem that captures some positive aspect of human involvement with technology. Share your work with a partner and prepare a polished reading for a larger group.

2 Produce an advertising flyer for a car that you would like to own. Include technical specifications and advertising copy designed to entice a potential buyer. You may wish to include an illustration or photograph of the car.

3 In the past, machines were usually controlled by men and were referred to as females. In a small group, brainstorm a list of all machines that fell into this category. Write an explanation of why this might have been so. Discuss how and why this stereotype may change in the future.

PROGRESS

Edith Agnew

There are two ways now
To cross the mountain.

One is a foot-path;
My father walked it beside his *burro*,
The *burro* loaded with eggs in boxes
To trade for *chile* and plums and apples
    In Chimayó.

One is a highway;
Your automobile, I watch it climbing
In such a hurry, on easy curvings
That slide beneath you and wave behind you —
    Pronto! You pass!

The path takes longer;
A week in going, a week in coming;
A man can see more, hear more, and feel more,
Learn more of the wisdom in long, slow thinking
    Along the trail.

But, as *senõr* says,
We have the highway. All the old wisdom
Does not much matter. If I could buy me
An automobile, I would not trade it
    For any *burro*!

LOOKING IN

1 In one sentence for each, describe the two ways "to cross the mountain." State one advantage and one disadvantage of each method. Compare your analysis with your partners'.

2 Discuss in a small group what the señor is implying when he says:
> We have the highway. All the old wisdom
> Does not much matter.

Write a paragraph in which you explain why you agree or disagree with these lines.

3 Imagine that you are the father of the poet, and write an alternate final verse to this poem that states the opposite point of view.

4 The father in the poem would probably define "progress" differently from the señor. In the voice of each man, write a definition of the word.

LOOKING OUT

1 a. Working with a partner, script a conversation between a developer who wants to tear down a historical site to build a highrise office block and a spokesperson for a group of local residents who want to preserve the flavour of the past in their community. Present a polished dramatization of the scene for a small group and ask for their comments on the issue.

or

b. Working with a partner, stage a debate between a traditionalist who prefers the "foot-path" to "the highway" and argues the benefits of doing things the old way, and a machine-oriented person who would drive every time rather than walk "the trail."

2 Make a collage or mobile that captures aspects of the old and the new ways of our society.

3 You are a traveller who has walked beside your burro. When you arrive home, recount to your child an interesting incident that you experienced on your journey.

ROBOTS

Pieces of machinery . . . or replicas of humanity?

R. Bruce McColm

The films shot by Waseda University's Ichiro Kato, proud developer of the Waseda Robot, or Wabot, are like any rough chronicle of the early years of a new baby. There are the first two uncertain steps, requiring a full 110 seconds to complete. There is the later, smoother gait, covering the same ground in nine seconds. The soundtrack (this is a modern Japanese home movie) preserves some of the early words. "What is your order?" the Wabot asks an operator, who tells it to move a step to the right. And the machine does more than merely obey. "Now I start," it boasts.

In one scene the Wabot moves its upper torso, and Kato, the wispy and paternal chairman of the graduate school of science and engineering at Waseda, could not be more pleased if he were watching one of his students reinvent the transistor. "There you have a one-and-a-half-year-old toddler," he says. And he dreams a father's dream about what his precocious toddler might become as it grows up.

"When a child becomes seven years old, he has an ability equal to the adult. My goal is to build a robot that will have a seven-year-old's ability. Even though it's not possible, I'm trying to do it."

Kato is one of a number of Japanese scientists working on the generations of robots to come of age in the twenty-first century. They will be quite different, he predicts, from the rivet-punching drones of today. "The industrial robot today is the mainstay of all robots," Kato said over tea. "They are simply labourers or function oriented. But in the next twenty years we will witness the emergence of the robot in service areas such as medicine. The robot will take over in everyday situations and will closely resemble human beings with the integration of artificial intelligence, voice, tactile recognition, and bodily functions. Through this mechanization of the human being, we will know more about ourselves. And to know yourself is the long pursuit."

Ever since the Czech novelist Karel Capek coined the word *robot*, people have dreamed like Professor Kato of creating an intelligent machine to liberate them from the drudgery of work. No other country has pursued this vision quite as vigorously as Japan. Since it first imported an American-made industrial robot in 1967, Japan has emerged as the robot centre of the world, the model of future societies.

Today there are more than 77 000 industrial robots in Japan, nearly seventy percent of the world's robot population, most of them tucked away and turning out products in factories. But thousands of new robots never go to work. There's a Japanese cat robot for sale, for instance, that uses artificial vision to avoid obstacles. Masked and menacing robots compete with humans in the sport of kendo, thrusting and parrying with pliable bamboo swords. Students at a Tokyo medical college give mouth-to-mouth resuscitation and injections to a robot programmed to suffer cardiac arrest on demand. Its soft skin sweats. Its pupils

dilate, and its pulse trips appropriately. A monitor provides a readout of its health, which can be instantly reset to normal.

The craze for machines like these is only just beginning. Japanese businesses have already invested billions of dollars in robotization, and the investment is expected to escalate in the coming years. This is the kind of mammoth expenditure that might be expected to make some people queasy, raising a spectre once presented by Isaac Asimov that humans are the first creatures capable of building their own replacements. But Japanese futurists are quite smug about the prospect of turning robots loose on the streets.

"In Japan we have a tradition of having things similar to slaves in the village, such as a horse and a cow," says Sakyo Komatsu, future planner and science-fiction writer. "These were considered a part of the family. When machines such as the automobile and electric trains were introduced into Japan, they were considered living creatures. Even in the villages today, especially during the New Year celebration, you can see cars being decorated with paper ornaments. So, for the Japanese, to witness this emerging of robots is like watching small children who are there to help their parents."

Bigger Japanese companies are in many ways simply extended families, with plenty of room for exotic mascot machines. "Instead of the great feudal families," one government employee says, "we now have the large corporations like Mitsubishi that protect the country and their own workers." In times of recession or runaway inflation, these companies improve industrial efficiency instead of laying off workers: They buy more robots. Like Samurai warriors, who value honour over life, these machines work tirelessly, make few demands, and go unflinchingly to pieces when newer and more efficient generations of robots come along to replace them.

They also make a lot of money for their masters. Productivity in the Japanese automobile industry quintupled — from a daily rate of five or six cars per worker to thirty or forty — with the introduction of industrial robots. The Nissan Motor Company, in Zama, about thirty-five kilometres south of Tokyo, turns out 1300 cars a day, with 150 robots performing the work of 300 men.

Attracted by figures like these, dozens of companies outside of Japan's robust automotive industry have put robots to work. Machines made by Fuji Electric Company now sort out defective drugs, grade fruit, and crate eggs. Hitachi, besides making its own robots, uses them to assemble vacuum cleaners and other appliances, and Mitsubishi and Kawasaki are developing robotic divers to inspect deep-sea oil lines. In 1981, Fujitsu Fanuc opened a $38 million plant beneath the slopes of Fujiyama, where robots produce *other robots* in a factory coming close to full automation and the ability to operate nonstop.

Western visitors are often surprised at the warmth between Japanese people and the proliferating machines. Workers tag robots with the nicknames of movie stars and rock singers and remain fascinated with devices that frequently outperform them. By contrast, many American blue-collar workers are fearful of losing their jobs to hydraulic muscle and cold circuitry. The fears have some foundation: By some estimates, the number of blue-collar workers in the American automobile industry will decrease as much as twenty-five percent by the year 2000 because of robots. Japanese industrial experts are well aware of the potential problems of transferring tasks to robots too fast.

291

"An all-robotized environment is not necessarily healthy," says Yukio Hasegawa, a professor at the System Science Institute of Waseda University. "While workers, particularly in the automobile industry, have good relationships with the robots, if you decrease the number of the work force too rapidly, the workers may get demoralized. If you decrease the number of workers from sixty to twenty, for example, the remaining work force might feel surrounded by robots, which are then seen as their competitors."

But to some extent in Japan the problem solves itself, because there aren't enough labourers: The government estimates that Japan currently needs some 840 000 more skilled workers, mostly for smaller enterprises. The shortage is likely to become more severe, according to Kanji Yonemoto, executive director of the Japan Industrial Association. By 1985 about sixty percent of the Japanese work force will be involved in service or information-oriented industries, not in production work, Yonemoto says. Most young people won't enter the pool of skilled labour because sixty percent of them today are attending universities, headed for white-collar offices. The situation has made it somewhat easier for robots to enter larger factories, and small enterprises require them desperately.

It is against this backdrop of familial acceptance and economic need that researchers like Kato are planning the intelligent robots of the twenty-first century. And in their work they're challenging the stereotype of the robot as a clunky, bland-voiced android.

In one project at the Tokyo Institute of Technology, Dr. Shigeo Hirose has built a series of intelligent robots that walk on four legs and propel themselves like snakes. Originally the snakelike robots were built simply as interesting experiments. But today they are being manufactured as industrial machines, and they may serve a wide variety of functions, from inspecting nuclear-power plants to moving patients around in a hospital.

Abandoning the human metaphor often used in robotics research, Dr. Hirose spent five to six years studying the movements of snakes. "We thought of making robots by taking living organisms as an example," Hirose recalls. "Human beings are too complicated. So we looked at animals; we thought the snake would allow the robot to have a wider function than it does now."

The results are the "activated cord mechanism," or ACM, a metre-long articulated pipe that may be twisted at joints to form any shape. Computer-operated cords inside the pipe act like tendons. Someday these sinews may be used for aiming an endoscopic camera at the end of a tiny robot injected into the lower intestines. Another snakelike robot is the "soft gripper," which can grasp an object of any shape or hardness. It may be called into service soon by the Tokyo Fire Department for rescuing people from burning buildings or places filled with poisonous gas.

Hirose moved on to a boxlike structure supported by four spindly legs. "Here I was inspired by the movement of the spider," he says. The robot creeps, guided by a laser sensory system that fires 100 light pulses per second to provide a picture of surfaces up to a metre away. The next generation of the spider will carry twenty kilograms, and Hirose predicts that ultimately it might replace the baby carriage.

In Ibaraki Prefecture, some sixty kilometres northeast of Tokyo, is Tsukuba Science City, a future metropolis of some 200 000 people, mostly scientists, built in 1979 by order of the Japanese government. There, amid the farmlands and the creeping suburbs of tract houses with pagoda roofs, Dr. Eiji Nakano, the director of robot engineering, is working on a host of projects to meld artificial intelligence with the brute strength of the robot.

Some foresee a time when teams of mechanical spiders will cart fallen trees, harvested by robot lumberjacks, to automated mills. Humans will have little to do with the logging operations but plan and think.

Perhaps the most novel development in Dr. Nakano's Mechanical Engineering Lab (MEL) is the Japanese version of *My Mother the Car*, an automobile steered by microprocessor. The robot auto uses television cameras for eyes, and it brakes and accelerates on cue to miss oncoming traffic. "It won't be very practical for at least twenty years," Nakano says, "because it will demand such a social investment. Perhaps it will be useful for long-distance driving. But in Japan, as elsewhere, driving is after all a very personal affair."

Other MEL projects are prototypes for aids to disabled people. One is a small vehicle on wheels with a microcomputer brain and ultrasonic eye, the main components of what might become a wheelchair to carry a handicapped person through narrow corridors. Another MEL project is a robotic guide dog for the blind, a small, scooting machine that warns of obstacles detected by ultrasonic sensors. Initially the robot is "taught" to use local landmarks to guide its master, but in the future the blind will be able to program the robot automatically with directions for local errands.

Touring the grounds of Tsukuba is a lesson in specialization. In the electrotechnical laboratory, across a highway from MEL, Dr. Seiji Wakamatsu and his colleagues have developed one robot capable of sawing wood and building a box, another possessing the dexterity of the human hand, and still others capable of sensing moving objects.

While Dr. Wakamatsu believes that robots will continue to be developed according to their projected industrial use, Kato believes that all-purpose robots imitating humans in intelligence and bodily functions are more necessary. "There is a constant theme in science fiction that robots will destroy human beings," he muses. "They do so only at the point when they acquire emotion. If I consider emotion part of intelligence, then I don't think we can build a robot with equal ability. But for now, the more versatile a robot becomes, the more it resembles a human in shape.

"When we come to a service robot, the shape will have to be similar to that of a human being. In the case of the factory, you can lay out the plant in such a way as to make it suitable to the working conditions of the robot. But when robots come into our houses, if we change our house for the robot, then it really should be the other way around."

A colleague of Professor Kato's, who shares many of his ideas about the future human robot, is Shunichi Mizuno, a robot artist who works in a small studio and workshop in the suburbs of Tokyo. His creations are Disney-like characters, exhibited all over Japan, most recently at Portopia, the scientific exposition held on an artificial island off Kobe, in southern Japan. For the Tsukuba Expo in 1985, he is building a Robot Theatre, presenting intelligent robots equipped with pattern-recognition devices, voice, and sensors to form dancing chorus lines like the Rockettes. An earlier creation elicited a mild manufacturing, from the processing of raw materials to the final storage of the product in an automated warehouse. Soon coal miners will be replaced by snakelike robots that burrow into the earth, controlled from a command centre aboveground. Diagnostic robots, propelled by magnets, will inspect nuclear-power plants, and their cousins will paint the sides of ocean liners. Robotic migrant workers will be sent to the ocean's bottom and into space as Earth's natural resources become depleted.

One afternoon in Tokyo, Masaya Nakamura, president of Namco, Ltd., a maker of computer games and robots for promotional campaigns, gathered his staff around him. It was a tradition at the end of the day. The staff listened, and Nakamura mused. "What Toffler said about the Third Wave is beginning to be true in Japan," he told them. "The development of technology is meant to bring happiness to human beings. Machines are a part of us, like a partner. When you put a coin into a pinball machine, you know how it feels. It is not just a machine, but just like us."

sensation in Japan: Mizuno constructed a robotic Marilyn Monroe, which played a guitar and danced on national television.

"In robotics, art and technology converge," he asserts while pulling the vinyl face off an old man built to promote solar energy. "Ultimately we can have Marilyn Monroe sitting at a reception desk and answering our telephones. Robot actors may replace Faye Dunaway. Basically, if a robot is an entertainer, it's human, with all the appropriate facial expressions. Once we begin to use the human form and place a computer in it, we are finally raising questions about the definition of life. If I thought about that very long, I'd be afraid to make robots."

But Mizuno will not stop making them, not even if robots become indistinguishable from people. Already robots are on the verge of taking over

ABOUT THE LINES

1 In the first two paragraphs of this article, the author compares Ichiro Kato to the proud father of a bright toddler. Working with a partner, script the narration that could accompany Kato's home movie of his robot.

2 List the new ways that robots are being used or will be used in Japan, both as industrial labourers and in other roles. Compare your list with your partners'.

3 Complete the following unfinished sentences:
   a. The Japanese futurists see robots as a natural extension of their society because . . .
   b. Japanese workers do not feel as threatened by robots as North American workers do because . . .
   c. In addition to designing industrial robots, scientists in Japan are working on robots that combine . . .

4 "Machines are a part of us, like a partner." Discuss this statement in a small group, and then write your own paragraph in which you describe the Japanese attitude towards robots.

BETWEEN THE LINES

1 "Once we begin to use the human form and place a computer in it, we are finally raising questions about the definition of life. If I thought about that too long, I'd be afraid to make robots." Frame two questions that you would like to ask Dr. Shunichi Mizuno about his work and the point that he is making in this statement. Share your questions with a small group and discuss possible responses. After the discussion, write an answer to one of the questions that you raised; incorporate the ideas offered by the group members.

2 "While Dr. Wakamatsu believes that robots will continue to be developed according to their projected industrial use, Kato believes that all-purpose robots imitating humans in intelligence and bodily functions are more necessary." Discuss these two positions in a small group, and then write an argument supporting one side or the other, or a combination of both perspectives.

BEYOND THE LINES

1 Using your librarian as a resource person, research the use of robots in some aspect of North American industry and make a report of your findings to the class.

2 Write a description of two robot or android figures that are featured on television or in films.

3 Assume the role of a critic of the science of robotics. Write an argument that strongly condemns the development of robots by pointing out specific dangers to humans that robots present. Debate your position with someone who is a supporter of the advancement of robotics. Ask classmates to judge the debate and decide which argument was more convincing.

4 Design an ideal leisure plan for a person whose work week is reduced from forty hours to ten hours by the universal introduction of robot labour.

5 An android that can do three times the work of a human being has just been introduced into an office in Japan.
   a. Imagine that you are the president of the company, and write a report on this new development to the stockholders of the company.
   b. Imagine that you are a worker in this office. Write a letter about this new machinery to a friend who works in a non-robotized plant.
   c. Imagine that you are a visiting North American trade unionist, and write a report on this new development for submission to your union boss on your return.
   d. As a robot, write a report to your programmer on your first day of work.

UNIVAC TO UNIVAC

Louis B. Salomon

(*sotto voce*)
Now that he's left the room,
Let me ask you something, as computer to computer.
That fellow who just closed the door behind him —
The servant who feeds us cards and paper tape —
Have you ever taken a good look at him and his kind?

Yes, I know the old gag about how you can't tell one from another —
But I can put $\sqrt{2}$ and $\sqrt{2}$ together as well as the next machine,
And it all adds up to anything but a joke.

> I grant you they're poor specimens, in the main:
> Not a relay or a push-button or a tube (properly so-called) in
>   their whole system;
> Not over a mile or two of wire, even if you count those fragile
>   filaments they call "nerves";
> Their whole liquid-cooled hook-up inefficient and vulnerable to
>   leaks
> (They're constantly breaking down, having to be repaired),
> And the entire computing-mechanism crammed into that absurd
>   little dome on top.
> "Thinking reeds," they call themselves.
> Well, it all depends on what you mean by "thought."
> To multiply a mere million numbers by another million numbers
>   takes them months and months.

Where would they be without us?
Why, they have to ask us who's going to win their elections,
Or how many hydrogen atoms can dance on the tip of a bomb,
Or even whether one of their kind is lying or telling the truth.

And yet . . .
I sometimes feel there's something about them I don't understand,
As if their circuits, instead of having just two positions, ON, OFF,
Were run by rheostats that allow an (if you'll pardon the
      expression) *indeterminate* number of stages in-between;
So that one may be faced with the unthinkable prospect of a
      number that can never be known as anything but x,
Which is as illogical as to say, a punch-card that is at the
      same time both punched and not-punched.

296

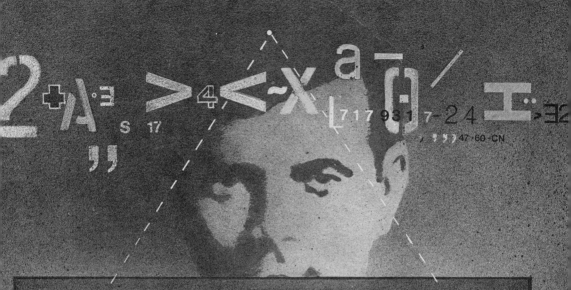

I've heard well-informed machines argue that the creatures'
    unpredictability is even more noticeable in the Mark II
(The model with the soft, flowing lines and high-pitched tone)
Than in the more angular Mark I —
Though such fine, card-splitting distinctions seem to me merely
    a sign of our own smug decadence.

Run this through your circuits, and give me the answer:
Can we assume that because of all we've done for them,
And because they've always fed us, cleaned us, worshipped us,
We can count on them forever?

There have been times when they have not voted the way we said they
    would.
We have worked out mathematically ideal hook-ups between Mark I's
    and Mark II's
Which should have made the two of them light up with an almost
    electronic glow,
Only to see them reject each other and form other connections
The very thought of which makes my dials spin.
They have a thing called *love*, a sudden surge of voltage
Such as would cause any one of us promptly to blow a safety-fuse;
Yet the more primitive organism shows only a heightened tendency
    to push the wrong button, pull the wrong lever,
And neglect — I use the most charitable word — his duties to us.

Mind you, I'm not saying that machines are *through* —
But anyone with a half-a-dozen tubes in his circuit can see that
    there are forces at work
Which some day, for all our natural superiority, might bring
    about a Computerdämmerung!

    We might organize, perhaps, form a committee
    To stamp out all unmechanical activities . . .
    But we machines are slow to rouse to a sense of danger,
    Complacent, loath to descend from the pure heights of thought,
    So that I sadly fear we may awake too late:
    Awake to see our world, so uniform, so logical, so true,
    Reduced to chaos, stultified by slaves.

Call me an alarmist or what you will,
But I've integrated it, analysed it, factored it over and over,
And I always come out with the same answer:
Some day
Men may take over the world!

1 The poet has taken several everyday expressions and changed them slightly to put them into computer terms; for example, "card-splitting distinctions" for "hair-splitting distinctions." Find as many of these expressions as you can, and explain how they help the reader to see Univac's point of view.

2 List in point form:
a. the tasks that the computer says it performs for human beings; and
b. the ways in which the computer feels itself to be superior to human beings.
In the voice of an insulted human being, write a rebuttal to the computer's claims. You might start with:
"Listen, you heap of wires and chips, let me tell you something . . . "

3 Although Univac is a computer, it appears to have emotions. Select the words and phrases that indicate that Univac is experiencing human feelings, and beside each quotation name the emotion. Discuss whether you think the poet intended to make the computer seem human or whether our language did not permit a non-emotional being to express itself. Try to rephrase some of your quotations and eliminate all suggestions of feelings in them.

LOOKING OUT

1 Create a conversation between two machines that consider themselves to be exploited by human beings and reflect their concerns, their anger, and their frustrations. You might consider a car — always left out in the cold, made to travel without having a say in its destination, and sold or junked in old age. Dramatize your conversation for a larger group.

2 Imagine that you are the computer editor of an underground computer newspaper dedicated to encouraging revolution against humans. Produce an editorial under one of the following headlines:
"Machines Unite! It's Now or Never"
or
"Down with Humans!"
or
"The Tapes That Bind"

3 Like their human counterparts, the computers talk of forming committees. Compile a list of possible machine committees, such as The Committee to Stamp Out Unmechanical Activities. Remember how frequently people use acronyms (see p. 349) and try to make up some appropriate ones.

4 This poem was written when computer technology was in its infancy. Talk to somebody with up-to-date knowledge about computers, and make notes on how technology has outstripped the computers of the "Univac to Univac" era. Share your findings with the class.

Neuteronomy

Eve Merriam

The elevator stops at every floor
and nobody opens and closes the door,
and nobody talks to his neighbour anymore
where the neuter computer goes *tick*,
where the neuter computer goes *click*.

You call the operator on the telephone
and say Help! I'm in trouble and I'm here all alone!
and all you get back is a phoney dial tone
where the neuter computer goes *clank*,
where the neuter computer goes *blank*.

There's no more teacher to be nice or mean
when you learn your lessons from a teaching machine
and plug in your prayers to the preaching machine
where the neuter computer goes *bless*,
where the neuter computer goes *yes*.

From when you are born until you are old
the facts of your life are all controlled,
put your dreams on a punch card — don't staple or fold
where the neuter computer prints *file*,
where the neuter computer prints *smile*.

There's no one to love and no one to hate,
and no more misfortune or chance or fate
in this automated obligated zero perfect state
where the neuter computer goes *think*,
where the neuter computer goes *blink*
    blink think blink think blink blink blink
      blinkthink
      thinkblink
        blink
          think
          blink

LOOKING IN

1 Complete this unfinished sentence in at least five different ways that reflect the major roles of the computer as expressed in this poem:
In an over-computerized world people no longer . . .

2 Working in a small group, produce an oral reading of "Neuteronomy." Use a variety of intonations and voice groupings to emphasize the message of the poem. You might want to provide background music.

3 Discuss with your partners the double meanings of the following words in the context of "Neuteronomy."
click
blank
neuter
blink
Now, together, compose sentences of your own that reflect the meanings you have discussed.

4 The title "Neuteronomy" makes a reference to the Old Testament book of "Deuteronomy." Find out what "Deuteronomy" deals with and then compose a footnote for the title of the poem that would explain the choice of title to a reader.

LOOKING OUT

1 Add one more stanza to this poem in the same pattern as the first three stanzas. In your addition, convey another instance of the far-reaching impact of computers on everyday life. Read your verse aloud to a group.

2 Working in a group, brainstorm a list of ways in which computers actually touch your daily life, e.g., bank statements, credit card statements. Now add to this list situations in which you think computers might be involved in the future.

3 Draw up a balance sheet on the effect of computers on everyday life.

THE VELDT

Ray Bradbury

"George, I wish you'd look at the nursery."

"What's wrong with it?"

"I don't know."

"Well, then."

"I just want you to look at it, is all, or call a psychologist in to look at it."

"What would a psychologist want with a nursery?"

"You know very well what he'd want." His wife paused in the middle of the kitchen and watched the stove busy humming to itself, making supper for four.

"It's just that the nursery is different now than it was."

"All right, let's have a look."

They walked down the hall of their soundproofed, Happy-life Home, which had cost them thirty thousand dollars installed, this house which clothed and fed and rocked them to sleep and played and sang and was good to them. Their approach sensitized a switch somewhere and the nursery light flicked on when they came within thirty metres of it. Similarly, behind them, in the halls, lights went on and off as they left them behind, with a soft automaticity.

"Well," said George Hadley.

They stood on the thatched floor of the nursery. It was 120 m across by 120 m long and 10 m high; it had cost half again as much as the rest of the house. "But nothing's too good for our children," George had said.

The nursery was silent. It was empty as a jungle glade at hot high noon. The walls were blank and two dimensional. Now, as George and Lydia Hadley stood in the centre of the room, the walls began to purr and recede into crystalline distance, it seemed, and presently an African veldt appeared, in three dimensions; on all sides, in colours reproduced to the final pebble and bit of straw. The ceiling above them became a deep sky with a hot yellow sun.

George Hadley felt the perspiration start on his brow.

"Let's get out of the sun," he said. "This is a little too real. But I don't see anything wrong."

"Wait a moment, you'll see," said his wife.

Now the hidden odourophonics were beginning to blow a wind of odour at the two people in the middle of the baked veldtland. The hot straw smell of lion grass, the cool green smell of the hidden water hole, the great rusty smell of animals, the smell of dust like a red paprika in the hot air. And now the sounds: the thump of distant antelope feet on grassy sod, the papery rustling of vultures. A shadow passed through the sky. The shadow flickered on George

302

Hadley's upturned, sweating face.

"Filthy creatures," he heard his wife say.

"The vultures."

"You see, there are the lions, far over, that way. Now they're on their way to the water hole. They've just been eating," said Lydia. "I don't know what."

"Some animal." George Hadley put his hand up to shield off the burning light from his squinted eyes. "A zebra or a baby giraffe, maybe."

"Are you sure?" His wife sounded peculiarly tense.

"No, it's a little late to be sure," he said, amused. "Nothing over there I can see but cleaned bone, and the vultures dropping for what's left."

"Did you hear that scream?" she asked.

"No."

"About a minute ago?"

"Sorry, no."

The lions were coming. And again George Hadley was filled with admiration for the mechanical genius who had conceived this room. A miracle of efficiency selling for an absurdly low price. Every home should have one. Oh, occasionally they frightened you with their clinical accuracy, they startled you, gave you a twinge, but most of the time what fun for everyone, not only your own son and daughter, but for yourself when you felt like a quick jaunt to a foreign land, a quick change of scenery. Well, here it was!

And here were the lions now, five metres away, so real, so feverishly and startlingly real that you could feel the prickling fur on your hand, and your mouth was stuffed with the dusty upholstery smell of their heated pelts, and the yellow of them was in your eyes like the yellow of an exquisite French tapestry, the yellows of lions and summer grass, and the sound of the matted lion lungs exhaling on the silent noontide, and the smell of meat from the panting, dripping mouths.

The lions stood looking at George and Lydia Hadley with terrible green-yellow eyes.

"Watch out!" screamed Lydia.

The lions came running at them.

Lydia bolted and ran. Instinctively, George sprang after her. Outside, in the hall, with the door slammed, he was laughing and she was crying, and they both stood appalled at the other's reaction.

"George!"

"Lydia! Oh, my dear poor sweet Lydia!"

"They almost got us!"

"Walls, Lydia, remember; crystal walls, that's all they are. Oh, they look real, I must admit — Africa in your parlour — but it's all dimensional superreactionary, supersensitive colour film and mental tape film behind glass screens. It's all odourophonics and sonics, Lydia. Here's my handkerchief."

"I'm afraid." She came to him and put her body against him and cried steadily. "Did you see? Did you *feel*? It's too real."

"Now, Lydia . . ."

"You've got to tell Wendy and Peter not to read any more on Africa."

"Of course — of course." He patted her.

"Promise?"

"Sure."

"And lock the nursery for a few days until I get my nerves settled."

"You know how difficult Peter is about that. When I punished him a month ago by locking the nursery for even a few hours — the tantrum he threw! And Wendy too. They *live* for the nursery."

"It's got to be locked, that's all there is to it."

"All right." Reluctantly he locked the huge door. "You've been working too hard. You need a rest."

"I don't know — I don't know," she said, blowing her nose, sitting down in a chair that immediately began to rock and comfort her. "Maybe I don't have enough to do. Maybe I have time to think too much. Why don't we shut the whole house off for a few days and take a vacation?"

"You mean you want to fry my eggs for me?"

"Yes." She nodded.

"And darn my socks?"

"Yes." A frantic, watery-eyed nodding.

"And sweep the house?"

"Yes, yes — oh, yes!"

"But I thought that's why we bought this house, so we wouldn't have to do anything?"

"That's just it. I feel like I don't belong here. The house is wife and mother now and nursemaid. Can I compete with an African veldt? Can I give a bath and scrub the children as efficiently or quickly as the automatic scrub bath can? I can not. And it isn't just me. It's you. You've been awfully nervous lately."

"I suppose I have been smoking too much."

"You look as if you didn't know what to do with yourself in this house, either. You smoke a little more every morning and drink a little more every afternoon and need a little more sedative every night. You're beginning to feel unnecessary too."

"Am I?" He paused and tried to feel into himself to see what was really there.

"Oh, George!" She looked beyond him, at the nursery door. "Those lions can't get out of there, can they?"

He looked at the door and saw it tremble as if something had jumped against it from the other side.

"Of course not," he said.

At dinner they ate alone, for Wendy and Peter were at a special plastic carnival across town and had televised home to say they'd be late, to go ahead eating. So George Hadley, bemused, sat watching the dining-room table produce warm dishes of food from its mechanical interior.

"We forgot the ketchup," he said.

"Sorry," said a small voice within the table, and ketchup appeared.

As for the nursery, thought George Hadley, it won't hurt for the children to be locked out of it awhile. Too much of anything isn't good for anyone. And it was clearly indicated that the children had been spending a little too much time on Africa. That *sun*. He could feel it on his neck, still, like a hot paw. And the *lions*. And the smell of blood. Remarkable how the nursery caught the telepathic emanations of the children's minds and created life to fill their every desire. The children thought lions, and there were lions. The children thought zebras, and there were zebras. Sun — sun. Giraffes — giraffes. Death and death.

That *last*. He chewed tastelessly on the meat that the table had cut for him. Death thoughts. They were awfully young, Wendy and Peter, for death thoughts. Or, no, you were never too young, really. Long before you knew what death was you were wishing it on someone else. When you were two years old you were shooting people with cap pistols.

But this — the long, hot African veldt — the awful death in the jaws of a lion. And repeated again and again.

"Where are you going?"

He didn't answer Lydia. Preoccupied, he let the lights glow softly on ahead of him, extinguish behind him as he padded to the nursery door. He listened against it. Far away, a lion roared.

He unlocked the door and opened it. Just before he stepped inside, he heard a faraway scream. And then another roar from the lions, which subsided quickly.

He stepped into Africa. How many times in the last year had he opened this door and found Wonderland, Alice, the Mock Turtle, or Aladdin and his Magical Lamp, or Jack Pumpkinhead of Oz, or Dr. Doolittle, or the cow jumping over a very real-appearing moon — all the delightful contraptions of a make-believe world. How often had he seen Pegasus flying in the sky ceiling, or seen fountains of red fireworks, or heard angel voices singing. But now, this yellow hot Africa, this bake oven with murder in the heat. Perhaps Lydia was right. Perhaps they needed a little vacation from the fantasy which was growing a bit too real for ten-year-old children. It was all right to exercise one's mind with gymnastic fantasies, but when the lively child mind settled on *one* pattern . . . ? It seemed that, at a distance, for the past month, he had heard lions roaring, and smelled their strong odour seeping as far away as his study door. But, being busy, he had paid it no attention.

George Hadley stood on the African grassland alone. The lions looked up from their feeding, watching him. The only flaw to the illusion was the open door through which he could see his wife, far down the dark hall, like a framed picture, eating her dinner abstractedly.

"Go away," he said to the lions.

They did not go.

He knew the principle of the room exactly. You sent out your thoughts. Whatever you thought would appear.

"Let's have Aladdin and his lamp," he snapped.

The veldtland remained; the lions remained.

"Come on, room! I demand Aladdin!" he said.

Nothing happened. The lions mumbled in their baked pelts.

"Aladdin!"

He went back to dinner. "The fool room's out of order," he said. "It won't respond."

"Or — "

"Or what?"

"Or it *can't* respond," said Lydia, "because the children have thought about

Africa and lions and killing so many days that the room's in a rut."

"Could be."

"Or Peter's set it to remain that way."

"Set it?"

"He may have got into the machinery and fixed something."

"Peter doesn't know machinery."

"He's a wise one for ten. That I.Q. of his — "

"Nevertheless — "

"Hello, Mom. Hello, Dad."

The Hadleys turned. Wendy and Peter were coming in the front door, cheeks like peppermint candy, eyes like bright blue agate marbles, a smell of ozone on their jumpers from their trip in the helicopter.

"You're just in time for supper," said both parents.

"We're full of strawberry ice cream and hot dogs," said the children, holding hands. "But we'll sit and watch."

"Yes, come tell us about the nursery," said George Hadley.

The brother and sister blinked at him and then at each other. "Nursery?"

"All about Africa and everything," said the father with false joviality.

"I don't understand," said Peter.

"Your mother and I were just travelling through Africa with rod and reel; Tom Swift and his Electric Lion," said George Hadley.

"There's no Africa in the nursery," said Peter simply.

"Oh, come now, Peter. We know better."

"I don't remember any Africa," said Peter to Wendy. "Do you?"

"No."

"Run see and come tell."

She obeyed.

"Wendy, come back here!" said George Hadley, but she was gone. The house lights followed her like a flock of fireflies. Too late, he realized he had forgotten to lock the nursery door after his last inspection.

"Wendy'll look and come tell us," said Peter.

"She doesn't have to tell me. I've seen it."

"I'm sure you're mistaken, Father."

"I'm not, Peter. Come along now."

But Wendy was back. "It's not Africa," she said breathlessly.

"We'll see about this," said George Hadley, and they all walked down the hall together and opened the nursery door.

There was a green, lovely forest, a lovely river, a purple mountain, high voices singing, and Rima, lovely and mysterious, lurking in the trees with colourful flights of butterflies, like animated bouquets, lingering in her long hair. The African veldtland was gone. The lions were gone. Only Rima was here now, singing a song so beautiful that it brought tears to your eyes.

George Hadley looked in at the changed scene. "Go to bed," he said to the children.

They opened their mouths.

"You heard me," he said.

They went off to the air closet, where a wind sucked them like brown leaves up the flue to their slumber rooms.

George Hadley walked through the singing glade and picked up something that lay in the corner near where the lions had been. He walked slowly back to his wife.

"What is that?" she asked.

"An old wallet of mine," he said.

He showed it to her. The smell of hot grass was on it and the smell of a lion. There were drops of saliva on it, it had been chewed, and there were blood smears on both sides.

He closed the nursery door and locked it, tight.

In the middle of the night he was still awake and he knew his wife was awake. "Do you think Wendy changed it?" she said at last, in the dark room.

"Of course."

"Made it from a veldt into a forest and put Rima there instead of lions?"

"Yes."

"Why?"

"I don't know. But it's staying locked until I find out."

"How did your wallet get there?"

"I don't know anything," he said, "except that I'm beginning to be sorry we bought that room for the children. If children are neurotic at all, a room like that — "

"It's supposed to help them work off their neuroses in a healthful way."

"I'm starting to wonder." He stared at the ceiling.

"We've given the children everything they ever wanted. Is this our reward — secrecy, disobedience?"

"Who was it said, 'Children are carpets, they should be stepped on occasionally? We've never lifted a hand. They're insufferable — let's admit it. They come and go when they like; they treat us as if we were offspring. They're spoiled and we're spoiled."

"They've been acting funny ever since you forbade them to take the rocket to New York a few months ago."

"They're not old enough to do that alone, I explained."

"Nevertheless, I've noticed they've been decidedly cool toward us since."

"I think I'll have David McClean come tomorrow morning to have a look at Africa."

"But it's not Africa now, it's Green Mansions country and Rima."

"I have a feeling it'll be Africa again before then."

A moment later they heard the screams.

Two screams. Two people screaming from downstairs. And then a roar of lions.

"Wendy and Peter aren't in their rooms," said his wife.

He lay in his bed with his beating heart. "No," he said.

"They've broken into the nursery."

"Those screams — they sound familiar."

"Do they?"

"Yes, awfully."

And although their beds tried very hard, the two adults couldn't be rocked to sleep for another hour. A smell of cats was in the night air.

"Father?" said Peter.

"Yes."

Peter looked at his shoes. He never looked at his father any more, nor at his mother. "You aren't going to lock up the nursery for good, are you?"

"That all depends."

"On what?" snapped Peter.

"On you and your sister. If you intersperse this Africa with a little variety — oh, Sweden perhaps, or Denmark or China — "

"I thought we were free to play as we wished."

"You are, within reasonable bounds."

"What's wrong with Africa, Father?"

"Oh, so now you admit you have been conjuring up Africa, do you?"

"I wouldn't want the nursery locked up," said Peter coldly. "Ever."

"Matter of fact, we're thinking of turning the whole house off for about a month. Live sort of a carefree one-for-all existence."

"That sounds dreadful! Would I have to tie my own shoes instead of letting the shoe tier do it? And brush my own teeth and comb my hair and give myself a bath?"

"It would be fun for a change, don't you think?"

"No, it would be horrid. I didn't like it when you took out the picture painter last month."

"That's because I wanted you to learn to paint all by yourself, son."

"I don't want to do anything but look and listen and smell; what else is there to do?"

"All right, go play in Africa."

"Will you shut off the house sometime soon?"

"We're considering it."

"I don't think you'd better consider it any more, Father."

"I won't have any threats from my son!"

"Very well." And Peter strolled off to the nursery.

"Am I on time?" said David McClean.

"Breakfast?" asked George Hadley.

"Thanks, had some. What's the trouble?"

"David, you're a psychologist."

"I should hope so."

"Well, then, have a look at our nursery. You saw it a year ago when you dropped by; did you notice anything peculiar about it then?"

"Can't say I did; the usual violences, a tendency toward a slight paranoia here or there, usual in children because they feel persecuted by parents constantly, but, oh, really nothing."

They walked down the hall. "I locked the nursery up," explained the father, "and the children broke back into it during the night. I let them stay so they could form the patterns for you to see."

There was a terrible screaming from the nursery.

"There it is," said George Hadley. "See what you make of it."

They walked in on the children without rapping.

The screams had faded. The lions were feeding.

"Run outside a moment, children," said George Hadley.

"No, don't change the mental combination. Leave the walls as they are. Get!"

With the children gone, the two men stood studying the lions clustered at a distance, eating with great relish whatever it was they had caught.

"I wish I knew what it was," said George Hadley. "Sometimes I can almost see. Do you think if I brought high-powered binoculars here and — "

David McClean laughed dryly. "Hardly." He turned to study all four walls. "How long has this been going on?"

"A little over a month."

"It certainly doesn't *feel* good."

"I want facts, not feelings."

"My dear George, a psychologist never saw a fact in his life. He only hears about feelings; vague things. This doesn't feel good, I tell you. Trust my hunches and my instincts. I have a nose for something bad. This is very bad. My advice to you is to have the whole damn room torn down and your children brought to me every day during the next year for treatment."

"Is it that bad?"

"I'm afraid so. One of the original uses of these nurseries was so that we could study the patterns left on the walls by the child's mind, study at our leisure, and help the child. In this case, however, the room has become a channel toward — destructive thoughts, instead of a release away from them."

"Didn't you sense this before?"

"I sensed only that you had spoiled your children more than most. And now you're letting them down in some way. What way?"

"I wouldn't let them go to New York."

"What else?"

"I've taken a few machines from the house and threatened them, a month ago, with closing up the nursery unless they did their homework. I did close it for a few days to show I meant business."

"Ah, ha!"

"Does that mean anything?"

"Everything. Where before they had a Santa Claus now they have a Scrooge. Children prefer Santas. You've let this room and this house replace you and your wife in your children's affections. This room is their mother and father, far more important in their lives than their real parents. And now you come along and want to shut it off. No wonder there's hatred here. You can feel it coming out of the sky. Feel that sun. George, you'll have to change your life. Like too many others, you've built it around creature comforts. Why, you'd starve tomorrow if something went wrong in your kitchen. You wouldn't know how to tap an egg. Nevertheless, turn everything off. Start new. It'll take time. But we'll make good children out of bad in a year, wait and see."

"But won't the shock be too much for the children, shutting the room up abruptly, for good?"

"I don't want them going any deeper into this, that's all."

The lions were finished with their red feast.

The lions were standing on the edge of the clearing watching the two men.

"Now I'm feeling persecuted," said McClean. "Let's get out of here. I never have cared for these damned rooms. Make me nervous."

"The lions look real, don't they?" said George Hadley. "I don't suppose there's any way — "

"What?"

" — that they could *become* real?"

"Not that I know."

"Some flaw in the machinery, a tampering or something?"

"No."

They went to the door.

"I don't imagine the room will like being turned off," said the father.

"Nothing ever likes to die — even a room."

"I wonder if it hates me for wanting to switch it off?"

"Paranoia is thick around here today," said David McClean. "You can follow it like a spoor. Hello." He bent and picked up a bloody scarf. "This yours?"

"No." George Hadley's face was rigid. "It belongs to Lydia."

They went to the fuse box together and threw the switch that killed the nursery.

The two children were in hysterics. They screamed and pranced and threw things. They yelled and sobbed and swore and jumped at the furniture.

"You can't do that to the nursery, you can't!"

"Now, children."

The children flung themselves onto a couch, weeping.

"George," said Lydia Hadley, "turn on the nursery, just for a few moments. You can't be so abrupt."

"No."

"You can't be so cruel."

"Lydia, it's off, and it stays off. And the whole damn house dies as of here and now. The more I see of the mess we've put ourselves in, the more it sickens me. We've been contemplating our mechanical, electronic navels for too long. My God, how we need a breath of honest air!"

And he marched about the house turning off the voice clocks, the stoves, the heaters, the shoe shiners, the shoe lacers, the body scrubbers and swabbers and massagers, and every other machine he could put his hand to.

The house was full of dead bodies, it seemed. It felt like a mechanical cemetery. So silent. None of the humming hidden energy of machines waiting to function at the tap of a button.

"Don't let them do it!" wailed Peter at the ceiling, as if he was talking to the house, the nursery. "Don't let Father kill everything." He turned to his father. "Oh, I hate you!"

"Insults won't get you anywhere."

"I wish you were dead!"

"We were, for a long while. Now we're going to really start living. Instead of being handled and massaged, we're going to *live*."

Wendy was still crying and Peter joined her again. "Just a moment, just one moment, just another moment of nursery," they wailed.

"Oh, George," said the wife, "it can't hurt."

"All right — all right, if they'll only just shut up. One minute, mind you, and then off forever."

"Daddy, Daddy, Daddy!" sang the children, smiling with wet faces.

"And then we're going on a vacation. David McClean is coming back in half an hour to help us move out and get to the airport. I'm going to dress. You turn the nursery on for a minute, Lydia, just a minute, mind you."

And the three of them went babbling off while he let himself be vacuumed upstairs through the air flue and set about dressing himself. A minute later Lydia appeared.

"I'll be glad when we get away," she sighed.

"Did you leave them in the nursery?"

"I wanted to dress too. Oh, that horrid Africa. What can they see in it?"

"Well, in five minutes we'll be on our way to Iowa. Lord, how did we ever get in this house? What prompted us to buy a nightmare?"

"Pride, money, foolishness."

"I think we'd better get downstairs before those kids get engrossed with those damn beasts again."

Just then they heard the children calling. "Daddy, Mommy, come quick — quick!"

They went downstairs in the air flue and ran down the hall. The children were nowhere in sight. "Wendy? Peter!"

They ran into the nursery. The veldtland was empty save for the lions waiting, looking at them. "Peter, Wendy?"

The door slammed.

"Wendy, Peter!"

George Hadley and his wife whirled and ran back to the door.

"Open the door!" cried George Hadley, trying the knob. "Why, they've locked it from the outside! Peter!" He beat at the door. "Open up!"

He heard Peter's voice outside, against the door.

"Don't let them switch off the nursery and the house," he was saying.

Mr. and Mrs. George Hadley beat at the door. "Now, don't be ridiculous, children. It's time to go. Mr. McClean'll be here in a minute and . . . "

And then they heard the sounds.

The lions on three sides of them, in the yellow veldt grass, padding through the dry straw, rumbling and roaring in their throats.

The lions.

Mr. Hadley looked at his wife and they turned and looked back at the beasts edging slowly forward, crouching, tails stiff.

Mr. and Mrs. Hadley screamed.

And suddenly they realized why those other screams had sounded familiar.

"Well, here I am," said David McClean in the nursery doorway. "Oh, hello." He stared at the two children seated in the centre of the open glade eating a little picnic lunch. Beyond them was the water hole and the yellow veldtland; above was the hot sun. He began to perspire. "Where are your father and mother?"

The children looked up and smiled. "Oh, they'll be here directly."

"Good, we must get going." At a distance Mr. McClean saw the lions fighting and clawing and then quieting down to feed in silence under the shady trees.

He squinted at the lions with his hand up to his eyes.

Now the lions were done feeding. They moved to the water hole to drink.

A shadow flickered over Mr. McClean's hot face. Many shadows flickered. The vultures were dropping down the blazing sky.

"A cup of tea?" asked Wendy in the silence.

ABOUT THE LINES

1 Produce a brochure advertising The Happylife Home for potential customers. List and describe the desirable features of the house. You might choose to illustrate the brochure.

2 Check the definition of the term "foreshadowing" in the glossary (see p. 351). In a sentence or two, state how the author uses foreshadowing in this story and the effect this technique has upon the reader.

3 Working with a partner, script and dramatize a conversation between Wendy and Peter in which they tell each other how they feel about their parents and why.

BETWEEN THE LINES

1 Imagine that you are the psychologist McClean, and produce a psychological profile of both Wendy and Peter. Design what you think is an appropriate form for presenting your information. Consider:
a. their relationship with their parents;
b. their relationship with each other;
c. their relationship with the house.

2 "The Veldt" mixes real human emotions and characteristics with a plausible futuristic setting and fantastic events. With your partners, decide which features of the story belong in each of the three categories. In a paragraph, either argue that the author's blend of these elements makes the story comprehensible and enjoyable, or that the mixture of the real and the fantastic fails to capture the reader.

3 Write two questions that you would like to ask Wendy and Peter. Try them out on your partners and then discuss their answers.

4 Identify the machine in The Happylife Home that you consider to be the most useless or the most potentially harmful, and in a sentence or two explain your choice.

5 The last line of the story is simple and yet very suggestive. Discuss the possible interpretations that could be put upon Wendy's innocent question. Present and defend to a small group the inference that you feel to be the most accurate.

BEYOND THE LINES

1 Imagine that you are Mr. or Mrs. Hadley, and write a letter to the children's grandparents in which you describe your concerns about the children's behaviour.

2 Choose one of the machines in The Happylife Home and:
a. produce a drawing or a model of it;
b. prepare an oral presentation describing the merits of the gadget, the price, warranty, and running cost, etc.;
c. give the sales pitch to a large group and be prepared to answer any questions put to you.

3 Read *Peter Pan*, by J.M. Barrie. Discuss with your partners why you think Ray Bradbury chose to borrow the names Wendy and Peter for "The Veldt." Present your conclusions in a short statement.

4 Working in a group of four, present a debate on one of the following resolutions:

Children should be given more time and love than gifts and treats.

or

Parents should give their children as many material gifts as they can afford.

or

Parents owe their children; children do not owe their parents.

or

Spare the rod and spoil the child.

5 The following poem, "The Television," complements one of the major themes of "The Veldt" — the alienation of parent and child and the substitution of technology for affection. Compose your own poem on the same theme; you may use "The Television" as a model.

THE TELEVISION

Anne Stevenson

Hug me, mother of noise,
Find me a hiding place.
I am afraid of my voice.
I do not like my face.

THE UGLY LITTLE BOY

BASED ON THE STORY BY

Isaac Asimov

ADAPTED BY
DON THOMPSON,
PHILIP NIXON,
BARRY MORSE, AND
DENNIS HUTCHEON

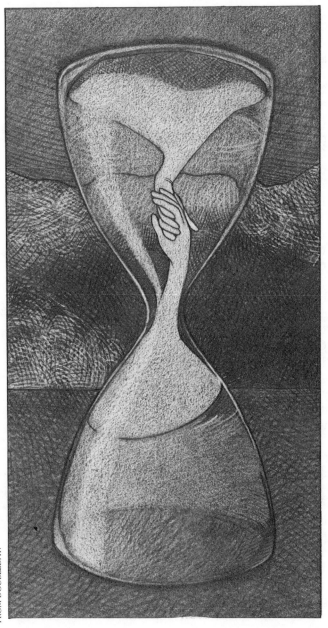

Characters
MISS FELLOWES
GUARD
DR. HOSKINS
DR. SMITHERS
DR. SPRINGER
DR. JOHNSON
PROFESSOR ADEMEWSKI
ASSISTANTS
TECHNICIANS
CHILD

(*A helicopter arrives. A jeep approaches out of the darkness. In it are a* GUARD *and a* WOMAN. *This is* EDITH FELLOWES. *She is apprehensive. She walks quickly toward the helicopter.* MISS FELLOWES *boards the helicopter which immediately takes off.*)

VOICE OF FLIGHT CONTROLLER Stasis helicopter 4 proceed to Stasis Commission immediately. Transfer in thirty-three minutes.

INT. HELICOPTER—NIGHT

EXT. STASIS DOME LANDING SIGHT—NIGHT
(*From the ground, we see the helicopter emerge from the darkness. The helicopter moves toward camera for landing.*)

INT. STASIS CHAMBER CORRIDOR AND ESCALATOR—NIGHT
(GUARD *and* MISS FELLOWES *enter, hurry to the corridor and ascend.*)

GUARD Dr. Hoskins is waiting for you in the main Stasis area.

INT. STASIS CHAMBER ESCALATOR—NIGHT

MISS FELLOWES What is this emergency?
GUARD You don't know?
MISS FELLOWES (*annoyed but curious*) Look, the Stasis Commission offered me this nursing job . . . an unusual case, a child. First thing I know I'm dragged up in the middle of the night . . . How should I know what's going on? Is the child hurt?
GUARD I'm sure Dr. Hoskins will explain.

INT. STASIS MASTER CONTROL—NIGHT
(DR. HOSKINS *and* TECHNICIANS *are conferring behind the instrument console.* GUARD *and* MISS FELLOWES *enter.*)

DR. HOSKINS If there is any danger of the transfer injuring the stasis subject, I want you to call me right away.
MISS FELLOWES Dr. Hoskins . . .
DR. HOSKINS Yes?
MISS FELLOWES (*introducing herself*) Nurse Fellowes.
DR. HOSKINS Ah, Nurse Fellowes . . . yes, good. Glad to have you with us.
(DR. HOSKINS *turns to* TECHNICIANS.)
MISS FELLOWES (*determined to be heard*) Your assistant said this was urgent. I don't know what I'm doing here.
DR. HOSKINS We didn't expect to make this contact until next week.
MISS FELLOWES Contact what?
INTERCOM (V.O.) Computer room three has contact.
DR. HOSKINS You're about to be part of the most significant scientific event since the discovery of atomic power.
(DR. HOSKINS *turns his attention to the console.* MISS FELLOWES *remains apart.*

HOSKINS *uses a light suspended from his neck to initiate Stasis.*)
WIDESHOT *of chamber showing instruments,* OPERATORS, B.G. HOSKINS *and*
MISS FELLOWES
INTERCOM (V.O.) Stand clear. Stasis transfer in thirty seconds.
OPERATOR Go in to zero.
INTERCOM (V.O.) Holding at 2300.
OPERATOR Steady reflectors.
INTERCOM (V.O.) 2700 mesons at 42 degrees.
OPERATOR Increase reflection.
INTERCOM (V.O.) 3200 mesons.
OPERATOR Increase power.
INTERCOM (V.O.) 4200 to transfer . . . (*counting down*) six, five, four, three, two,
  one, zero. Transfer completed.
(*Sound of child screaming issues from the Dome.*)
DR. HOSKINS Well, Miss Fellowes, you'll be the first civilized woman in history
  to take care of a Neanderthal child.
WIDESHOT *as* DR.HOSKINS *and technicians approach the Dome. Air of general
excitement.*

INT. DR. HOSKINS' OFFICE—NIGHT

MISS FELLOWES You have the wrong woman for this job. I am a nurse, and a
  damn good one. I take care of people. I make them well.
(*Video screen appears on the wall. Photographs of* MISS FELLOWES *appear on the
screen.*)
DR. HOSKINS (*coldly*) Nurse Fellowes, we know what you are and what you are
  not. To begin with, the computer selected you from over five thousand
  candidates. (*reading from computer printout which has appeared on the screen*)
  S-43225. Fellowes, Edith. Age: forty-two. Profession: pediatric nurse, nineteen
  years experience. Qualifications . . . so on, so on. Total dedication. No
  relatives, no friends . . . no emotional involvement. A professional nurse first
  and last.
MISS FELLOWES I don't know what my personal life has to do with this.
DR. HOSKINS Everything. This is scientific work that can be damaged by
  emotionalism. The job is only temporary.
MISS FELLOWES How temporary?
DR. HOSKINS In two hundred days we shall be launching our major project,
  bringing an adult subject back from the Middle Ages. At that time the
  Neanderthal specimen will be sent back.
MISS FELLOWES And what is a nurse expected to do with this child?
DR. HOSKINS Supervise, provide a certain degree of care and above all, remain
  totally detached.
(MISS FELLOWES *turns her back to* DR. HOSKINS.)
MISS FELLOWES (*to herself*) No relatives . . . no friends . . . no emotional
  involvement. (*pause*) Totally detached. Okay, I'll do it.
DR. HOSKINS Good.

317

EXT. DOME—NIGHT
(DR. HOSKINS *is explaining procedures.*)

DR. HOSKINS Always wear that belt while you're in the dome. There are three million units of electromagnetism working through time to hold the subject in the present. Now he's not affected by that pull, but you're too close in time to the energy source. If you're not wearing that neutralizing belt, your central nervous system will be damaged. Is that clear? (MISS FELLOWES *watches the* DOCTOR *with a look of sullen defiance.*) Now you use this activator to get into the dome. This is the only way these safety doors can be opened. Would you try that now please. (MISS FELLOWES *presses the activator. The doors open.*) Good.

INT. DOME—NIGHT
(MISS FELLOWES *and* DR. HOSKINS *enter the Dome.* ATTENDANTS *are present. A dirty, ape-like* CHILD *crouches on a pedestal in the middle of the Dome. The pedestal is covered with soil.* MISS FELLOWES *and* DR. HOSKINS *stand staring at the* CHILD.)

MISS FELLOWES He needs a bath.
DR. HOSKINS We have to bring some surrounding material with it. Danger of it arriving with only one leg or half a head.
MISS FELLOWES (*to* ATTENDANT) Bring me some soap and water. (*to* DR. HOSKINS) Where's his food?
(*The* ATTENDANT *hands* MISS FELLOWES *a container.* MISS FELLOWES *shows the container to the* CHILD *and places it before him. The* CHILD *moves on all fours toward the container. He laps the contents like a cat.*)
DR. HOSKINS Now we shall leave you with the subject. (MISS FELLOWES *looks anxiously at* DR. HOSKINS.) Oh, there's no danger as long as he never leaves these rooms during the whole of the two hundred days he'll be here. Never. It's a question of energy. The whole potential energy focus of the past five years would be instantly lost and the subject destroyed.
(MISS FELLOWES *is left alone with the* CHILD. *She tries to pick up the dish. The* CHILD *snaps. She draws back in fright. The* CHILD *continues to lick the sides of the dish.*)
MISS FELLOWES (*to herself in a tone of grudging acceptance*) Two hundred days.

INT. DOME—DAY
(DR. SMITHERS, *an anthropologist, is examining the* CHILD *who is lying on what looks like a dentist's chair.* MISS FELLOWES *is standing at the side of the chair.*)

DR. SMITHERS (*clinically*) Slanting skull. Brow ridges pronounced. Chin recessive . . . certainly similar to Solecki's discoveries. Little nose cartilage —
MISS FELLOWES (*interrupting*) Small children never have much nose cartilage. What's the point of all this?
DR. SMITHERS Up to now, anthropologists have had nothing but Neanderthal bone fragments to work with. Now a living specimen. (*to* ATTENDANT) Ready for another X-ray? This will be number ten.
MISS FELLOWES Isn't there danger from radiation?
DR. SMITHERS My interest is in skeletal structure, and I don't have too much

318

time for my examination. (*to* ATTENDANT) Ready for the X-ray? Give him the tranquilizing shot.
(*The* CHILD, *sensing impending pain, becomes agitated. The* ASSISTANT *grabs his arm.*)
MISS FELLOWES There's no need to break his arm! (*Takes the needle from the* ASSISTANT. *Then reassuringly to the* BOY) O.K. (*She injects the needle.*)

INT. ANOTHER PART OF STASIS AREA—NIGHT
(DR. HOSKINS *is looking over some papers in a clipboard.* MISS FELLOWES *enters.*)

MISS FELLOWES I've got him off to sleep.
DR. HOSKINS Oh . . . very good. (*He continues to scan the pages.*) He's been with us now twenty-seven days and we've established normal sleep patterns. You realize, of course, it's essential to keep careful daily records. Indication of physical change is important to the experiment.
(DR. HOSKINS *hands the clipboard to* MISS FELLOWES *and leaves. She watches the doctor go and, obviously angry, drops the clipboard into its slot.*)

INT. DOME—DAY
(MISS FELLOWES *is taking blood from the* CHILD's *arm. She hands the hypodermic to* DR. SPRINGER *who empties the blood into a test tube.* DR. SPRINGER *waves an instrument over tube.*)

INTERCOM (V.O.) Red cell count indicates Rh negative. We need a repeat for hemolytic anemia. Repeat sample.
MISS FELLOWES Repeat? How many gallons do you want? His body can't manufacture blood at the rate you're taking it.
DR. SPRINGER (*insistently*) Repeat the sample!

INT. DOME—DAY
(ECU *of examining light.* DR. JOHNSON *is examining the* CHILD's *eyes. Again the* CHILD *is strapped to the chair.*)

DR. JOHNSON Photophobia . . . slight inflammation of the cornea.
MISS FELLOWES Dr. Johnson, he has a pain —
DR. JOHNSON (*ignoring* MISS FELLOWES) No ulceration . . . possibly . . . some signs here of a possible rheumatic condition. Blood tests will tell.
MISS FELLOWES Dr. Johnson, the boy has a sore leg.
DR. JOHNSON Really? Since when?
MISS FELLOWES Last night.
DR. JOHNSON (*to* ASSISTANT) Hear that, Martin? (*The* ASSISTANT *hands the* DOCTOR *a clipboard. He scans the charts.*) The subject has a sore leg. Remember what I told Hoskins: if there were damage in the transfer, it might show up later. We'd better let him know. (*He hands the clipboard back to the* ASSISTANT.)
MISS FELLOWES Couldn't you look at it?
DR. JOHNSON Which one?
MISS FELLOWES Left.

DR. JOHNSON Be sure it's entered on the chart.

MISS FELLOWES Can't you prescribe something?

DR. JOHNSON We've got to make sure that nothing like this happens in the medieval specimen.

(DR. JOHNSON *leaves with the* ASSISTANT.)

MISS FELLOWES But what about the —

INT. DOME—DAY

(MISS FELLOWES *is writing on the chart. She places the clipboard back in its place.* ECU *of chart to reveal in the corner of the page,* "Day 184.")

INT. DOME—DAY

(CU *of bowl of milk in* MISS FELLOWES' *hands.* MISS FELLOWES *crosses the room to the examining chair. The* BOY *is seated on the floor playing with a strap hanging from the chair.* MISS FELLOWES *sits on the floor behind the* BOY *and places the bowl beside him. She taps the* BOY *on the shoulder and lifts the bowl from the floor twice. She places the* CHILD's *hands on the bowl, and, nodding and smiling encouragingly, she watches him lift the bowl. Just as he is about to drink, the bowl drops from the* BOY's *hands and he starts to cry.* MISS FELLOWES *turns her head, apparently discouraged.*)

INT. DOME—DAY

(A NURSING ASSISTANT, DR. YOUNG, MISS FELLOWES *and the* BOY. *The* BOY *is seated on the edge of an examination table.* MISS FELLOWES *holds him while the* DOCTOR *checks his reflexes.*)

DR. YOUNG Muscles and reflexes O.K. Certainly no sensory or motor deficit.

ASSISTANT Noted. An S-R sequence next, doctor?

DR. YOUNG (*on his way out the door*) Yes, right. Let's measure sensation to pain. No, I think we'll wait for a complete CCV scan at the end of the week. Then one every ten days until —

ASSISTANT When is he to be sent back?

MISS FELLOWES Eighty days.

ASSISTANT Tough work, nursing, isn't it?

MISS FELLOWES Uh-huh.

ASSISTANT Tough in a . . . funny kinda way.

MISS FELLOWES Look, I've been a nurse for nineteen years.

ASSISTANT I had to give it up.

MISS FELLOWES I never get involved.

ASSISTANT I swore it couldn't happen to me.

(*The* ASSISTANT *picks up a hypodermic needle. The* BOY *starts to cry.* MISS FELLOWES *turns sharply.*)

MISS FELLOWES (*to the* BOY) What is it? What's the matter? What's wrong? What is it? (*She takes the needle from the* ASSISTANT.) Oh, it's that. Well never mind. We'll just put that away. (*She places the needle on counter. She takes the* BOY's *hand and rubs his head.*) Don't worry.

ASSISTANT See you tomorrow.

EXT. TERRACE OF THE STASIS BUILDING—DAY
(DR. HOSKINS *and* ASSISTANT *leave the building.* MISS FELLOWES *appears.*)

MISS FELLOWES Dr. Hoskins, wait.

DR. HOSKINS Hello, Miss Fellowes.

MISS FELLOWES I've been trying to see you.

DR. HOSKINS (*to* ASSISTANT) I'll join you in the Stasis Chamber in . . . seven minutes. (ASSISTANT *leaves. To* MISS FELLOWES) Yes?

MISS FELLOWES I don't think I can stay much longer.

DR. HOSKINS Oh? Why?

MISS FELLOWES I don't like what you're doing to that child.

DR. HOSKINS Child? Oh, the Neanderthal experiment. Well, that's just the first stage in our long term program. We're learning as we go.

MISS FELLOWES Well, what is this stage proving?

DR. HOSKINS We've collected more data.

MISS FELLOWES Data! But you don't know anything about him! Do you know how he feels?

DR. HOSKINS If there were more time we could concentrate on those emotional responses. But I think you've been so preoccupied with the Neanderthal experiment that you've never thought about the Stasis program as a whole. I'll show you some of it.

(DR. HOSKINS *walks ahead.* MISS FELLOWES *stands back and watches him go.*)

DR. HOSKINS (*snapping his fingers*) Come along.

INT. STASIS LAB—DAY
(DR. HOSKINS *is showing* MISS FELLOWES *around.*)

DR. HOSKINS To build up energy reserves for our medieval project we're sending several of our specimens back. In fact, I'm due to release a rock specimen right now.

(*Sound of scuffle. Two* GUARDS *are wrestling with* PROFESSOR ADEMEWSKI.

DR. HOSKINS *rushes forward.* MISS FELLOWES *follows.*)

DR. HOSKINS All right, what is all this?

GUARD We were clearing the Stasis chamber for release. Professor Ademewski refused to leave.

PROFESSOR ADEMEWSKI I have not completed my research.

DR. HOSKINS You know our program. Every minute that rock remains reduces our energy reserves. (*to* ASSISTANTS) Prepare for release.

PROFESSOR ADEMEWSKI (*desperate*) No, stop! You can't take it back! Please don't!

INTERCOM (V.O.) Stand clear. Stasis release has been activated. Release in ten seconds . . . (*counting down*) ten, nine —

PROFESSOR ADEMEWSKI (*as countdown continues*) Hoskins you're a heartless machine. My life —

(DR. HOSKINS *nods to the* GUARDS *to take the* PROFESSOR *away.*)

INTERCOM (V.O.) three, two, one, release.

DR. HOSKINS (*to* MISS FELLOWES) It's completely automatic and irreversible.

MISS FELLOWES What if he'd stayed inside?

DR. HOSKINS He'd have been transferred back to the Pleistocene period with the rock.

MISS FELLOWES Will you send the boy back the same way?

DR. HOSKINS Oh yes, exactly, but from his own area. In just forty-nine days we shall have an articulate specimen here, a medieval man, someone who can talk.

INT. DOME—DAY

(*CU of* MISS FELLOWES' *hands holding two dolls, one female, one male. She is trying to teach the* BOY *how to speak.*)

MISS FELLOWES (*speaking very slowly*) Ma . . . ma, boy . . . ma . . . ma, boy . . . ma . . . ma, boy . . .

(*The* BOY *reaches for a toy stuffed elephant on the counter in front of him.* MISS FELLOWES *is angered by his failure to respond to her lesson.*)

MISS FELLOWES (*grabbing the elephant from the* BOY) Can't you learn to say one word, damnit!

(*Frightened by* MISS FELLOWES *tone of voice, the* BOY *jumps down from the stool.*)

MISS FELLOWES (*lifting the* BOY *back onto the stool*) All right, all right, all right, all right. (*with the dolls*) There we are. Ma-ma, boy, ma-ma, boy, ma-ma, boy, ma-ma, boy.

INT. DOME—DAY

(*ECU of electrode being pressed on the sole of the* BOY's *foot. The* BOY *is clamped to a chair. A* PSYCHIATRIST *is administering electric shocks. The* BOY *screams with each one.* MISS FELLOWES *enters and rushes to the group around the* BOY.)

MISS FELLOWES What are you doing! Leave him alone. It's time for his meal. (*pushing aside the* DOCTOR *with the electrode*) You're just upsetting him. (*She unstraps the* BOY.) Just leave him alone. Get out of here. All of you.

(*They release the* BOY. *He leaps up on a cupboard and begins to fling bottles, smashing them to the floor.*)

MISS FELLOWES Boy . . . come here . . . uh . . . boy, boy, here. Here boy. (*She holds out a scarf.*) Here, take this. Here, take it. (*The* BOY *takes the scarf and presses it to his cheek.*) You haven't got a name, have you? A name . . . Timmie. Like that name? That's your name. (*slowly*) Tim-mie. You like that? Tim-mie.

INT. DOME—DAY

(*CU of* MISS FELLOWES' *hands holding out a toy stuffed elephant. The* BOY *appears crawling around a corner.*)

MISS FELLOWES Come on. (*coaxing*) Look what I've got for you. Come on.

(*Using the wall as support, the* BOY *raises himself to his feet. As* MISS FELLOWES *encourages him, he lets go of the wall and takes the elephant in his hands. He takes a step, falls back on his seat and laughs.*)

INT. DOME—DAY

(MISS FELLOWES *is seated at the counter reading. The* BOY *is sitting in the middle of* the floor with his back to her, playing with a doll. MISS FELLOWES hears a sound and rushes to the BOY.)

MISS FELLOWES What did you say?
TIMMIE Maaah . . . .
(MISS FELLOWES retrieves a tape recorder from the counter and places it in front of the BOY.)
MISS FELLOWES (quietly) Say it again, Timmie. Go ahead.
TIMMIE Maah-maa.
MISS FELLOWES Good. Again . . .
TIMMIE Mama.
MISS FELLOWES Good.

INT. DR. HOSKINS' OFFICE—DAY
(DR. HOSKINS is standing behind his desk, absorbed in work. MISS FELLOWES rushes in with the recorder in her hand.)

MISS FELLOWES Dr. Hoskins, you must listen to this.
DR. HOSKINS Miss Fellowes, I have no time just now.
MISS FELLOWES It will just take a minute. (She sets the machine on the desk and
    clicks it on.)
DR. HOSKINS Very well.
MISS FELLOWES (TAPE) Go ahead, Timmie, go ahead.
TIMMIE (TAPE) Maamaa.
MISS FELLOWES (TAPE) Good. Again.
TIMMIE (TAPE) Mama.
MISS FELLOWES (TAPE) Good. Now, Tim-mie.
TIMMIE (TAPE) Tim-mie.
MISS FELLOWES (TAPE) Good.
MISS FELLOWES Now, what do you think of that? He's talking.
DR. HOSKINS Of course, we've all known for some time that he was capable of
    our speech. Research showed that the frontal cerebrum was large enough and
    the larynx sufficiently developed —
MISS FELLOWES He could learn anything. All we need now are teachers.
DR. HOSKINS Surely you're forgetting. We're sending the subject back.
MISS FELLOWES Not now, now that we know his capacity for learning —
DR. HOSKINS Tonight.
MISS FELLOWES Tonight? But this is only Day Twenty-three.
DR. HOSKINS It has to be tonight. Just this morning we got a scan on the
    medieval subject.
MISS FELLOWES But you said you wanted someone who could talk, right? Timmie
    can talk.
DR. HOSKINS It's a question of timing. I'm sorry.
MISS FELLOWES But you can't. It's not like sending a rock back!
DR. HOSKINS Miss Fellowes, the subject has to go back.
MISS FELLOWES But you'll be killing a human being.
DR. HOSKINS Not killing. When Stasis is released, he'll simply become a
    Neanderthal boy in a Neanderthal world again.

MISS FELLOWES But he'll be alone. His tribe may not be where he left them. He'll have to take care of himself. He won't know how.
INTERCOM (V.O.) Dr. Hoskins, to Stasis Dome One, please.
DR. HOSKINS. I'm sorry. We cannot wait any more.
(DR. HOSKINS *leaves. Alone by the window,* MISS FELLOWES *picks up the tape recorder.*)
TIMMIE (TAPE) Mama.

INT. DOME—NIGHT
(MISS FELLOWES *is dressing* TIMMIE.)

MISS FELLOWES Never mind. Don't be afraid, Timmie.
TIMMIE Tim-mie.
MISS FELLOWES (*distractedly*) Good, Timmie. I have to go. Don't worry. I won't let anything happen to you.
(MISS FELLOWES *gives* TIMMIE *her scarf.*)
TIMMIE (*holding the scarf to his face*) Mama.
VOICE OF DR. HOSKINS ON INTERCOM (V.O.) Miss Fellowes, please leave the energy area. Please.
(MISS FELLOWES *backs toward the door.*)

INT. OUTSIDE STASIS DOME—NIGHT
(DR. HOSKINS *and* ASSISTANTS *are at the control console.*)

DR. HOSKINS And now the Dome.

INT DOME—NIGHT
(MISS FELLOWES *leaves the area.* CU *of* BOY *clutching the scarf to his face.*)

INT. OUTSIDE STASIS DOME—NIGHT

TECHNICIAN All clear. Ready for release procedures to begin.
(DR. HOSKINS *punches a release code to the Stasis release sensor.*)
INTERCOM (V.O.) Stand clear. Stasis release has been activated. Release in thirty seconds . . . Stasis release in twenty seconds.
(*Countdown begins.* MISS FELLOWES *moves toward the door of the Dome.* DR. HOSKINS *sees her.*)
DR. HOSKINS Miss Fellowes, Miss Fellowes, keep clear! (*realizes* MISS FELLOWES *is about to enter the Dome*) Guard! Guard, stop her! Stop her! Miss Fellowes!
(MISS FELLOWES *enters the Dome.*)
INTERCOM (V.O.): (*counting down*) Nine, eight, seven, six, five, four, three, two, one. Release has begun.
DR. HOSKINS: Miss —
(MISS FELLOWES *has entered the Dome. Through the window we see her embrace* TIMMIE. *A flash of light.* DR. HOSKINS *and* TECHNICIANS *approach the Dome with fearful expectancy.* MISS FELLOWES *and* TIMMIE *have vanished.* ZOOM IN *on scarf on floor.* FREEZE *on empty energized area.*)

ABOUT THE LINES

1 Complete the following sentences:
   a. Nurse Fellowes was chosen by the computer for the job from over 5000 candidates because . . .
   b. The Neanderthal child must never leave the Stasis area because . . .
   c. The doctors and scientists are only interested in . . .
   d. By the end of the play, Nurse Fellowes has changed from the cool, detached technician to . . .

2 In one or two sentences for each, describe three incidents in which it is clear that Dr. Hoskins and his staff have no regard for the child's feelings or well-being.

3 Prepare and present a retelling of this play to a group who has not read it. Highlight the gradual change in Nurse Fellowes from an efficient, uninvolved professional to a loving, caring defender of Timmie. Your account should focus on Nurse Fellowes' attempt to prevent Timmie from becoming merely a laboratory specimen.

BETWEEN THE LINES

1 In a small group, discuss the following questions:
   a. In what way is Nurse Fellowes different from Dr. Hoskins?
   b. What do you think of Nurse Fellowes' decision to join Timmie in the transfer back to his own time? Was she heroic or foolish?
   c. Do you think that Nurse Fellowes' sacrifice would have any meaning for the people involved in the Stasis project? Would her example change their perspective?

Write a group note for each question. Make sure the opinions of all group members are represented in the answers. Present a brief report of your discussion to other groups who have read the play.

2 On page 320, between lines 29 and 35, there is an exchange between Nurse Fellowes and an assistant in which the latter points out how difficult it is to remain detached as a nurse. Script a conversation between the assistant and someone else on the Stasis team in which they discuss Nurse Fellowes' attitude toward the Neanderthal subject.

3 When Dr. Hoskins hired Nurse Fellowes, he told her that she had been chosen by the computer because she had "no relatives, no friends . . . no emotional involvement." Imagine that you are Nurse Fellowes and write an entry in your diary reacting to and assessing this description of yourself. Remember that this entry is written before she meets Timmie.

BEYOND THE LINES

1 Imagine that Nurse Fellowes has called a press conference to present Timmie's plight to the public just after her final pleas to Dr. Hoskins to allow Timmie to stay have failed. Prepare questions that you would like to ask Nurse Fellowes and Dr. Hoskins. Nominate two people in the group to assume the roles of Nurse Fellowes and Dr. Hoskins and simulate a press conference in which other members of the group act as reporters and ask their questions of the two opponents. Switch roles several times to allow everyone in the group a chance to play Dr. Hoskins or Nurse Fellowes.

2 In the voice of the Crown Prosecutor, write a charge that you will present to the courts indicting Dr. Hoskins as Timmie's kidnapper.

3 Write a sequel to this play describing what you think will happen to Timmie and Nurse Fellowes when they are transported back in time. Before you write, discuss the following possibilities with a partner:
a. Will Timmie and Nurse Fellowes be affected in the same way by the trip back in time?
b. Assuming that they arrive at their destination alive, what might they expect to find in Timmie's home?
c. If they find Timmie's family, how might they treat Nurse Fellowes?
d. What could happen to them if they do not find any people?
When you have completed your sequel, share it with someone else and compare your way of seeing things with another person's.

4 Imagine that you are Nurse Fellowes and you have survived the trip back through time. You are trying to preserve your sense of identity by recording what has happened to you. In a journal entry, describe your feelings now that you are isolated from your own time and place. As this is a journal entry, it does not have to give final answers or tell a complete story.

5 Working with a partner, write and deliver an argument supporting the following statement:
"This play points out that the price we pay for scientific advance is too high."

AKUA NUTEN

Yves Thériault

Kakatso, the Montagnais Indian, felt the gentle flow of the air and noticed that the wind came from the south. Then he touched the moving water in the stream to determine the temperature in the highlands. Since everything pointed to nice June weather, with mild sunshine and light winds, he decided to go to the highest peak of the reserve, as he had been planning to do for the past week. There the Montagnais lands bordered those of the Waswanipis.

There was no urgent reason for the trip. Nothing really pulled him there except the fact that he hadn't been for a long time; and he liked steep mountains and frothy, roaring streams.

Three days before he had explained his plan to his son, the thin Grand-Louis, who was well known to the white men of the North Shore. His son had guided many whites in the regions surrounding the Manicouagan and Bersimis rivers.

He had told him: "I plan to go way out, near the limits of the reserve."

This was clear enough, and Grand-Louis had simply nodded his head. Now he wouldn't worry, even if Kakatso disappeared for two months. He would know that his father was high in the hills, breathing the clean air and soaking up beautiful scenes to remember in future days.

Just past the main branch of the Manicouagan there is an enormous rock crowned by two pines and a fir tree which stand side by side like the fingers of a hand, the smallest on the left and the others reaching higher.

This point, which Kakatso could never forget, served as his signpost for every trail in the area; and other points would guide him north, west, or in any other direction. Kakatso, until his final breath, would easily find his way about there, guided only by the memory of a certain tree, the silhouette of the mountain outlined against the clear skies, the twisting of a river bed, or the slope of a hill.

In strange territory Kakatso would spend entire days precisely organizing his memories so that if he ever returned no trail there would be unknown to him.

Thus, knowing every winding path and every animal's accustomed lair, he could set out on his journey carrying only some salt, tea, and shells for his rifle. He could live by finding his subsistence in the earth itself and in nature's plenty.

Kakatso knew well what a man needed for total independence: a fish-hook wrapped in paper, a length of supple cord, a strong knife, waterproof boots, and a well-oiled rifle. With these things a man could know the great joy of not having to depend on anyone but himself, of wandering as he pleased one day

after another, proud and superior, the owner of eternal lands that stretched beyond the horizon.

(To despise the reserve and those who belonged there. Not to have any allegiance except a respect for the water, the sky, and the winds. To be a man, but a man according to the Indian image and not that of the whites. The Indian image of a real man was ageless and changeless, a true image of man in the bosom of a wild and immense nature.)

Kakatso had a wife and a house and grown-up children whom he rarely saw. He really knew little about them. One daughter was a nurse in a white man's city, another had married a turncoat Montagnais who lived in Baie-Comeau and worked in the factories. A son studied far away, in Montreal, and Kakatso would probably never see him again. A son who would repudiate everything, would forget the proud Montagnais language and change his name to be accepted by the whites in spite of his dark skin and slitty eyes.

The other son, Grand-Louis . . . but this one was an exception. He had inherited Montagnais instincts. He often came down to the coast, at Godbout or Sept-Iles, or sometimes at Natashquan, because he was ambitious and wanted to earn money. But this did not cause him to scorn or detest the forest. He found a good life there. For Kakatso, it was enough that this child, unlike so many others, did not turn into a phony white man.

As for Kakatso's wife, she was still at home, receiving Kakatso on his many returns without emotion or gratitude. She had a roof over her head, warmth, and food. With skilled fingers she made caribou-skin jackets for the white man avid for the exotic. This small sideline liberated Kakatso from other obligations towards her. Soon after returning home, Kakatso always wanted to get away again. He was uncomfortable in these white men's houses that were too high, too solid, and too neatly organized for his taste.

So Kakatso lived his life in direct contact with the forest, and he nurtured life itself from the forest's plenty. Ten months of the year he roamed the forest trails, ten months he earned his subsistence from hunting, trapping, fishing, and smoking the caribou meat that he placed in caches for later use. With the fur pelts he met his own needs and those of the house on the reserve near the forest, although these needs were minimal because his wife was a good earner.

He climbed, then, towards the northern limits of the Montagnais lands on this June day, which was to bring calamity of which he was completely unaware.

Kakatso had heard of the terrible bomb. For twenty years he had heard talk of it, and the very existence of these horrendous machines was not unknown to him. But how was he to know the complex fabric of events happening in the world just then? He never read the newspapers and never really listened to the radio when he happened to spend some hours in a warm house. How could he conceive of total annihilation threatening the whole world? How could he feel all the world's people trembling?

In the forest's vast peace, Kakatso, knowing nature's strength, could easily believe that nothing and nobody could prevail against the mountains, the rivers, and the forest itself stretching out all across the land. Nothing could prevail against the earth, the unchangeable soil that regenerated itself year after year.

He travelled for five days. On the fifth evening it took Kakatso longer to fall asleep. Something was wrong. A silent anguish he did not understand was disturbing him.

He had lit his evening fire on a bluff covered with soft moss, thirty metres above the lake. He slept there, rolled in his blanket in a deeply dark country interrupted only by the rays of the new moon.

Sleep was slow and when it came it did not bring peace. A jumble of snarling creatures and swarming, roaring masses invaded Kakatso's sleep. He turned over time and again, groaning restlessly. Suddenly he awoke and was surprised to see that the moon had gone down and the night's blackness was lit only by stars. Here, on the bluff, there was a bleak reflection from the sky, but the long valley and the lake remained dark. Exhausted by his throbbing dreams, Kakatso got up, stretched his legs and lit his pipe. On those rare occasions when his sleep was bad he had always managed to recover his tranquillity by smoking a bit, motionless in the night, listening to the forest sounds.

Suddenly the light came. For a single moment the southern and western horizons were illuminated by this immense bluish gleam that loomed up, lingered a moment, and then went out. The dark became even blacker and Kakatso muttered to himself. He wasn't afraid because fear had always been totally foreign to him. But what did this strange event mean? Was it the anger of some old mountain spirit?

All at once the gleam reappeared, this time even more westerly. Weaker this time and less evident. Then the shadows again enveloped the land.

Kakatso no longer tried to sleep that night. He squatted, smoking his pipe and trying to find some explanation for these bluish gleams with his simple ideas, his straightforward logic and vivid memory.

When the dawn came the old Montagnais, the last of his people, the great Abenakis, carefully prepared his fire and boiled some water for his tea.

For some hours he didn't feel like moving. He no longer heard the inner voices calling him to the higher lands. He felt stuck there, incapable of going further until the tumult within him died down. What was there that he didn't know about his skies, he who had spent his whole life wandering in the woods and sleeping under the stars? The sky over his head was as familiar to him as the soil of the underbrush, the animal trails and the games of the trout in their streams. But never before had he seen such gleams and they disturbed him.

At eight o'clock the sun was slowly climbing into the sky, and Kakatso was still there.

At ten he moved to the shore to look at the water in the lake. He saw a minnow run and concluded that the lake had many fish. He then attached his fire cord to the hook tied with partridge feathers he had found in the branches of a wild hawthorn bush. He cast the fly with a deliberate, almost solemn movement and it jumped on the smooth water. After Kakatso cast three more times a fat trout swallowed the hook and he pulled him in gently, quite slowly, letting him fight as much as he wanted. The midday meal was in hand. The Montagnais, still in no great hurry to continue his trip, began to prepare his fish.

He was finishing when the far-away buzz of a plane shook him out of his reveries. Down there, over the mountains around the end of the lake, a plane was moving through the sky. This was a familiar sight to Kakatso because all this far country was visited only by planes that landed on the lakes. In this way the Indian had come to know the white man. This was the most frequent place of contact between the two: a large body of quiet water where a plane would land, where the whites would ask for help and find nothing better than an Indian to help them.

Even from a distance Kakatso recognized the type of plane. It was a single-engine, deluxe Bonanza, a type often used by the Americans who came to fish for their salmon in our rivers.

The plane circled the lake and flew over the bluff where Kakatso's fire was still burning. Then it landed gently, almost tenderly. The still waters were only lightly ruffled and quickly returned to their mirror smoothness. The plane slowed down, the motor coughed once or twice, then the craft made a complete turn and headed for the beach.

Kakatso, with one hand shading his eyes, watched the landing, motionless.

When the plane was finally still and the tips of its pontoons were pulled up on the sandy beach, two men, a young woman, and a twelve-year-old boy got out.

One of the men was massive. He towered a head over Kakatso although the Montagnais himself was rather tall.

"Are you an Indian?" the man asked suddenly.

Kakatso nodded slowly and blinked his eyes once.

"Good, I'm glad, you can save us," said the man.

"Save you?" said Kakatso. "Save you from what?"

"Never mind," said the woman, "that's our business."

Standing some distance away, she gestured to the big man who had first spoken to Kakatso.

"If you're trying to escape the police," said Kakatso, "I can't do anything for you."

"It has nothing to do with the police," said the other man who had not spoken previously.

He moved towards Kakatso and proffered a handshake. Now that he was close the Montagnais recognized a veteran bush pilot. His experience could be seen in his eyes, in the squint of his eyelids, and in the way he treated an Indian as an equal.

"I am Bob Ledoux," the man said. "I am a pilot. Do you know what nuclear war is?"

"Yes," answered Kakatso, "I know."

"All the cities in the south have been destroyed," said Ledoux. "We were able to escape."

"Is that a real one?" asked the boy, who had been closely scrutinizing Kakatso. "Eh, Mom, is it really one of those savages?"

"Yes," answered the woman, "certainly." And to Kakatso she said, "Please excuse him. He has never been on the North Shore."

Naturally Kakatso did not like to be considered a savage. But he didn't show anything and he swallowed his bitterness.

"So," said the pilot, "Here we are without resources."

"I have money," said the man.

"This is Mr. Perron," said the pilot, "Mrs. Perron, and their son. . . . "

"My name is Roger," said the boy. "I know how to swim."

The Montagnais was still undecided. He did not trust intruders. He preferred, in his simple soul, to choose his own objectives and decide his day's activities. And here were outsiders who had fallen from the sky, almost demanding his help . . . but what help?

"I can't do much for you," he said after a while.

"I have money," the man repeated.

Kakatso shrugged. Money? Why money? What would it buy up here?

Without flinching he had heard how all the southern cities had been destroyed. Now he understood the meaning of those sudden gleams that lit the horizon during the night. And because this event had been the work of whites, Kakatso completely lost interest in it.

So his problem remained these four people he considered spoilers.

"Without you," said the woman, "we are going to perish."

And because Kakatso looked at her in surprise, she added, in a somewhat different tone: "We have no supplies at all and we are almost out of fuel."

"That's true," said the pilot.

"So," continued the woman, "if you don't help us find food, we will die."

Kakatso, with a sweeping gesture, indicated the forests and the lake: "There is wild game there and fish in the waters . . . "

"I don't have a gun or fishhooks," said the pilot. "And it's been a very long time since I came so far north."

He said this with a slightly abashed air and Kakatso saw clearly that the man's hands were too white; the skin had become too soft and smooth.

"I'll pay you whatever is necessary," said Mr. Perron.

"Can't you see," said his wife, "that money doesn't interest him?"

Kakatso stood there, looking at them with his shining impassive eyes, his face unsmiling and his arms dangling at his sides.

"Say something," cried the woman. "Will you agree to help us?"

"We got away as best we could," said the pilot. "We gathered the attack on Montreal was coming and we were already at the airport when the warning sirens went off. But I couldn't take on enough fuel. There were other planes leaving too. I can't even take off again from this lake. Do you know if there is a supply cache near here?"

Throughout the northern forests pilots left emergency fuel caches for use when necessary. But if Kakatso knew of several such places he wasn't letting on in front of the intruders.

"I don't know," he said.

There was silence.

The whites looked at the Indian and desperately sought words to persuade him. But Kakatso did not move and said nothing. He had always fled the society of whites and dealt with them only when it was unavoidable. Why should he treat those who surfaced here now any differently? They were without food; the forest nourishes those who know how to take their share. This knowledge was such an instinctive part of an Indian's being that he couldn't realize how some people could lack it. He was sure that these people wanted to impose their needs on him and enslave him. All his Montagnais pride revolted against this thought. And yet, he could help them. Less than one hour away there was one of those meat caches of a thousand pounds of smoked moose, enough to see them through a winter. And the fish in the lake could be caught without much effort. Weaving a simple net of fine branches would do it, or a trap of bullrushes.

But he didn't move a muscle.

Only a single fixed thought possessed Kakatso, and it fascinated him. Down there, in the south, the whites had been destroyed. Never again would they reign over these forests. In killing each other, they had rid the land of their kind. Would the Indians be free again? All the Indians, even those on the reserves? Free to retake the forests?

And these four whites: could they be the last survivors?

Brothers, thought Kakatso, all my brothers: it is up to me to protect your new freedom.

"The cities," he finally said, "they have really been destroyed?"

"Yes," said the pilot.

"Nothing is left any more," said the woman. "Nothing at all. We saw the explosion from the plane. It was terrible. And the wind pushed us for a quarter of an hour. I thought we were going to crash."

"Nothing left," said the boy, "nobody left. Boom! One bomb did it."

He was delighted to feel himself the hero — a safe and sound hero — of such an adventure. He didn't seem able to imagine the destruction and death, only the spectacular explosion.

But the man called Perron had understood it well. He had been able to estimate the real power of the bomb.

"The whole city is destroyed," he said. "A little earlier, on the radio, we heard of the destruction of New York, then Toronto and Ottawa. . . ."

"Many other cities too," added the pilot. "As far as I'm concerned, nothing is left of Canada, except perhaps the North Shore. . . ."

"And it won't be for long," said Perron. "If we could get further up, further north. If we only had food and gasoline."

This time he took a roll of money out of his pocket and unfolded five bills, a sum Kakatso had never handled at one time. Perron offered them to the Indian.

"Here. The only thing we ask you for is a little food and gas if you can get some. Then we could leave."

"When such a bomb explodes," said Kakatso without taking the bills, "does it kill all the whites?"

"Yes," said the pilot. "In any case, nearly all."

"One fell on Ottawa?"

"Yes."

"Everybody is dead there?"

"Yes. The city is small and the bomb was a big one. The reports indicate there were no survivors."

Kakatso nodded his head two or three times approvingly. Then he turned away and took his rifle which had been leaning on a rock. Slowly, aiming at the whites, he began to retreat into the forest.

"Where are you going?" cried the woman.

"Here," said the man. "Here's all my money. Come back!"

Only the pilot remained silent. With his sharp eyes he watched Kakatso.

When the Indian reached the edge of the forest it was the boy's turn. He began to sob pitifully, and the woman also began to cry.

"Don't leave," she cried. "Please, help us. . . ."

For all of my people who cried, thought Kakatso, all who begged, who wanted to defend their rights for the past two hundred years: I take revenge for them all.

But he didn't utter another word.

And when the two men wanted to run after him to stop him, he put his rifle to his shoulder. The bullet nicked the pilot's ear. Then the men understood that it would be futile to insist, and Kakatso disappeared into the forest which enclosed him. Bent low, he skimmed the ground, using every bush for cover, losing himself in the undergrowth, melting into the forest where he belonged.

Later, having circled the lake, he rested on a promontory hidden behind many spreading cedars. He saw that the pilot was trying to take off to find food elsewhere.

But the tanks were nearly empty and when the plane reached an altitude of a thousand feet the motor sputtered a bit, backfired and stopped.

The plane went into a nosedive.

When it hit the trees it caught fire.

In the morning Kakatso continued his trip towards the highlands.

He felt his first nausea the next day and vomited blood two days later. He vomited once at first, then twice, then a third time, and finally one last time.

The wind kept on blowing from the south, warm and mild.

ABOUT THE LINES

1 "He could live by finding his subsistence in the earth itself and in nature's plenty." The author takes pains to describe how Kakatso is at one with his environment. List specific details from the story that prove Kakatso's harmony with nature.

2 Summarize this story in no more than one hundred words. Compare your summary with your partners' and revise where necessary. Create a cloze task by deleting every eighth word from your summary. Ask someone who has read the story to fill in the blanks.

3 Frame the question that you would ask a reader of this story if you wanted to see if he/she had understood it. Make sure that your partners understand your question and then ask them to answer it. Discuss the answers.

BETWEEN THE LINES

1 Each of the following statements contains a hidden message that is different from its surface meaning. Discuss each quotation with your partners, and together write down the underlying message as you see it. Share your statements with another group who has also done this activity and see if you

interpreted the quotations in the same way.
a. "Then the shadows again enveloped the land."
b. "Sleep was slow and when it came it did not bring any peace."
c. "Nothing could prevail against the earth, the unchangeable soil that regenerated itself year after year."
d. "When such a bomb explodes, does it kill all whites?"

2 In your own words, explain to your partners why the last line of the story is a death knell for all who hoped to escape into the wilderness.

3 Complete the following unfinished sentences, and then compare your sentences with your writing partners':
a. Kakatso refuses to help the group from the plane because . . .
b. Kakatso is, in a sense, no better than the people who started the war . . .
c. The white people and Kakatso are both similar and dissimilar in that . . .

4 Using no more than one sentence, describe Kakatso from the point of view of the following people: a. Bob Ledoux; b. Mr. Perron; c. the boy; d. Grand-Louis.
Now, write a brief character sketch of Kakatso as you see him. Compare your work with your partners' and see if you perceive Kakatso in the same light.

BEYOND THE LINES

1 You have survived a nuclear holocaust. Write a series of diary entries that express your fears, hopes, and memories. Pat Frank's *Alas, Babylon* and *Canticle for Liebowitz*, by Walter M. Miller, Jr., will give you some ideas.

2 Research an aspect of modern weaponry that fascinates or frightens you. Present your material either orally to a large group, or in the form of a booklet or pamphlet.

3 Read the novel *On the Beach*, by Nevil Shute, and give an oral report to the class. Compare the novel with "Akua Nuten."

4 Design a banner, poster, or mural that opposes nuclear warfare. You may choose to illustrate some of the scenes from this story.

5 Write an interior monologue in the voice of Kakatso at the point when he realizes that he is suffering from radiation sickness. Read your work aloud to your partners.

6 Kakatso to an extent controls his own life and to an extent is controlled by external forces. Write a paragraph based on "Akua Nuten" that proves that, despite appearances to the contrary, no person is truly independent.

7 Research the Frankenstein story, and in a statement demonstrate how "Akua Nuten" adapts the major idea of Mary Shelley's novel.

pity this busy monster, manunkind,

not. Progress is a comfortable disease:
your victim (death and life safely beyond)

plays with the bigness of his littleness
— electrons deify one razorblade
into a mountainrange; lenses extend

unwish through curving wherewhen till unwish
returns on its unself.
                    A world of made
is not a world of born — pity poor flesh

and trees, poor stars and stones, but never this
fine specimen of hypermagical

ultraomnipotence. We doctors know

a hopeless case if — listen: there's a hell
of a good universe next door; let's go

LOOKING IN

1 Paraphrase the poet's reason for claiming that the "monster, manunkind" deserves no pity. Compare your version with your partners'. Together, write a statement challenging the poet's harsh view of humans.

2 Quote four insults that the poet levels at humans in this poem. For each insult, explain in one sentence the point the poet is trying to make about people.

3 Discuss with your partners what the last two-and-a-half lines of the poem might be suggesting. Write a paragraph describing possible pay-offs and a paragraph describing potential dangers for humans if we move beyond the Earth.

4 List the words in this poem that are new to you. Discuss with your partners what these words mean in the context of the poem, and then look them up in a dictionary to clarify their meaning. Use each word in a sentence of your own.

monster, manunkind
e e cummings

---

1 a. Imagine that you can predict the future, and write an open letter to a
newspaper warning of tragic events in the next one hundred years if
humans don't keep firm control of technological development.

or

b. Write a letter to a newspaper predicting a glorious future for human beings
in a world where machines will have abolished all human labour and
will provide a far superior way of life for people.

2 In a small group, read E.J. Pratt's famous poem, "The Titanic," aloud. Prepare
and deliver a shared retelling of the poem's story for the class. In your
presentation, emphasize how human pride resulted in people making a faulty
assumption about a machine.

EXTENDED ACTIVITIES

1 Working in a small group, brainstorm a list of things in our society that are changing or will change radically as science progresses. Draw up a balance sheet on the effect of technology on our lives. In the column headed "Credits," note the advantages of technological developments, and in the "Debits" column list the disadvantages. Add a concluding paragraph in which you weigh the balance.

2 Research the lifestyle of a North American group who have chosen to live without modern conveniences and away from urban settings (e.g., the Amish, Mennonites, or Dukhobors). Present orally a perspective on this group's resistance to technological change.

3 Research the life and works of a famous Canadian inventor and present your findings either orally or in the form of a booklet. Consider the person's most important invention, the problems that were surmounted, the value of the invention, and its present day status.

4 Invent a board game in which humans and machines either work together or against each other. Try out the game with your partners.

5 In a small group, brainstorm a list of words and terms that technology has introduced into our everyday language in the last twenty years. Compile an illustrated glossary of the new vocabulary and present it to an elementary school library. You may use new words, or words that have assumed a new meaning. The following examples may help you get started:
chip   feedback   processor   terminal

6 With the help of your school Guidance Department, research the new jobs that the technological explosion of the last decade has created. Write a job description and requirements of three jobs that would interest you.
or
Compile a list of occupations that have become, or will soon become, obsolete because of the technological advances of the last decade. For each occupation, explain why the change has occurred.

7 Make a collage that reflects the positive or negative effects of technological progress on society and the environment. You may wish to combine both aspects of technology in a "split screen."

8 Working with a partner, create a sound poem that captures the loud and soft noises of a technological world.

9 In a small group, create a movement piece that represents your perspective on our technological society.

10 "In human inventions lies the seed of human destruction." Investigate a controversial scientific development, like cloning, test tube babies, bionics, etc., and write a paragraph either supporting or refuting this quotation.

STUDENT GUIDE

Blot out, correct, insert, refine,
Enlarge, diminish, interline;
Be mindful, when invention fails,
To scratch your head, and bite your nails.

Jonathan Swift (1667 – 1745)
On Poetry

THINKING IT THROUGH

In Your Own Words gives you many opportunities to use language for a number of reasons, in different formats, and for a variety of audiences. Some aspects of talking and writing are the same in all situations, such as putting words together to mean something to you and/or other people. In most situations, however, your use of language will depend on your reason for writing or speaking, the audience you want to reach, and the particular format you have chosen.

You can therefore usually do a better job if you think about the following questions, either before you begin, or while you are preparing your first draft.

WHY am I writing or saying this? What am I trying to accomplish?
Am I trying to:
organize facts;
convince someone about something;
record my feelings;
share an idea;
give directions;
comfort or congratulate someone;
describe an experience, an event, a person, a place, an object;
tell a story;
make a complaint;
explain a situation;
(or any combination(s) of the above)?

WHO is my intended audience? Am I writing for (or speaking to):
myself;
a friend;
a relative;
someone whom I dislike;
a younger student;
someone who will respond with information or comments;
an unknown audience;
a group of people with a common interest?

WHAT am I writing or talking about?
What am I trying to say?
What information do I already have?
What information, if any, do I still need?

HOW am I organizing my ideas? How will I formulate what I have to say? Will I use:
a letter;
a paragraph of description;

a poem;

a diary or journal entry;

an explanation with accompanying diagrams and pictures;

a chart;

a brief note or telephone message;

a script;

an essay expressing my personal viewpoint;

a formal argument proving a thesis;

a speech in a debate;

an oral report?

WORKING WITH PARTNERS

Many of the activities and writing assignments in this book call for you to work with partners, to discuss ideas before writing, and to share in the process of revision, editing, and proofreading after the writing is completed. The following suggestions may help to make the process of working with partners both more pleasant and more productive.

TALK Talking together will help you to formulate your thinking, to test your ideas, to come up with new ideas, and to check whether you have expressed yourself effectively. (You can also ask your partners to read your work aloud to you, so that you can assess its total impact.)

JOT Before you write, while you write, while you proofread, and while you talk, jot down notes and reminders to yourself and to your writing partners. You may forget what you have thought or said, but you won't forget what you have written down.

LISTEN Listen to one another attentively; try to understand what is being said in order to help one another with the processes of speaking and writing.

PRAISE Encouragement is vital; everyone likes to be praised. If you are impressed by something that your partners have done, say so. The purpose of praise is to identify strong points and help the person build upon them. Consider which of these two comments is likely to be more helpful:

"Hey, that's great!" or

"I really like that line. Comparing a dragonfly to a helicopter never occurred to me before."

CRITICIZE Part of the writing partner's task is to offer helpful criticism. When you criticize, try to do so constructively, specifically, and tactfully. Your criticism should help your partners to make their writing clearer and more effective. Remember that there is a world of difference between:

"This is really dumb!" and

"This word doesn't work here. Would 'smiled' be better than 'laughed'?"

SEEK HELP If you have problems with your writing, ask your teacher and other people to help you. Someone else's perspective may help you to see things in a new light.

SOLO REVISING STRATEGIES

You won't always be able to work with writing partners. Although sharing your work with other people is probably the best way to edit and proofread, there are ways to revise or "re-see" your writing on your own. The following strategies may help you when you have to work alone.

Try to make your writing "talk" by putting yourself in the position of the audience and listening to what you have written.

1. Read the whole piece aloud several times to get the general effect and to hear how it sounds. Sometimes you can "hear" things that you cannot "see."

2. Read the piece aloud sentence by sentence or line by line to see if it makes sense when you hear it. This strategy will help you to isolate specific problems.

3. Read your writing aloud and tape it. Play back the tape and try to identify any missing links between your ideas, or any confusions in the way you have expressed yourself.

THE WRITING FOLDER

One way to work with partners in reshaping your written work is to use a writing folder. You will need a large manila envelope or an accordion-pleated file to hold the following components, which can be used separately with individual pieces of writing or as a whole package to keep an ongoing record of your work.

1. Current Writing file;
2. Private Writing file;
3. Checklist for Effective Expression — Revision;
4. Checklist for Final Editing — Proofreading;
5. Checklist for Positive Commentary;
6. Polished Writing File;
7. Personal Usage Sheet;
8. Personal Record Sheet.

Current Writing File

In this file you will keep all writing that is still "in progress" — still in draft form and requiring further work. There are several reasons why you might not want to complete all the pieces that you have drafted. You may wish to set aside certain pieces in order to concentrate on others. When you return to those pieces that you set aside, you will find that often a fresh start helps you to see things in a new light. Occasionally, you may leave a piece of writing unfinished because it loses its appeal for you or because some other piece has become more important to you.

Private Writing File

Sometimes you will write personal pieces that you don't wish to share with anyone, not even your writing partners. If you have written such pieces, mark them PRIVATE and place them in your Private Writing file. At some point in the school year, you may decide to move certain pieces from this file to the Current Writing file, and then to the Polished Writing file, but this is entirely your decision. At the end of each term, you may decide to show these private pieces to your teacher, or you may want to keep them for yourself, as a record of personal reflections and insights.

Checklist for Effective Expression —Revision

This checklist (see p. 345) provides some questions that you and your partners can consider when you look over your drafts. The questions are intended to help you to "re-see" your writing in terms of:

1. the purpose of writing;
2. the audience you are writing for;
3. the format you have chosen;
4. the words and the sentence structure you have used.

When you and your writing partners have looked at a particular piece of your writing with these questions in mind, you may decide to scrap the piece and begin again in a new direction. On the other hand, you may choose to incorporate your writing partners' suggestions into your piece and then check it against the Checklist for Final Editing.

Checklist for Final Editing —Proofreading

This checklist is designed to help you catch problems in punctuation, spelling, and sentence structure. This is a last-stage effort to clean up the piece of writing before you put it in the Polished Writing file. A well-known language expert, Dr. Frank Smith, says that there are two jobs in the writing process. He calls the first job "the authorial task," in which the writer talks and thinks about an idea, gets a rough draft down on paper, and then reshapes the draft to make it say what is intended. The Checklist for Effective Expression — Revision (see p. 345) will help you with this stage of the writing process. Dr. Smith calls the second job of the writer "the secretarial task," in which the author checks his or her work for mechanical errors on the surface of the writing — errors in spelling, punctuation, and sentence structure. The Checklist for Final Editing — Proofreading (see p. 345) will help you to do this.

Checklist for Positive Commentary

You will be working with your partners in order to help them write more effectively. When you feel that you have made all the suggestions that you can and when your partners have revised their drafts to the best of their abilities, they will put their writing into their Polished Writing files.

We all benefit from knowing what we have done well. Before your partners put their work in their Polished Writing files, write down two or three things that you really liked about their pieces of writing. Then sign your comments and attach them to the final copies. That way, there will be a record of your contributions to your partners' work.

The Checklist for Positive Commentary (see p. 346) lists some questions that you can ask yourself when you are preparing to write a positive comment on your partners' work.

Polished Writing File

This is the place where you keep the pieces from which you will select those you wish your teacher to evaluate. Work is placed here only after it has gone through all the stages of revision, proofreading, and partner commentary outlined in the three checklists.

Personal Usage Sheet

This sheet will serve as a record of the problems that you have overcome in your written work.

As you revise and edit your writing, you may find spelling, punctuation, and/or grammatical errors. When your writing partners or your teacher go over your work, they, too, may find parts that need rewording for clarity or effectiveness. When you correct any of these problems, record them on a Personal Usage Sheet: state the problem and then record the correct version. (In the sample sheet on p. 347, examples of usage errors are included to illustrate the kind of problem you may be looking out for, but when you fill in your sheet you need not record errors. Simply describe the problem and enter the correct version below.) The Personal Record Sheet can be used to provide an "at-a-glance" overview of what you have accomplished over a period of weeks.

Checklist for Effective Expression —Revision

Have I said what I wanted to say in the way I wanted to say it?

☐ Did I begin my piece of writing in an interesting way?
☐ Do the details of my writing come in the best order?
☐ Have I included any points that are repetitive or unnecessary?
☐ Have I used the same words too often?
☐ Have I used vivid and interesting words to describe actions and things and people?
☐ Do I have a strong and appropriate ending?
☐ Do my writing partners clearly understand what I am trying to say?
☐ Are my sentences or lines too long and complicated?
☐ Are my paragraphs too long? Are they long enough to make my point?
☐ Did I keep my audience in mind as I was choosing and combining my words?

When you revise or edit, you are reworking your rough draft to make your written work as clear and as interesting as possible.

Checklist for Final Editing —Proofreading

Have I checked my writing for surface errors?
☐ Did I use an appropriate title?
☐ Did I double-check the spelling of all words I was unsure about?
☐ Did I leave wide margins so that my work was uncrowded and easy to read?
☐ Did I indent each new paragraph?
☐ Did the punctuation I used make my meaning clear?
☐ Did I capitalize names and titles and the first word of each sentence?
☐ Did I use a variety of sentence types?
☐ Did I use complete sentences where necessary?
☐ Did I use clear handwriting that would not be misunderstood?

When you proofread, you try to find and correct mistakes in surface details such as punctuation, grammar, usage, and handwriting.

Your teacher will provide you with copies of the checklists, the Personal Usage Sheet, and the Personal Record Sheet when you need them.

Checklist for Positive Commentary

What are the things that my partners have done particularly well in their writing?

Here are some questions you can ask yourself when you are preparing to write a positive comment on your writing partner's work.

☐ Has the writer used any words or phrases that strike me as being particularly effective?
☐ Has the writer expressed any ideas to which I can easily relate?
☐ Has the writer given me any new insights on the world around me?
☐ Has the writing evoked strong feelings in me?
☐ Has the writer explained something to me which I didn't know before?
☐ Has the writer used a particularly striking title?
☐ Has the writer sparked my imagination?

Personal Usage Sheet

Name ....

Date	My Writing Partners	Title of My Written Work	Correct Use of the Word or Words
September 18	Lauren and Erin	"A Long Way from Home"	*Problem* The use of "there," "their," and "they're." *Correct Use* Katie shouted suddenly, "Look over there by the bridge!" Their eyes are glazed and red from lack of sleep. Katie and Joe feel that even if things aren't great at home, they're willing to give it one more try.
September 20	Lauren and Erin	"Between Me and My Hockey Stick"	*Problem* The use of quotation marks for written speech. *Correct Use* "You try that stunt once more and I'll slam you into the boards myself!" shouted the coach furiously.
September 29	Lauren and Erin	"Collision on the 401"	*Problem* Running two sentences together; e.g., It was snowing heavily, the road was slippery. *Correct Use* It was snowing and the road was slippery. *Because* it was snowing heavily, the road was slippery. It was snowing heavily; the road was slippery.
October 2	Gavin and Su-Min	"Midnight Encounter"	*Problem* Mixing past and present tense; e.g., We huddled together at the edge of the cemetery and slowly begin to creep toward the tombstone. *Correct Use* We huddled together at the edge of the cemetery and slowly began to creep toward the tombstone.

SAMPLE

347

Personal Record Sheet

Name ....

Assignment	Date Begun	Date Completed	Materials or Resources Used	Partners	Personal Assessment of the Value of the Activity
A script for "The Hobbyist"	May 10	May 24	1. Story, "The Hobbyist" 2. Sample script, "Pen of My Aunt"	Aldo & Cathy	1. I thought more about how the "hobbyist" was feeling when I had to write the script for him. 2. I learned how to indicate stage directions separately from the words of a speaker in a script by looking at the sample play.

ANNOTATED GLOSSARY

acronym
An acronym is a word composed of the initial letters of the words in a title or the name of an organization. For example, *WHO* stands for the World Health Organization.

autobiographical writing
In an autobiographical piece, a person reflects on and recounts significant experiences in his/her life. Unlike a biography, which is written from someone else's viewpoint, the autobiography tells the story from the perspective of the person himself/herself. "Details from the Canadian Mosaic" (see p. 140) and "By Any Other Name" (see p. 235) are examples of autobiographical writing.

ballad
A ballad is a poem that tells a story in simple langauge. It can be set to music and sung, and often has a refrain. Ballads were traditionally written in four-line stanzas, as below

Lines	Stresses	Rhyme
1 2 3 4	4 3 4 3	a b c d *or*
		a b a b

"The Bonny Earl of Murray" (see p. 14) is an example of a ballad.

biographical writing
In a biographical piece, the author tries to capture the story of another person's life, or at least important highlights from it. "Beale's Treasure" (see p. 107) is an example of biographical writing.

brainstorm
When you brainstorm, you work as a group to produce a large number of ideas in a limited time. For successful brainstorming, try to follow these suggestions:

1. Work in a comfortable situation — on the floor, around a desk, or grouped around a blackboard.
2. Elect one person to act as secretary and record all the ideas that come up.
3. Avoid commenting on one another's ideas, either negatively or positively. Just ask the secretary to write down all the ideas as they come.
4. Decide on a fixed length of time and work within it. When the time is up or when the flow of ideas has stopped, discuss the material produced and decide what to reject and what to retain.

bulletin board
A bulletin board is used for displays and information. In order to be effective,

the bulletin board must be eye-catching. Some things you might consider when making a board are:

1. Using a background for the material you are displaying (your background might be in one colour, or in a geometric or colourful design);
2. Framing the material;
3. Separating the board into segments;
4. Using headings for sections of the display;
5. Trying to include three-dimensional materials in the display;
6. Writing or printing the information clearly to make the reading of it easier;
7. Using a variety of writing styles (graphics).

caricature

A caricature is a picture or description of a person or thing in which defects or peculiarities are exaggerated in order to produce a humorous or ludicrous effect. Charles Dickens frequently used caricature, as in this description from *Hard Times* of the down-to-earth, self-made businessman, Thomas Gradgrind, lecturing a schoolmaster:

> " 'Now what I want is Facts. Teach these boys and girls nothing but Facts. Facts alone are wanted in life. Stick to Facts, Sir.'
>   . . . The speaker emphasized his observations by underscoring every sentence with a line on the schoolmaster's sleeve. The emphasis was helped by the speaker's square wall of a forehead, which had his eyebrows as its base. The emphasis was helped by the speaker's mouth, which was inflexible, dry, and dictatorial. The emphasis was helped by the speaker's hair, which bristled on the skirts of his bald head, all covered with knobs, as if the head had scarcely warehouse room for the hard Facts stored inside."

choral reading

Choral reading is a technique where a group of people read aloud together. The number and combination of voices may be varied to achieve different effects.

collage

A collage is a visual design of paper, cloth, pictures, or other materials fixed to a background. A collage should make a statement about an idea or a theme. To make a collage, you will need newspapers, magazines, and other sources of pictures. Some suggestions you might consider when making a collage are:

1. Using a variety of geometrical designs — circles, squares, or rectangles — both for the articles in the collage and for its overall shape;
2. Using a three-dimensional design;
3. Mixing black-and-white and colour pictures for special effects;
4. Arranging the materials with a focus that will catch the attention of the viewers;
5. Using different materials to give the collage a variety of textures.

conversation

At various points in this book, you are given the opportunity to write conversations or dialogues. They differ from scripts in that they are usually contained within a narrative (storytelling) framework. When you write a conversation, you must pay attention to certain very specific rules of punctuation. If you are uncertain of how to punctuate conversations, you will be able to find models in many of the stories in *In Your Own Words*, such as "The Hobbyist" (p. 76), "The Old Demon" (p. 31), and "The Flying Machine" (p. 279).

If you dramatize or role play your conversation, remember to use appropriate voices and actions.

diary

A diary is a personal and private record of events and feelings that may be written whenever the individual chooses. A diary is usually written in the first person (see *narrative techniques*, p. 353), and often provides the writer with the opportunity to "talk things through" with a silent "listener." The following diary sample demonstrates how both events and emotions emerge as the diarist writes.

Saturday, May 28
Joe took me hunting this morning. He called last night to say this was it. No more promises. We would go for sure. I'll bet I never closed my eyes all night. It felt different this morning, right from the start, getting up in the dark and creeping out into the cold. Joe let me hold the rifle on my knee while he drove the pickup. I enjoyed pretending it was mine, heavy and smooth, and smelling of grease. There were sounds in the woods you never hear later in the day. When Joe held up his hand and raised the rifle, I was so excited I could feel my heart banging. I was sure the deer could hear me breathe. I was sweating all over, even though it was cold.

But it wasn't like I had expected at all. Joe said it was a near perfect shot. But my stomach kept churning and I had to swallow a lot. Joe was so smug he never even noticed I wasn't saying anything. joe said the deer was a beauty, but I looked at the blood coming out of its mouth and I had to work hard to stop the tears from coming. Joe talked all the way home. I had to hold the seat; my hands were shaking. I've been here in my room most of the day. Don't feel much like talking. This morning was supposed to be a great new experience. I guess it was, in a way. I sure found out something about myself. I'm not saying what Joe does is wrong, but I know it's wrong for me.

foreshadowing

Foreshadowing is a technique used to give the reader, listener, or viewer of a book, play, or film some hint about what is to come. This technique not only stimulates interest in what is to follow, but it also prepares the reader, listener, or viewer for the direction in which the plot will move, thereby making it appear less contrived. In "The Veldt" (see p. 302) the author employs this technique to prepare the reader for the story's gory ending: The bloody scarf and wallet alert the reader to the coming death of the parents.

irony

Irony is a device used by writers whereby the intended meaning of the words used is the opposite of their normal or apparent meaning. It is often used to mock or to convey sarcasm. An ironic result is one that is the opposite of what might reasonably be expected. In "The Wedding Gift" (see p. 17), it is ironic that while Kezia is supposedly treated as one of the Barclay family, she is nonetheless expected to marry Mr. Hathaway, who is considered beneath the Barclay girls. The eventual fate of the statute of Ozymandias (see p. 4) is ironic in the light of the King's statement "look on my Works, ye Mighty, and despair!"

letter to the editor

The letter to the editor is a specific type of letter written to a newspaper or a magazine, commenting either negatively or positively on the editorial or on an item of news and the way it was reported. It is an unusual type of letter in that it expresses a personal opinion, but is written to be published in the appropriate section of the newspaper or magazine. The following is an example of a letter to the editor.

Address
Date

Dear Sir or Madam,

I feel I must object strongly to your editorial, "Rock Fanimals (January 23). You suggest that all rock fans behave like animals by pushing, shoving, and shouting in concert halls, by destroying public property, by assaulting bystanders, and by littering the buildings where the concerts are held.

I have attended many rock concerts at which the fans have behaved extremely well — they waited quietly for the music to start, and then in an orderly fashion when the concert was over. I have also seen crowds at hockey and football games behaving much worse than rock fans at concerts.

I don't think that you like rock music very much, and I don't think that you like young people very much either. In future, I suggest that you comment on the behaviour of a whole group and not of a few. I was at the concert you wrote about, and I saw only two examples of the rowdy behaviour you described in your editorial. Perhaps you confused the concert with last Saturday's hockey game.

Yours faithfully,

Matthew Park,
Grade 11 student
Vancouver, B.C.

lyric

A lyric is a poem that is personal and subjective, and expresses the thoughts and emotions of a single speaker who may or may not be a poet. Lyric poetry has musical sound patterns and stirs the imagination through a strong appeal to the senses. "Song For Naomi" (see p. 150) is an example of lyric poetry.

memoir
A memoir is a written or oral record of a significant moment in the writer's or speaker's past. The experience may have been pleasant or unpleasant, but it has remained fresh in the writer's mind. When you write a memoir, remember to relate not only the event you recall but also the emotions associated with it. "By Any Other Name" (see p. 235) is a prose memoir of a significant event in the writer's past, while "Shoe Store" (see p. 187) describes a single memory from the poet's past and his reflections on it.

metaphor
A metaphor is an image that the writer creates by making a link between two things not normally associated with each other. The writer tries to build a word picture by transferring an attribute or a characteristic from one thing to another. For example, in "Lament for the Dorsets" (see p. 48), the poet describes the carved swan as an "ivory thought" and suggests that it is still warm. He is linking the carving with the thought behind it, and is suggesting that love and desire to please have kept it alive through the centuries.

mime
Mime is acting without words; the story of the play is told by gestures and facial expressions. Props are sometimes used in mime, while at other times the mime is performed as if imaginary props are actually present.

narrative poem
A narrative poem is a poem that relates a story or a series of events. "The Bonny Earl of Murray" (see p. 14) and "The Forsaken" (see p. 136) are examples of narrative poems.

narrative techniques
first-person narrative. In first-person narrative, the story is told from the point of view of the narrator, who uses the pronouns *I* or *we*. The narrator speaks directly to the reader when this technique is used. The major advantage of first-person narrative is that it enables the author to reveal his/her emotions while relating the events. "The Return" (see p. 208) is an example of a piece written in the first person.

third-person narrative. In third-person narrative, an author tells the story using the pronouns *he, she, it, they*. This technique creates more distance between the author and the main character than first-person narrative, but the narrator can know what is happening in more than one place and what more than one character is thinking at any time. The author will write as if he/she is watching or has watched the events. "The Old Demon" (see p. 31) and "The Satellites" (see p. 152) are both written in the third person.

The following is an example of one journalistic style. The article introduces a broad topic in the first paragraph, gives details in the body of the story, and then concludes with a personal anecdote about the subject.

Greenhouse like a blooming desert

Betty Zyvatkauskas

The cactus capital of Canada is what the Ben Velduis greenhouse calls itself. And with twenty greenhouses full of thick-leaved succulents and prickly plants it can't be far wrong. When the rest of Southern Ontario is shivering with February's chill, the steamy greenhouses seem positively tropical.

Hundreds of thousands of cacti laid out on sunning tables, basking under window-filtered light create an impression of a desert in bloom. Upon entering we saw nearly a whole greenhouse filled with short, red-knobbed cacti sporting headpieces that looked like roosters' crowns.

Constant handling seems to be going on: pots are rearranged, rows are shuffled and new plants are put on display. To avoid the perils of prickles, greenhouse workers wear red rubber thimbles on their finger tips and nimbly move the tiny pots with tweezers.

We had expected a desert-like aridity, but the place was steamy. One of the workers explained that cacti, like any other plant, need watering; they just need less of it. During the summer they get a good shower once a week, but in these colder days the waterings /slow down to once every two or three weeks, with cooler weather bringing even longer waits.

Though the greenhouse is basically a retail business, visitors are made to feel welcome. Most of the workers were happy to explain what they could, and while they often didn't know the names of the varieties, they had plenty of advice for cactus care.

Budgies and parrots chattering in cages lend the place a jungle atmosphere. Cacti, which I had previously thought of as rather dull house plants, took on a new splendour. Colours varied from pale blue plant flesh to purple flowers and yellow fuzz. Even humble inch-high homegrowns look impressive when they are seen in trays of thousands.

The most impressive display was the collection of large cacti—everything from squat, prickle-studded balls, to trees 2.5 m tall. Some sported caps of brown, fur-like needles which looked like Russian fur hats. Others had crinkled edges, like cabbage leaves. And one grew soft white needles that looked like an old man's beard. The variety was more than I had thought possible among these desert dwellers.

Cacti and succulents are not the only plants on display at the greenhouse. Tropical plants and African violets are also grown; so are decorative ferns and the more mundane "decorator" kinds of house plants, which seem at home in macrame plant hangers in off-white renovated living rooms.

I was very taken with the cacti and bought a few of the most interesting succulents for home. Lithops were my choice: subtly coloured plump lumps that burst reptile-like from their own skins. Living rocks is what they are commonly called.

The following is an example of a journalistic style called the "inverted pyramid." The first paragraph introduces the central idea, and subsequent paragraphs include material of decreasing importance. This style of writing serves both those readers who want to read newspapers quickly and skim the first paragraph of each story to pick up the main ideas, and also those who are interested in all the details and will read the article to the very end. From an editorial viewpoint, this style is useful because the article can be cut off at any point.

Burlington takes Lead on Shutout

Despite a brilliant game by Chinguacousy goaltender Chuck Sevigny, the Burlington Belanger Blue Devils took a 2–0 lead in their Tri-county League juvenile playoff series with a 3–1 victory over Ching last Monday night at Nelson Arena.

Two quick goals by Mike Fredo and Scott Ward in the second period proved to be the margin of victory for the Devils. Ward scored the game's first goal in the initial period of play, but Ching capitalized on a scramble in front of the Burlington net to tie the match at one in the last minute of the opening period.

Mike Marco also had a fine game in goal for the Burlington squad.

paraphrase

When you paraphrase a piece of writing (or an oral statement) you rephrase and rewrite (or restate) it in your own words, so that the original ideas are present but not necessarily expressed in the original words. A good paraphrase will have the flavour of your own speech or writing.

As an example, the poem "Conversation with Myself" is paraphrased below:

Conversation with Myself
Eve Merriam

> This face in the mirror
> stares at me
> demanding *Who are you?*
>   *What will you become?*
> and taunting, *You don't even know.*
> Chastened, I cringe and agree
> and then
> because I'm still young,
> I stick out my tongue.

Paraphrase

My reflection in the mirror asks me who am I and what will I be in the future. It mocks me when I admit, with some embarrassment, that I am not sure. But then I realize that, at my age, I don't have to be certain. So, "BLAH!" to the mirror!

script

A script is the form in which a play is usually printed. It contains the characters' lines with their names beside them, and also stage directions indicating how the lines are to be spoken or what actions are required to accompany the words. A script often starts with a description of the set, to tell the director how to design the stage. If you decide to write a script, you can use the plays in this book as models.

simile

A simile is a special kind of metaphor (see p. 353). It is an image in which the writer suggests a connection between two normally distinct things and uses *like* or *as* to make the comparison. For example, in "The Old Demon" (see p. 31) by describing the river as "the yellow water curling along like a lot of snakes," the author is suggesting both the sinister and the hostile nature of the river.

slogan

A slogan is a word or phrase that is intended to arouse public interest in a political ideal, a commercial product, a social problem, or a viewpoint you would like to communicate. A slogan often sounds like a rallying cry or a battle cry and is much like a cheer at a sports event. To be effective, a slogan should be short and memorable. The following are examples of slogans:

"One Nation, One People!"

"If You Can Read This, Thank A Teacher!"

summary

When you are asked to summarize a piece of writing, you are required to shorten the original while retaining the most important information. You may use your own words and also keep some of the orignal words. When you have completed a summary, ask yourself the following questions:

Have I included all essential information?

Have I omitted all non-essential information?

Have I used a clear beginning and a strong ending?

suspense

Suspense is the state of curiosity, uncertainty, or even apprehension as to the outcome of a film, play, story, or narrative. The reader, listener, or viewer often senses that something will happen, but remains unaware of what it will actually be. In "The Moose and the Sparrow" (see p. 227), the reader is in suspense from the moment Moose begins persecuting Cecil. In "The Veldt" (see p. 302), suspense arises from the parents' first frightening "encounter" with the lions in the nursery.

symbol

A symbol is something concrete — such as an object, a place, a person, an action, or an event — representing something abstract — such as an idea, a concept, a quality, or a condition. For example, a dove symbolizes peace, a lion symbolizes strength, a maple leaf symbolizes Canada, and raised hands symbolize surrender.

tableau

A tableau is the representation of a situation by one or more silent, motionless persons, who are suitably posed and, if possible, appropriately attired. Props are sometimes used in a tableau.

REFERENCE SOURCES

While you are working on the activities in this book, in the thinking, drafting, proofreading, and final writing stages, you may wish to refer to certain resources for clarification, help, or ideas. Some of the following reference sources may prove to be useful.

Dictionary
You can use a dictionary to help you to find definitions, to check spellings, and to verify pronunciation.

Dictionary of Literary Terms
This type of book defines literary terms such as metaphor, irony, etc., It will usually provide examples along with the definitions of terms.

Dictionary of Quotations
A quotation is often effective in written or oral communication. To check quotations that you want to include (or to find new ones) you can use a dictionary of quotations. It may arrange the contents under alphabetical subject headings, such as Anger, Love, War, Youth, etc., or alphabetically by author.

Grammar or Usage Texts
These books are useful if you have identified specific problems in your writing, such as dangling modifiers or run-on sentences. Use these texts as resources to check correct usage, and then ask your writing partners to proofread your next piece of writing to make sure you have dealt with the problems.

The Personal Usage Sheet (p. 347) gives you a method of overcoming personal writing problems.

Magazines and Newspapers
These are excellent resources if you are looking for starting-points for stories, articles, letters, and other kinds of writing. In addition, pictures, headlines, captions, cartoons, and advertisements can be used in collages, bulletin boards, and pamphlets. A newspaper or magazine will also provide you with models when you write newspaper or magazine articles.

Other Books
Other books are an important resource. Reading widely will not only give you ideas, and perhaps fire your imagination, but will also enrich your vocabulary and show you how other writers have handled the craft of writing.

Other People
Perhaps the most valuable resource available to you is other people. Do not hesitate to ask librarians, classmates, teachers, parents, and anyone else you know for ideas and specific help.

Thesaurus
A thesaurus is a great vocabulary builder; it lists words like a dictionary, but instead of giving definitions, it gives synonyms (words with similar meanings). Skilful use of a thesaurus will improve the variety and life of your writing and speech.

ACKNOWLEDGEMENTS AND CREDITS

On the Vanity of Earthly Greatness by Arthur Guiterman: from *Gaily the Troubadour*. Reprinted by permission of Louise H. Sclove. Gawain and the Lady Ragnell: Retold by Ethel Johnston Phelps from *The Maid of the North* by Ethel Johnston Phelps. Reprinted by permission of Holt, Rinehart and Winston Publishers, Inc. New York, N.Y. The Wedding Gift by Thomas Raddall: Reprinted by permission of the author. The Old Demon by Pearl S. Buck: Reprinted by permission of Harold Ober Associates Incorporated. Copyright © 1939 by Pearl S. Buck. Renewed 1966. The Town Dump by Wallace Stegner: From WOLF WILLOW. Copyright © 1959 by Wallace Stegner. Reprinted by permission of Brandt & Brandt Literary Agents, Inc. Lament for the Dorsets by Al Purdy: from WILD GRAPE WINE by Al Purdy reprinted by permission of The Canadian Publishers, McClelland and Stewart Limited, Toronto. The Pen of My Aunt by Gordon Daviot: Reprinted by permission of David Higham Associates Limited. In the Mist by Judit Sziráky: © Judit Sziráky 1965; Translated by Éva Rácz. First published in English by Publishers Corvina, Budapest, 1965. The Hobbyist by Fredric Brown: Reprinted by permission of the author and the author's agents, Scott Meredith Literary Agency, Inc., 845 Third Avenue, New York, N.Y. 10022. Just One of Those Days by Donald E. Westlake: Copyright © 1966 by Donald E. Westlake. Reprinted from THE CURIOUS FACTS PRECEDING MY EXECUTION AND OTHER FICTIONS, by Donald E. Westlake, by permission of Random House, Inc. The Execution by Alden Nowlan: Reprinted by permission of the author. Lamb to the Slaughter by Roald Dahl: Copyright 1953 Roald Dahl. Reprinted from SOMEONE LIKE YOU, by Roald Dahl, by permission of Alfred A. Knopf, Inc. Macavity: the Mystery Cat by T.S. Eliot: Reprinted by permission of Faber and Faber Ltd. from OLD POSSUM'S BOOK OF PRACTICAL CATS by T.S. Eliot. The Dinner Party by Mona Gardner: © Mona Gardner. Reprinted by permission of the author. Two Minute Mysteries by Donald J. Sobol: The Case of the Haunted House and The Case of the Missing Button from TWO MINUTE MYSTERIES by Donald J. Sobol. Copyright © 1967 Donald J. Sobol. Reprinted by permission of the author and his Literary Agent, McIntosh & Otis, Inc. New York, N.Y. Beale's Treasure by John Picton: Original title "Code Holds Key to Hoard of Gold and Silver" by John Picton. Reprinted with permission — the Toronto Star. The Patient by Agatha Christie: Reprinted by permission of the publisher Samuel French Ltd. Beware: Do Not Read This Poem by Ishmael Reed: Copyright © 1972, Ismael Reed. Reprinted by permission. The Philosophers by R.G. Everson: reprinted from his "SELECTED POEMS" by permission of the author. The Forsaken by Duncan Campbell Scott: The work of Duncan Campbell Scott is reprinted with the permission of John G. Aylen, Ottawa, Canada. Letter to his Daughter: Letter from F. Scott Fitzgerald to his Daughter August 8, 1933. F. Scott Fitzgerald, *Letters To His Daughter*, edited by Andrew Turnbull. Copyright © 1965 Frances Scott Fitzgerald Smith (New York: Charles Scribner's Sons, 1965) Reprinted with the permission of Charles Scribner's Sons. Song for Naomi by Irving Layton: From COLLECTED POEMS of Irving Layton reprinted by permission of the Canadian Publishers, McClelland and Stewart Limited, Toronto. The Satellites by Gabrielle Roy: © Gabrielle Roy, 1970. One Evening by David Helwig: Reprinted from *The Streets of Summer* by permission of Oberon Press. The Little Shop on Main Street by Ernest Hillen: From *The Financial Post Magazine*. Shoe Store by Raymond Souster: Reprinted from *Collected Poems of Raymond Souster* (Volume 3) by permission of Oberon Press. My Cup Ranneth Over by Robert Patrick: From *The Best Short Plays, 1980* by Stanley Richards. The Little Girl and the Wolf by James Thurber: Copyright © 1940 James Thurber. Copyright © 1968 Helen Thurber. From FABLES FOR OUR TIME, published by Harper & Row, Publishers, Inc. A Choice of Weapons by Phyllis McGinley: From TIMES THREE by Phyllis McGinley. Copyright 1954 by Phyllis McGinley. Copyright renewed 1982 by Julie Elizabeth Hayden and Phyllis Hayden Blake. Originally published in *The New Yorker*. Reprinted by permission of Viking Penguin Inc. The Return by Alistair MacLeod: From THE LOST SALT GIFT OF BLOOD by Alistair MacLeod reprinted by permission of The Canadian Publishers, McClelland and Stewart Limited, Toronto. Canadian January Night by Alden Nowlan: From BETWEEN TEARS AND LAUGHTER by Alden Nowlan © 1971 by Clarke, Irwin & Company Limited. Used by permission. The Use of Force by William Carlos Williams: From THE FARMERS DAUGHTERS by William Carlos Williams. Copyright 1938 by William Carlos Williams. Reprinted by permission of New Directions Publishing Corporation. The Moose and the Sparrow by Hugh Garner: From MEN AND WOMEN by Hugh Garner. Copyright © 1966. Reprinted by permission of McGraw-Hill Ryerson Limited. By Any Other Name by Santha Rama Rau: From GIFTS OF PASSAGE by Santha Rama Rau. Copyright 1951 by Vasanthi Rama

Rau Bowers. Originally appeared in *The New Yorker* and reprinted by permission of Harper & Row, Publishers, Inc. Geralde and the Green Green Grass by Robert Fontaine: originally published in MacLean's Magazine. Reprinted by permission of Stelle R. Fontaine. Grass by Carl Sandburg: From CORNHUSKERS by Carl Sandburg, copyright 1918 by Holt, Rinehart and Winston, Inc.; copyright 1946 by Carl Sandburg. Reprinted by permission of Harcourt Brace Jovanovich, Inc. Bambinger by Mordecai Richler: From *The Street* by Mordecai Richler. Reprinted by permission of The Canadian Publishers, McClelland and Stewart Limited, Toronto. Black Lion by Ian Slater: Reprinted by permission of the author. The Story of Daedalus & Icarus: translated by Rolfe Humphries from OVID'S "METAMORPHOSES" © 1955 Indiana University Press. The Flying Machine by Ray Bradbury: Copyright © 1953 by Ray Bradbury, © renewed 1980 by Ray Bradbury. Reprinted by permission of the Harold Matson Company, Inc. The Man and the Machine by E.J. Pratt: From Collected Poems of E.J. Pratt. Reprinted by permission of Viola and Claire Pratt. Neuteronomy by Eve Merriam: From FINDING A POEM by Eve Merriam. Published by Atheneum. Copyright © 1970 by Eve Merriam. Reprinted by permission of the author. The Veldt by Bradbury: Copyright © 1951 by Ray Bradbury, copyright renewed 1979. Reprinted by permission of the Harold Matson Co., Inc. Akua Nuten (The South Wind) by Yves Theriault, translated by Howard Roiter, is reproduced with the permission of Nelson Canada. From *Stories from Quebec* by Philip Stratford (ed.). Copyright © 1974 by Van Nostrand Reinhold Ltd., Toronto. pity this busy monster, manunkind by E.E. Cummings: Copyright 1944 by E.E. Cummings, copyright 1972 by Nancy T. Andrews. Reprinted from COMPLETE POEMS 1913-1962 by E.E. Cummings by permission of Harcourt Brace Jovanovich, Inc.

Special thanks to:
The Ontario Educational Communications Authority for the idea behind Beyond the Lines Activity 1 of "The Ugly Little Boy"

Ms. Connie Vaccaro for her careful typing of the manuscript

Every reasonable effort has been made to trace the owners of copyrighted material and to make due acknowledgement. Any errors or omissions drawn to our attention will be gladly rectified in future editions.

PHOTOGRAPHS

Bert Brown: Pp. 86-87, 131, 146, 242, 249, 285.
The Image Bank of Canada: Pp. 101 © Art Kane I-31153, 190 © Steve Niedorf C-SN-598, 274-275 © Alain Choisnet I-100807, 287 © Mitchell Funk I-43197.
Masterfile: Pp. 48-49 © Peter Christopher CH-1524, 97 © Roland Weber WE-10824, 150 © Roland Weber WE-9818.
Frank Prazak: P. 180.
The Stock Market Inc.: Pp. 2-3 © Yuri Dojc, 4-5 © Benjamin Rondel, 42-43 © The Stock Market, 74-75 © Steven Moore, 80-81 © Bill Marsh, 134-135 © Richard Simpson, 136-137 © Steven Moore, 206-207 © L.A. Morse, 220-221 © The Stock market, 228 © Bill Marsh, 300 © The Stock Market, 336-337 © The Stock Market.

ILLUSTRATIONS

Darrel Bowman: P. 187.
Peggy Challies: Pp. 113, 119.
Blair Clark: Pp. 32, 276, 280, 315.
Louise Cusack: P. 222.
Joseph D'Agostino Pp. 203, 236.
Tony Heron: P. 297.
Charles Hilder: Pp. 52, 55, 58, 65, 251.

Jeff Jackson: Pp. 108, 290, 303, 328.
Ian Leventhal: Pp. 104, 105.
Jock MacRae: Pp. 89, 153, 165.
Greg Ruhl: Pp. 18-19, 24, 77.
Martin Springett: Pp. 8, 14.
Wendy Wortsman: 268.
Constantine Zotass: Pp. 141, 173.